A House Divided

A House Divided

The diary of a
Chief Executive of the
Royal Opera House

MARY ALLEN

SIMON & SCHUSTER
A VIACOM COMPANY

First published in Great Britain by Simon & Schuster UK Ltd, 1998
A Viacom company

1 3 5 7 9 10 8 6 4 2

Simon & Schuster UK Ltd
Africa House
64-78 Kingsway
London WC2B 6AH

Simon & Schuster Australia
Sydney

A CIP catalogue record for this book is available from the British Library

ISBN 0-684-85865-7

Typeset by SX Composing DTP, Rayleigh, Essex
Printed and bound in Great Britain by
Butler & Tanner Ltd, Frome and London

If a house be divided against itself, that house cannot stand.
Mark, chapter 3 verse 25

For Nigel

DRAMATIS PERSONAE

ROYAL OPERA HOUSE

Members of The Main Board Between September 1997 and March 1998

Lord Chadlington	Chairman 1996–1997
Sir Colin Southgate	Chairman from 1998
Sir James Spooner	Deputy Chairman to 1997
Vivien Duffield	Board member from 1990 and Deputy Chairman from 1998
Bob Gavron	Board member to 1998
Jim Butler	Board member to 1998
Rudi Mueller	Board member to 1998
Lord Eatwell	Board member from 1998
Sir David Lees	Board member from 1998
Stuart Lipton	Board member from 1998
Carolyn Newbigging	
Michael Berkeley	
Colin Nears	

Previous Board Members

Lord Sainsbury	Chairman (1980s)
Sir Angus Stirling	Chairman 1991–1996
Baroness Blackstone	Board member 1987–97
Sir Kit McMahon	Board member 1989–97

Members of The Senior Management Between September 1997 and March 1998

Mary Allen	Chief Executive
Richard Hall	Finance Director
Nicholas Payne	Opera Director
Sir Anthony Dowell	Artistic Director of the Royal Ballet
Anthony Russell-Roberts	Artistic Administrator of the Royal Ballet
Malcolm Warne Holland	Orchestra Director
John Harrison	Technical Director
Mike Morris	Personnel Director
Keith Cooper	Director of Sales and Broadcasting
John Seekings	Development Director
Judy Grahame	Director of External Relations
Phyllida Ritter	Director of the Friends of Covent Garden
Jackie McDougall	Director of the Royal Opera House Trust

Previous Members of Senior Management

Sir Jeremy Isaacs	General Director 1987–1997
Genista McIntosh	Chief Executive 1997

ARTS COUNCIL OF ENGLAND

Council Members Referred to in the Diary

Lord Gowrie	Chairman
Richard Cork	Chairman, Visual Arts Panel
Christopher Frayling	Chairman, Education Panel
Sir David Harrison	Chairman, Eastern Arts Board
Gavin Henderson	Chairman, Music Panel

Thelma Holt	Chairman, Drama Panel
Lady MacMillan	Chairman, Dance Panel
Trevor Phillips	Chairman, London Arts Board
David Reid	Chairman, Audit Committee
Prue Skene	Chairman, Lottery Panel

Officers

Mary Allen	Secretary-General 1994–1997
Graham Devlin	Acting Secretary-General 1997–1998*
Peter Hewitt	Chief Executive from 1998
Jeremy Newton	Lottery Director
Nigel Copeland	Finance Director
Kathryn McDowell	Music Director
Hilary Carty	Dance Director
Nicole Penn-Symons	Head of Lottery Monitoring

DEPARTMENT OF CULTURE, MEDIA AND SPORT**

Rt Hon Chris Smith MP	Secretary of State from 1997
Mark Fisher	Arts Minister 1997–1998
John Newbigin	Policy adviser from 1997
Sir Hayden Phillips	Permanent Secretary 1992–1998
Melanie Leech	Assistant Secretary (Head of Arts) to 1998

*Normally there would have also been a Deputy Secretary-General. Sue Hoyle had been my deputy; she had left in March 1997 and Graham Devlin had taken over. He occupied the post for six weeks before I left and he became Acting Secretary-General

**The Department was renamed after the 1 May 1997 election. It had been previously called the Department of National Heritage.

NOTE ON THE STRUCTURE AND ORGANIZATION OF THE ROYAL OPERA HOUSE COVENT GARDEN

The Royal Opera House Covent Garden – generally known just as the Royal Opera House – is a registered charity. It owns a theatre (the Royal Opera House) and its staff include three performing companies: a chorus, an orchestra and a ballet company. Although the Royal Opera and the Royal Ballet are often referred to as separate entities, they are structurally and constitutionally part of the Royal Opera House. The Royal Ballet has a separate group of Governors, who are responsible in broad terms for the welfare of the Royal Ballet, the Birmingham Royal Ballet and the Royal Ballet School. The Governors of the Royal Ballet delegate to the Board of the Royal Opera House responsibility for managing the Royal Ballet.

The Royal Opera House is governed by a voluntary Main Board. During my time at the Royal Opera House the number of Board members varied between seven and nine. Board members are chosen in consultation with the Secretary of State for Culture, Media and Sport and the Arts Council of England, but new Board members can only be appointed by the Board itself. Likewise, the Chairman is elected by the Board from among its own members. In addition, there have for some years been two subsidiary Boards: the Opera Board and the Ballet Board. During the time of Lord Chadlington's chairmanship these were suspended in order to rethink the role of these bodies and their membership. Sir Colin Southgate re-established them. During the period covered by this diary there were three sub-committees of the Main Board: the Finance and Audit Committee, the Remuneration Committee, and the Development Steering Committee.

The development has been in progress for over twenty years. In 1975 the Government purchased land to enable the redevelopment of the Covent Garden site, to upgrade the facilities of the theatre and to create the necessary studio and office space to enable the Royal Ballet to move from its rented premises in Baron's Court and join the rest of the company in Covent Garden. In 1981 this land was given to an organization called the Development Land Trust, which had two trustees: the Royal Opera House and the Arts Council. The day-to-day running of the development was delegated to the Royal Opera House, with the Arts Council and the Government being involved only in certain types of decision, for example the sale or mortgaging of parts of the property.

The development itself is undertaken by a company called Royal Opera House Developments Limited. During the period covered by this diary the development was overseen on the part of the Royal Opera House Main Board by the Development Steering Committee. There was also a Design Sub-Group, which looked at the detail of the interior design and considered certain operational issues such as catering.

The development was made possible by the award, in 1995, of £78.5 million from the arts' share of the proceeds from the National Lottery. In addition funds were to be raised through an Appeal (original target £100 million) and through the sale of some or all of those parts of the site which were to be developed commercially. The intention was that sufficient funds would be available to enable not only the completion of the development but also the establishment of an endowment, which would help to fund the running costs of the new theatre.

The Friends of Covent Garden is a separately constituted organization. There is also the Royal Opera House Trust, an independent charitable trust, established in order to raise money for the Royal Opera House. It raised money both for the revenue operation – productions, other projects, running costs – and for the development, the latter through a special Appeal. Also of relevance to this account is the Floral Charitable Trust. Although the terms of its Trust Deed describe very broadly the use to which the Floral Trust's funds could be put, in terms of supporting the Royal Opera House and its performing companies, they were originally intended for the development.

At the point at which I left the Royal Opera House, many aspects of the structure described above were under review, with a view to simplifying the relationship between the different bodies and committees. This is a description, therefore, of the position as it was in late 1997 and early 1998.

It is also useful to summarize the relationship between the Arts Council of England and the Royal Opera House. The Arts Council is a Non-Departmental Public Body, or quango, through which funds voted by the Government are channelled to the arts, in the form of annual grant-in-aid. Every year the Arts Council agrees with each arts organization it funds the level of its revenue grant and the type and amount of art the organization will produce in return. This is set out in a written agreement, together with any other targets, for example, projected attendances. In addition, the Arts Council makes it a condition of revenue grants that, before any funds are released, the recipient organization has to produce a balanced budget for the year in question.

The Arts Council also distributes funds to the arts from the lottery. Lottery awards are covered by another range of conditions, more detailed and more stringent than those applying to revenue grants. Some are standard, applying to all awards, and some are individually tailored. The award to the Royal Opera House was subject to eighteen such individual conditions.

Each funded arts organization has an Arts Council assessor, an officer who takes lead responsibility for the relationship between the two bodies. In the case of the Royal Opera House this was the Deputy Secretary-General. The Royal Opera House was the only funded organization to have as its assessor a member of the Arts Council's top management.

INTRODUCTION

Near the end of 1997, when I had been Chief Executive of the Royal Opera House for three months, some friends of mine who live in a mid-sized town in one of the southern states of America wrote to me and said, 'There's just been an article about you in our local paper – what on *earth* have you been doing?'

The Royal Opera House is possibly one of the most controversial organizations in the world. Everything it does is scrutinized, analysed, interpreted, and commented upon to a degree that is virtually without equal.

In recent years the organization has been criticized for failing to live within its means, for being elitist and snobbish because of the high ticket prices it charges, and above all for being poorly managed. However, at the same time as being held up as an example of mismanagement, the Royal Opera House has also had an impressive array of talents associated with it. Its chairmen have included Lord Drogheda, Sir Claus Moser, Lord Sainsbury, Sir Angus Stirling and Lord Chadlington. Sir Jeremy Isaacs, the first Chief Executive of Channel 4, was the most recent General Director. All these people have a distinguished track record in their own professional fields. Why is it, then, that after fifty years of such leadership the Royal Opera House came to the brink of collapse?

I believe that the events of the last two years had their genesis in long-standing structural weaknesses coupled with profound change over a relatively short period of time.

The Royal Opera House has a structure that is inherently unstable. There are two governing bodies (the Main Board of the Royal Opera House and the Governors of the Royal Ballet); three groups of performers (the Royal Ballet, the Royal Opera Chorus and the Orchestra of the Royal Opera House); and three brand names (the

Royal Opera House, the Royal Opera and the Royal Ballet). Each of these entities attracts its own vehement supporters. There is also an independent Royal Opera House Trust, which raises funds using the name of the Royal Opera House to do so, but which then retains the discretion as to how those funds will be spent.

When the interests of these different groups converge, the Main Board of the Royal Opera House is able to take decisions on the basis of what benefits the organization as a whole. But once there is any divergence the different entities tend to move apart and to function in a quasi-independent fashion, sometimes to the detriment of robust overall management and adequate financial control. It is this tendency to split apart under pressure, one part of the organization in conflict with another, that left the Royal Opera House for so long balanced precariously on the edge of a management precipice.

A period of unprecedented change tipped it over. As long as the Royal Opera House was doing the same thing year after year – planning for and presenting opera and ballet in its own theatre – the differences and tensions could be ignored, fudged, glossed over or temporarily resolved. Indeed, at the point at which the lottery award was granted, in 1995, the organization was in reasonably good shape. There had been two reports on its management and operation three years earlier; both had made a number of recommendations for cost-cutting, which by and large had been implemented. A substantial donation had written off most of the accumulated deficit that had been run up in the late 1980s, and for two out of the previous three years the organization had made a small operating surplus. Even wanting to develop their building, but not being able to for lack of funds, was a position with which the Royal Opera House Board and management were familiar and knew how to manage.

Then came the lottery award. This precipitated an entirely new situation with which the management was unfamiliar: that of being able to demolish and rebuild the theatre – paradoxically the easy part[1]

[1] At the time of writing, more than half-way through the building project, it remains on time and on budget, and its management has been commended in a number of reports.

– while at the same time transferring the operation of the performing companies elsewhere. Virtually all the financial difficulties faced by the Royal Opera House during the last two years have arisen because of the decisions, taken in the run-up to the closure period, about what to do with the companies while the theatre was being rebuilt.

One option was to go to the Lyceum, a newly-refurbished theatre of a similar size and ambience to the Royal Opera House, a couple of hundred yards down Bow Street. A problem with this plan was that the Lyceum had very little space backstage, and so it was not possible to store more than one set on site at any one time. Given the restrictions on night-time loading and movement of heavy vehicles, sets could not have been moved in and out at a rate that would have enabled the Royal Opera House to continue playing a number of productions simultaneously in rep. Instead they would have had to mount short seasons of performances of a single opera or ballet, and then change to another one. The management feared that this would have an adverse impact on artistic standards, and since it would not be possible to present so many performances the box office income would be lower than at the Royal Opera House. Going to the Lyceum would also have meant making around 300 members of staff redundant, something the management hoped to avoid.

The proposed alternative option was to build a new, temporary theatre on the south bank of the River Thames, close to Tower Bridge. It would have been constructed so as to enable the same number and pattern of performances as at the Royal Opera House, with slightly more seats. Assuming audiences were willing to travel to Tower Bridge, box office income would have been maintained at around the same level, and it would not have been necessary to make any staff redundant. There were opposing views about the viability of this approach. On the one hand there were artistic and revenue benefits. On the other hand the theatre would cost a further £20 million to build; the site did not have planning permission for the construction of a temporary theatre; and an organization with no experience in major construction projects would have to embark on two simultaneously.

The options were discussed at a succession of Board meetings during the summer of 1995, different Board members proposing different courses of action. Lord Gowrie and I (at that point Chairman and Secretary-General respectively of the Arts Council) gave informal but emphatic advice[2] on a number of occasions to individual Board members, and to Jeremy Isaacs, that the Royal Opera House should go to the Lyceum. The owners of the Lyceum needed a decision before it was known whether the Tower Bridge site would receive planning permission. Eventually the Royal Opera House chose the Tower Bridge option. *Jesus Christ Superstar* went into the Lyceum. Three months later the planning application for the Tower Bridge project was called in by the Department of the Environment, causing substantial delay. By the time planning permission was eventually granted, it was too late for work to start – the Tower Bridge theatre would not have been completed on time to receive the Royal Opera and the Royal Ballet.

There were no other theatres available of a suitable size. The Theatre Royal Drury Lane was occupied by *Miss Saigon*, and *Beauty and the Beast* was going into The Dominion. The Royal Opera House therefore had to rethink their approach to the period in which their own theatre was closed. By this time it was early 1996, and there were only eighteen months to go before the main part of the reconstruction work began. The opera and ballet managements made independent contact with a number of theatres, and the organization effectively split down the middle into two touring companies. This was considerably more expensive than running a single operation, and by June 1996 the plans as they then stood would have cost very substantially more than the Royal Opera House had available for the closure period. The Board took the decision that it would go over

[2] Our advice was informal because officers and members of the Arts Council were not permitted to participate in the running of a funded arts organization, in order to avoid the risk of the Arts Council becoming a shadow director and thus, in the event of an insolvent liquidation, becoming liable for a share of the debt, which would then have to be met from public funds.

budget by £3.5 million, £2.5 million of which would be found from the fund-raising for the building project, and asked the management to revise the plans with a view to eliminating the balance of the overrun. The unfamiliarity of the proposed operation, combined with a disaggregated management structure, made it difficult to take a strong, unified approach to the management of change. By the end of 1996, only six months before the Royal Opera House was due to close, contracts with the receiving theatres had not been signed and the budgets were still out of balance.

I had joined the Arts Council in 1992, and had taken over as Secretary-General in early 1994, immediately after Lord Gowrie had become Chairman. At the point we took office the Arts Council had been weakened by three, successive, Government-driven restructurings during the previous year, as well as the first ever cash cut in its grant. We spent our first year or so restoring the organization's credibility, stopping funded arts organizations going bust, strengthening the relationship between the Arts Council and the regional arts boards, and building a strong distribution system for the arts' share of the national lottery funds for good causes. During this period the Royal Opera House was beginning to pose an increasing number of problems for the Council and its senior staff.

At the end of 1995 it became apparent that the Royal Opera House was having some difficulty in meeting one of the first seven lottery conditions.[3] Rather late in the day, shortly before it was necessary to begin drawing down lottery funds to keep the project on track, it transpired that the Royal Opera House had not fully understood what the Arts Council wanted to see in terms of cash flow forecasts for the period the theatre would be closed. Meetings were held, strong words were uttered, tempers were lost, liquidation was threat-

[3] The lottery award to the Royal Opera House, which was split into two tranches, was subject to eighteen conditions, seven of which had to be satisfied before the first tranche of the award could be paid; a further three before the Royal Opera House could have access to the second tranche; and a final eight, the agreement to which was a precondition of the award but the meeting of which could only be achieved over time.

ened, professional advisers were brought in and, after several traumatic weeks, the condition was finally met. The next set of conditions involved drawing up finalized plans for the closure period. Rather than repeat these scenes, the Arts Council decided to allocate a dedicated monitor to the Royal Opera House, who would make regular reports to the Arts Council while at the same time ensuring that the Royal Opera House understood fully what was required.

Richard Pulford was chosen to be the monitor: he had been joint chief executive of the South Bank Centre for several years, prior to which he had been the Arts Council's Deputy Secretary-General. He understood the needs of, and constraints upon, the Arts Council in distributing public funds and monitoring the use to which they were put; he also had substantial experience of running a large, building-based arts organization. Since leaving the South Bank Centre a few years earlier he had become one of the country's most able and respected freelance arts consultants.

Richard Pulford worked closely alongside the Royal Opera House senior management throughout most of 1996, during which time he presented three reports to the Arts Council. In the first, dated July 1996, he said he thought the closure plans, although tight, would be achievable. His report made reference to the demands that would be made of the Royal Opera House's financial systems and management, but was not unduly pessimistic. In the second report, presented in September, he commented that, although there were aspects of the financial procedures that could be tightened, there were no fundamental deficiencies in them. He also took another look at the closure budgets and said they were achievable as long as box office targets were reached. The third report, presented in December 1996, was not so sanguine. Richard Pulford said that the original closure plans, about which he had reported in July, had metaphorically been left on the shelf while planning had continued throughout the autumn without reference to them. However, although the situation was critical it was recoverable with decisive management action, and such action was now urgently required.

In March 1997 the Royal Opera House management, by this time under new leadership at both Board and executive level, presented revised plans and budgets for the closure period to the Arts Council. The Arts Council had them reviewed by a firm of professional advisers. They, too, said the budgets were tight but achievable, as long as costs were rigidly controlled and box office targets attained. The second tranche of the Royal Opera House's lottery award was confirmed for release. There were two further conditions attached: that the relatively small deficit remaining in the closure budgets should be ironed out during the summer and revised budgets presented to the Arts Council by the end of September 1997, and a business plan for the first sixteen months' operation in the new building should be completed by the end of March 1998.

Up until this point the organization had more or less hung together. There then followed a series of events that intensified the pressure, including the resignation and replacement of the Chief Executive. Genista McIntosh, previously Executive Director of the Royal National Theatre, had been appointed as successor to Jeremy Isaacs in July 1996,[4] and had taken up her post in January 1997. In May 1997 she resigned and left the Royal Opera House immediately. When, later in the year, she was asked why she had done so, she said that she had been extremely unhappy in the job and thought she might become ill if she continued in it.

Lord Chadlington,[5] who had taken over as Royal Opera House Chairman in September 1996, asked me if I would take on the job. I said that I would consider doing so on condition that each member of the Royal Opera House Board, on an individual as well as a collective basis, believed that this was the right thing to do and supported my appointment. I suggested that he discuss the matter with the Department of National Heritage in order to determine whether

[4] At that point the title of the job also changed, from General Director to Chief Executive. The intention was to emphasize the business-like nature of the new management.

[5] Lord Chadlington, or Peter Gummer as he was then, had been a member of the Arts Council until early 1996, and Chairman of its Audit Committee and its Lottery Advisory Panel.

the urgent need for a replacement Chief Executive at this particular time warranted not going through a full recruitment process, and said that I would want to discuss my proposed move with Lord Gowrie. Lord Chadlington spoke to Chris Smith, the new secretary of State for National Heritage, and to each of his Board members; I talked to Lord Gowrie, and then accepted the job. The whole affair generated enormous controversy for a number of reasons, chief among which were the view that, irrespective of the circumstances, the Royal Opera House should have gone through a full recruitment process; speculation about what had made Genista McIntosh so unhappy; and a belief that I should not have gone from the Arts Council to its largest funded organization. The Arts Council, moreover, was unhappy that Lord Chadlington had gone over its head in seeking advice from Chris Smith.

I left the Arts Council immediately, to avoid any conflict of interest between my old responsibilities and my new ones. Lord Chadlington said he thought it important that there was a three month 'insulation' period between my departure from the Arts Council and my arrival at the Royal Opera House, during which time I had nothing to do with either organization.

The establishment of three inquiries followed almost immediately. Chris Smith announced an inquiry into the Royal Opera House development,[6] following which the Arts Council announced its own inquiry into the Royal Opera House, including the nature of the relationship between the two organizations, to be undertaken by an eminent City lawyer, Edward Walker-Arnott. A month later the Select Committee for National Heritage, chaired by Gerald Kaufman, announced a further inquiry into the Royal Opera House, the terms of reference for which included an investigation of the circumstances surrounding Genista McIntosh's resignation and my appointment.

At the same time as all this was happening in the background,

[6] This first inquiry by Chris Smith was subsumed within the Arts Council's inquiry. Chris Smith's second inquiry – that by Sir Richard Eyre – was not announced until November 1997.

the Royal Opera House had discovered in June 1997 a hole in its cash flow of £2 million, and only escaped from its immediate financial difficulties by loans from two donors. To add to the problems a production of *Macbeth* failed to be ready in time for its first night and only concert performances could be given, losing substantial sums at the box office. Meanwhile staff threatened to strike about certain aspects of their payments during the closure period, and over 300 staff were made redundant when the old theatre closed. So by the time I joined the Royal Opera House as Chief Executive, in September 1997, the organization was badly shaken and very apprehensive.

Earlier in the year Richard Hall had been appointed as Finance Director, and he joined the Royal Opera House in July 1997, having previously been an audit partner with one of the major accounting firms. Prior to my arrival he had begun a review of the closure budgets, with a view to eliminating the small remaining deficit before presenting revised budgets to the Arts Council. A few days after I arrived he told me the results: rather than eliminating a deficit of £800,000 over the closure period, his forecast was for a deficit of around £10 million.[7] I did not believe it at first: I thought that either the finance department had made a mistake or that the rest of the organization was trying it on because the Finance Director and I were both new. During the following four weeks we went through repeated budget reviews, trying to reduce the deficit, and uncovering an almost total absence of proper financial information or controls.[8]

[7] The detailed reasons for this huge variance emerged during the following few weeks, and are set out in the diary itself.

[8] The absence of financial procedures was perplexing. Although expressing some reservations, the Royal Opera House's auditors had voiced no major concerns about the nature of the controls in place. Richard Pulford had remarked that although financial procedures could be tightened in certain respects they were broadly adequate. Yet only nine months later a new Finance Director was saying they were virtually non-existent. It is possible that the finance department more or less collapsed under the weight of change when the organization moved out of the House.

That was the point at which the structural weaknesses became exposed. At an executive level it became apparent that the Royal Opera and Royal Ballet effectively regarded themselves as autonomous entities, not coming under the jurisdiction of the overall management, although neither had the infrastructure to exist separately. As a result there was no sense of the management being a single team, all trying to achieve the same objective, and there was no practice of departmental heads working together to reach collective decisions. This perpetuated a sense of opposition, and a belief that problems were the responsibility of the general managers – mainly the Chief Executive and Finance Director – to solve. This is not to say that individuals were unhelpful: everyone was horrified at the prospect of imminent bankruptcy and participated in trying to find savings. It was more the case that artistic decisions had tended to be made without always assessing their financial impact on other parts of the organization, and as a result it was exceedingly difficult suddenly to bring everyone together in order to take tough decisions in response to a crisis.[9]

When the problems reached the Board, this sense of being unable to grapple with them was magnified. The Board, too, responded first with disbelief to the news about the forecast deficit. They had been involved in the detail of drawing up the budgets for the first of the three closure years, and had known the outline but not the details of the following two years' budgets.[10] Disbelief gave way to panic, which exposed divisions within the Board itself, as different groups of Board members tried to drive through different solutions. The Chairman, together with the Finance Director and I, wanted to find a way to keep the Royal Opera House going. Other Board members

[9] During my time at the Royal Opera House I sought to rationalize its structure and operation.

[10] The closure period lasted from September 1997 to December 1999, spanning three financial years. The problems in the first year were due to income shortfalls, as a result of over-optimistic box office projections. The figures in the second two years had, it transpired, been prepared over a very short period of time and the cost projections contained a number of errors and omissions.

wanted to put it into administrative receivership. One Board member – possibly more at times – believed that if the organization was allowed to reach the brink of bankruptcy the Government would step in at the last moment with additional public funds. In fact a charitable source of sufficient funds to avert the immediate crisis was identified relatively early on (the Floral Trust), but there were then repeated Board wranglings over whether that money – which would otherwise have gone towards the building project – should be used instead to ensure the survival of the performing companies. Eventually it was, but only as part of an agreement, jointly negotiated between the Floral Trust, the Board, and the Arts Council, which laid a number of further constraints upon the Royal Opera House.

At the same time another source of funding, the Royal Opera House Trust, began to make its own continued support of both the opera and ballet companies, and the development project, subject to further conditions relating to solvency. As the conditions and constraints being applied by different sources of funds multiplied, the standing and authority of the Board diminished. Then, only a week after the solvency of the Royal Opera House had been assured, the report of the Select Committee for Culture, Media and Sport[11] was published, resulting in the resignation of the Chairman. The remainder of the Board stated their intention to resign[12] and said that they would remain, with caretaker status only, until a new Board had been formed. By the end of 1997 the governance of the organization had more or less fallen apart.

[11] When the name of the Department changed from National Heritage to Culture, Media and Sport, so did that of the Select Committee.

[12] The Select Committee's report had also recommended that I resign. I offered my resignation to the Board but they refused it, insisting I should remain.

Sir Colin Southgate was appointed as the new chairman in January 1998 and during the next few weeks began to rebuild the Board. He also took a fresh look at the management. In an early conversation with Colin Southgate I made it clear to him that if he wanted a different kind of leadership I would step aside. He rapidly came to the view that the organization should be led by an artistic director. Although I disagreed with him at the time, and told him so, with the benefit of the distance of several months I have come to share his views. The experiment begun by the Board in summer 1996, of having the Royal Opera House run by an arts administrator who would build a team around them, has not worked. The only way in which the organization can begin to heal its differences and start to function properly is if it unites behind a really senior, heavy-hitting artistic director of international stature. The management needs to be led by someone who is responsible for executing the business of the organization – putting on opera and ballet – and who leads by imposing his or her weight of experience. The coherence and single-mindedness that the organization needs will only come about through the appointment of an intendant as recommended by Sir Richard Eyre.[13]

This all makes my departure sound, from my own point of view, much more straightforward than it was at the time. In practice there were a couple of months while Colin Southgate was deciding which approach he wished to take towards management during which I was in a rather uncomfortable limbo. At the point at which I actually left the Royal Opera House I was very upset indeed, although I think that was in part a reaction to the intense difficulties I had experienced while I was there. Also, I regretted not being able to finish the job of turning the organization around and taking it back into the new building. Now that I have been away from it for a while my overwhelming sense is one of relief, and I think anyone who reads this diary will understand why.

[13] In fact it is now being proposed that the job is divided into two: an Artistic Director and an Executive Director.

So why publish this diary? Firstly because it offers an informed snapshot of a highly controversial organization, giving an internal perspective on matters that have otherwise received attention mainly from a variety of external points of view. Despite there being a great deal of useful analysis in Richard Eyre's report I think there are critically important issues that have not yet been properly addressed. The most important to my mind is this question of structure: how to heal the divisions that make the Royal Opera House so vulnerable. For example, although Richard Eyre's report emphasized the need for parity between opera and ballet, and discussed the respective roles of an intendant and the Royal Ballet's artistic director, it did not consider the role of the Governors of the Royal Ballet, who – while I was still there – were increasingly coming to shadow the Board and management of the Royal Opera House in wanting to take decisions about the Royal Ballet and its future.

Another critically important question not examined by Richard Eyre is the role of the donors: a major contributing factor to the divisions that characterize the Royal Opera House. In effect the Royal Opera House is caught between two types of master. On the one hand it receives more public subsidy than any other arts organization in the country: it is held to account for that money and must meet various obligations towards the public in order to justify continuing to receive it. On the other hand, because the public subsidy is not large enough to run an international opera house, the Royal Opera House needs to raise substantial funds from companies and individuals. These people, quite rightly, care about what is happening to their money and are entitled to express their views. However, at present they have a direct role in how the organization is run, which creates a tension between the demands of public accountability and the demands of the donors. Until the issues this raises – such as whether donors should be represented on the Board, or be able to place constraints on management's capacity to manage – are resolved, this tension will continue to undermine the organization.

The other reason for publishing this diary is that it is an adventure story. I remember, at one of the most stressful points in the narrative, telling an acquaintance something of what was going on and she said, 'Think of it as an adventure story. Most people don't have the chance to live through adventures; of course there are going to be caves with dragons in them as well as happy endings – at the moment you are facing a dragon in a cave.' The sense of living in a thriller was accentuated on occasions when I had to explain to outsiders, for example at a meeting I had with the Charity Commissioners, what had been going on at the Royal Opera House. Listeners would move from a stance of interested sympathy to one of fascinated horror, sitting on the edge of their seats and saying, 'Yes, and then what happened?' It is hard to resist telling a good story.

This, then, is the story of a group of men and women who found themselves unexpectedly faced with a catastrophe, and describes how they reacted to it. There is no point in pretending this is a dispassionate account: the tapes on which it is based were often dictated while I was experiencing a variety of extreme emotions. Although I do not, now, necessarily agree with everything I said at the time I hope this account conveys a sense of what it was like to go through these experiences. There is an interesting moral question about publishing diaries: would people have spoken as openly, and acted as they did, if they had known that their words and actions were being recorded? In fact, for most people at least, this was not a secret diary. Having decided to keep a diary I told the Board and senior management of the Royal Opera House on a number of occasions that I was doing so in the hope of injecting some sanity into events. It is a matter of opinion whether this tactic succeeded.

It is perhaps presumptuous to hope that this record might also make a contribution, however minor, to the debate about the organization and its future. There are a large number of exceedingly able, committed and energetic people involved in one way or another with the Royal Opera House: none of them has ever wanted anything other than its long-term health and survival, but rarely has so much good intention foundered on so many rocks of disaster. Richard Eyre's report has done much to take that debate forward. It remains to be seen what will result from the proposals announced in

September 1998. But to my mind a successful and popular Royal Opera House will only be achieved once all those with a stake in its success can work together harmoniously, in partnership.

My thanks go to the staff of the Royal Opera House, for their unfailing courtesy, dedication, professionalism and hard work, which enabled the organization to continue producing opera and ballet despite the chaos going on at Board and senior management level. But my deepest and most heartfelt thanks go to my husband, who had to put up with me during this period and who was unfailingly kind, loving, supportive and wise.

Mary Allen
September 1998

Monday 1 September

After three months of waiting I finally had my first day at the Royal Opera House.

Forty-five Floral Street is a Dickensian labyrinth of what look as though they were once warehouses. I located my office, which is filled with large pieces of brown furniture and the walls of which are covered in tatty yellow paint, met Pippa, secretary to Lord Chadlington, and then set out to meet as many other people as I could find. I spent the morning in 45 Floral Street, and in the Bow Street office:[14] most people were enthusiastic about their work and about the prospect of moving to the new theatre. Particularly enjoyed talking to Fay Fullerton in the production wardrobe and Ron Freeman, who is Head of Wigs. The wig department is in the attic: long rows of windows looking out over the roofs of Covent Garden.

In the afternoon I went round the other Floral Street building and met the marketing and music staff, and then had a meeting with Keith Cooper, the Director of Corporate Affairs, and his Marketing Director, Andrew Stokes, about the poor ticket sales at the Labatt's Apollo,[15] which are presently £1.5 million below target. Unless sales improve substantially we could be facing a serious cash crisis.

I returned to my office feeling somewhat stunned, and tried to make a few notes about the people I had met during the day.

[14] The Royal Opera House's administrative offices are located in three buildings adjacent to the theatre: 45 Floral Street, which included my office; 51 Floral Street, and 9 Bow Street.

[15] The Labatt's Apollo was the first London theatre in which the ballet company would be performing during the closure period. It is located in Hammersmith, alongside the flyover, and had been the Hammersmith Odeon when I saw the Beatles there in 1964. It has a large, 3000-seater auditorium, and the programme mostly comprised musicals, such as *Summer Holiday*, and shows like *Riverdance*.

Tuesday 2 September

After a long day I came home feeling confused.

I arrived at work early, in order to read some of the documents I'd been given the previous day. I spent time with Esther – the temp who is helping me out until I have recruited my own PA – setting up some systems, and then off to the meeting of the senior management group. It is far too large, about twelve people, and the agenda comprised mainly tactical matters that had arisen during the previous few days, which were discussed in general terms, mostly without reaching conclusions.

At one point John Harrison, the Technical Director, asked the group to approve expenditure on quite a large item of machinery. I asked whether or not the senior management group had the authority to approve expenditure at that level – no one seemed to know whether the group had any authority at all.

We discussed the financial position of the Royal Opera House, and Richard Hall, the new Finance Director, told the senior management group that it would be undesirable to finish the closure period with a deficit larger than that with which we had started it: £5 million.[16] I pointed out that, since we were already looking at a possible deficit of £1.5 million on the Labatt's season alone, and since there had to be some doubt as to whether the other opera and ballet seasons would achieve their box office targets this year, it was likely that we were going to face a deficit of £7 million or more. Everyone agreed this was not acceptable, but there was no sense of urgency about needing to find a solution.

I had a quick lunch at my desk and then had a series of meetings during the afternoon with those senior staff I had not managed to meet the previous day. John Seekings, the Development Director,[17]

[16] This had arisen mainly during the previous two financial years.

[17] The construction project – known generally as the development – was managed by a team led jointly by John Seekings, a member of the Royal Opera House staff, and John Fairclough, who had been seconded from Stanhope. John Seekings had

seems to have the whole building project well under control. He has views on everything, including the overall management of the new building, all of which are sensible and constructive. I am looking forward to working with him. Other meetings during the afternoon were with Malcolm Warne Holland, the Orchestra Director, and John Harrison. Overall my impression is of a group of able and experienced people working with minimal coordination.

Just before I went home Richard Hall came in, and started discussing next week's management away-day. He has a number of ideas for restructuring the organization, based around the notion of separate profit centres, that he hopes will be adopted following the away-day. I said it sounded as though his ideas might fragment the organization rather than unify it; and said that, as the new Chief Executive, I will wish to participate in developing a new management structure. We were unable to finish the conversation, but will continue it tomorrow.

Wednesday 3 September

Today was better. I felt more in control of what was going on and managed to delude myself, for part of the day at least, that I was managing the Royal Opera House. It is rather like an organizational Gormenghast – everything takes place just out of sight: fascinating goings-on just around corners and along dark passages; most of the important decisions being taken way out of my reach with, I suspect, the intention that they shall remain so.

At the moment, I am at that stage in a new job that when a piece of paper arrives on the desk I look at it and I wonder, what is this about? Why is it being sent to me? What am I meant to do with it now? This process takes several minutes – and I know that in a few months' time the equivalent will be taking only a few seconds.

been with the Royal Opera House for eighteen years, and before he had taken on the job of Development Director had been Deputy Technical Director.

I had good meetings with both Mike Morris[18] and Richard Hall, during which I explained my concern that a new management structure was being cooked up for presentation to me with the expectation that I would endorse it there and then. They both, separately, reassured me that this was not the case, and that the management away-day was merely the beginning of a process in which everyone hoped I would become involved.

Thursday 4 September

Today was another confused blur, talking to people and reading bits of paper whose meaning thus far still largely eludes me. I met several more departments: the orchestra management, the IT department, and the technical department including a long discussion with Eric, the Head of Sound, who struck me as an immensely capable man.

Peter (Lord Chadlington, formerly Peter Gummer, Chairman of the Board) came in half-way through the morning. I had not seen him for over two months and I greeted him by informing him that the financial position was far worse than he imagined, and that if the ticket sales to the Labatt's Apollo did not pick up we were in serious danger of going bust. Peter looked considerably more harassed when he left my office than when he had entered it.

I spent a further two hours with Peter in the afternoon, during which time I outlined what I hoped to achieve before the end of the year in terms of identifying a unified artistic vision for the Royal Opera House as a whole, and firming up plans for making the work of the House much more accessible. Everything, of course, has to add up financially and this is where the difficulty will come. However, Peter agrees with me that it is better to expose these difficulties and work together with the Government and the Arts Council in trying

[18] Personnel Director. Mike had been with the Royal Opera House since 1994 and had done a great deal of work to transform the union agreements, particularly with the technical staff.

to find a solution, rather than to behave belligerently, metaphorically lying on our backs waving our arms and legs in the air and screaming for more money.

After the meeting with Peter I went out for a drink with Keith Cooper in order to discuss how we might structure his job in future. In a meeting we had had shortly before I arrived at the Royal Opera House, Keith had said he thought his job covered too wide a range of tasks. I said that I thought the press element should be separated from the rest; that a new job of External Relations Director should be created, incorporating press relations and government relations; and that he should concentrate on marketing, together with general access initiatives, and the development of broadcasting and large screen relays around the country. The aspects of the new House dealing with sales, such as catering and merchandizing, could become the responsibility of a new Director of Theatre Operations. Keith was not entirely happy with the notion that sales might not be coupled with marketing, and we agreed to keep this particular boundary flexible for the time being. But he is adamant that he wishes to let go of press relations, which I think will help both him and the organization greatly.

Home on the tube; arrived back at 9.30; brief chat to my husband Nigel and then to bed.

Friday 5 September

Yet another day goes by in a mixture of meetings, paperwork, new ideas and exploration of muddle.

The day began with a meeting with John Seekings, the Development Director, who once again impressed me with his competence and energy. I went through with him my idea about setting up staff working groups[19] to deal with different aspects of access to the new

[19] I had decided to set up a number of working groups to explore ways in which the Royal Opera House could be made more accessible. The reason for taking this approach was partly because I believed that the staff were likely to have better ideas

House and he seemed to support what I was planning. He himself wants to be on as many working groups as possible, preferably leading them himself. This is entirely consistent with a man who has already told me that the job he would really like to be doing is mine.

I then went up to the finance department and Richard Hall introduced me to his staff. He also explained the system of internal recharging he would like to put in place, which gave me an opportunity to say that I did not wish to create a gargantuan internal bureaucracy of the kind that has been the tendency in recent years in large institutions such as the National Health Service.

At lunch-time I went up to the model room to hear a presentation by Graham Vick about *The Merry Widow*, accompanied by models and costumes. It is going to be visually stunning – very severe, with mainly black and white costumes against sets that are brilliant purple or pink, mostly comprising painted cloths. It was good to meet Graham who has directed a number of productions at the Royal Opera House that I have admired greatly, particularly *Mitridate* and *Meistersinger*.

During the afternoon I asked a number of people where I could find Nicki Spencer, the Front of House Manager. No one appears to know where her office is located – I will just have to set out into the labyrinth and look for her.

I had a meeting with Keith, following on from our discussion the previous evening, during which I told him that I had gone through our restructuring proposals with Peter, who was excited about them and thought we should implement them immediately. I don't know whether I was imagining it, but Keith looked faintly taken aback. I reassured him about what the remainder of his job would comprise.

I then had two hours with Richard Hall while we dissected the financial crisis facing the Royal Opera House. The budget review that he had initiated earlier in the summer has now been completed.

than the management of what would work in practice, and partly because I wanted to promulgate the idea, throughout the organization, that accessibility was a priority.

It appears that the deficit for the current year, and for each of the two following years, is likely to be in the region of £3 million,[20] giving a total deficit of around £9 million for the twenty-seven month closure period, compared to the £800,000 shown in the budgets presented to the Arts Council in March. *In addition*, no source of funds has yet been identified for the overrun of £3.5 million, which had been agreed by the Board in June 1996, but which now, apparently, the Board are saying they don't know how to fund. We will need to discuss all of this with the senior management group: it cannot be possible that the costs have increased so much in such a short time. I assume that budget holders are trying it on, going for more money, knowing that Richard and I are new.

We also talked about some of the changes Richard wants to make to the existing financial procedures, in order to improve the quality and amount of financial information available. He and I had met shortly before I had started at the Royal Opera House and he had presented me with a list of improvements that he wanted to introduce during his first few months. Some of them will now have to be delayed while we deal with the budgets.

We then discussed the sale of the commercial properties[21] – part of the overall development – and the position of both the Government and the Arts Council in refusing to allow us to use any of the proceeds from the sale to support the continuing operation of the opera and ballet companies. Mark Fisher, the Arts Minister, is presently going so far as to say that none of 'The People's Opera House' should be sold at all. He should look back at the original lottery application, which made it quite clear that most if not all of the commercial properties needed to be sold just to get the thing built at all.

[20] The 1997/98 deficit was due mainly to forecast underachievement at the box office; those for 1998/99 and 1999/2000 were because costs were higher than budgeted.

[21] A substantial amount of the funding required to complete the construction project was to come from selling those parts of the site which were to be developed commercially.

Another meeting with the development team to talk about their budgets – fine (at least there's one part of the organization which isn't hell-bent on bankrupting itself), and the agenda of the Development Steering Committee[22] which is coming up next week. This is a small group of people including both John Sainsbury (ex-Chairman and major benefactor) and Vivien Duffield (major benefactor and Member of the Board) who, apparently, are at their most outspoken in this particular forum.

Nigel collected me at about 7.30 and we went to Suffolk.[23]

Saturday 6 September

Spent most of the day gardening, feeling relaxed and happy to be out in the open. The garden is looking autumnal. I cut back the remainder of the big bed and then cleared all the bushes along the rabbit fence. Nigel was cutting back the large bush that we had decided to get rid of, and while he did so listened to Diana's funeral.

I heard part of it. I have found the whole reaction to her death mystifying. When I first heard the news on Sunday I was shocked but watching the public grief grow during the week, and also attach itself to Dodi Fayed, I began to be bewildered by the extent of the public emotion. I suppose it is rather like the death of Marilyn Monroe, when the very suddenness of it creates a myth instantly.

It also struck me when listening to the funeral, in particular the hymn *I vow to thee my country*, that I have very ambivalent feelings about any event such as this that generates an outpouring of British

[22] The development was being undertaken by a company called Royal Opera House Developments Limited (ROHDL). It was overseen on the part of the Royal Opera House Main Board by the Development Steering Committee, which included among its membership several members of the Main Board. In addition there was a Design Sub-Group, which looked at the detail of the design and considered certain operational issues such as catering.

[23] During the week we lived in Highbury, but at weekends we tried to get away to our house in Suffolk as often as possible.

patriotism, or a sense of Britishness. Although I was born and brought up in this country, my mother has emphasized her Irishness all my life and, as I once explained to her, I could not be British without rejecting her and her Irishness; and yet I am not Irish. This means that sometimes I have a feeling of not really belonging here – of being stateless. When I heard the Westminster Abbey congregation singing *I vow to thee my country* there was a part of me that wished I, too, could sing a song like that and feel a real sense of belonging to this land.

We gardened for most of the day until I went off to Ipswich to do some minor shopping, and to Woodbridge to buy bulbs. I came back and planted them – always far more of a chore than I remember when I am buying them – and then watched Nigel at the bonfire.

Later I went in to play the piano, which had been delivered that morning. It is the most beautiful piece of furniture with art deco casing and foot plate. I think the tone is all right – always when I buy something I am convinced, once it is truly mine, that I have made a mistake and it is not good enough.

We lit a fire and read and listened to music for the rest of the evening. There was not a sound apart from the Schubert and the noise of the fire logs crackling.

Sunday 7 September

Spent the morning working. Nigel went off to play tennis with John Huntingford, a regular tennis partner, at 11.30 and I carried on working until I went over to join the Huntingfords at 1.00 p.m.

Their house was looking mellow among the autumn colours. At one point Nigel and I went out to pick tomatoes from the vines in the greenhouse and the air was warm and scented as we picked off the yellow and red fruit. I felt an almost physical pang of envy at the Huntingfords' lifestyle: moving through each day in a leisurely fashion, their physical needs met, living in an ancient house and large garden with their family, all together.

We returned home and continued working for the rest of the day, with a brief interlude for a swim – an error on my part, since although the water was 84° the ambient temperature was considerably lower and the overall effect chilling.

Monday 8 September

Got up at 5.00 in order to drive back to London. Into work by 9.00.

Spent the morning going on a site visit around the development. The project is far, far larger than one would imagine from having heard about it. It covers many acres and does not just involve constructing – or reconstructing – a theatre, but also building new offices, studios, workshops and vast spaces for the storage of sets.[24] Although it is still at a very early stage there is enough of the building already constructed to begin to get a sense of how monumental, and visionary, it will be.

I then had back-to-back meetings with Nicholas Payne (the Opera Director), Anthony Russell-Roberts (the Ballet Administrator)[25] and Keith Cooper, during which I talked with them about my ideas for broadcasting and relays to other venues; public relations; and the possibility of developing a more unified approach to artistic policy. Everyone was polite. I am beginning to realize that this merely

[24] One of the most important aspects of the development was that it would enable the sets to be stored on wagons, which would be kept in large storage bays. Up to seven shows could be stored on site, with a turnaround time of two hours between taking one show off the stage and putting another on. This innovation would reduce the number of technical staff employed, whle at the same time enabling a more intensive use to be made of the stage.

[25] Nicholas Payne was responsible for the opera programme and Sir Anthony Dowell for the ballet programme. Anthony Dowell worked closely with Anthony Russell-Roberts, who was responsible for the administrative aspects of running the ballet company. All three were members of the senior management group although Anthony Dowell did not attend regular meetings unless the ballet programme was being discussed.

signifies a disinclination explicitly to disagree with me at that particular point in time.

Vivien Duffield came to see me at around 5.30. We had a hugely enjoyable hour during which she jumped from one subject to another, expressing herself with great vigour on all of them. She said quite categorically that if we did not receive more money from the Government she would withdraw not only her own funds, but also those of all the other donors. Richard Hall has already told me that she has been expressing these views frequently during the last couple of months. I said to Richard that she had been saying as much to me almost constantly during the last five years. However, when she repeated these sentiments to me today, they seemed to have a force that I had not heard from her before. But it was good to see her again. I love Vivien's energy and her passion about the Royal Opera House.[26]

Tuesday 9 September

I came home shattered. The first part of the day, from 9.00 until 2.00 was taken up by the management away-day. This is the third such meeting that has taken place during the last four months, and is the culmination of a process that began when Genista McIntosh resigned, in response to a sense on the part of some members of the senior management group that if there was no one to lead them towards a more coordinated mode of working then they needed to start thinking about that for themselves.

The day began with an inconclusive discussion about a unified artistic vision, during which both Anthony Russell-Roberts and

[26] I had known Vivien Duffield for several years while I had been at the Arts Council and she had been on the Board of the Royal Opera House. She had always been one of the more articulate and outspoken Board members, well aware of the need for proper financial controls. She was also a generous donor and an extremely effective fund-raiser.

Nicholas Payne said that they did not think that such a thing was either desirable or possible. I suggested that such a vision might not relate specifically to individual projects, or even working together on joint projects, but rather to a number of artistic aspirations to which both companies could subscribe – for example, commissioning new work, musical excellence, and innovative design. There was a lot of nodding while I was speaking but I did not feel convinced that there was any desire to convert this into action.

The meeting went on to consider management structures; there was much interesting discussion but luckily nothing that even began to lead towards a decision. I said at the end that I would want to consider further everything I had heard before reaching any conclusions.

During the afternoon we had the regular senior management meeting during which I took the decision that it was time to begin alarming the senior management about the present financial position. I am not sure how successful I was in alarming them, although I was certainly very successful in alarming myself. I first set out the position regarding the budgets for the coming years. The finance department has done some more work on the figures, which now show deficits of £3.7 million for 1998/99 and £3.1 million for 1999/2000, in addition to the substantial income losses – £3 million or so – forecast for 1997/98. I remarked that I found it hard to understand how budgets and plans that had been submitted to the Arts Council in March, showing a total deficit of £800,000 for the entire closure period, could have altered so much in the last six months.

I then suggested we might start by analysing the changes that had taken place since the March budgets had been prepared, in order to identify their financial consequences. Judging by the demeanor of colleagues this was an unorthodox approach, which was not welcomed. Richard Hall suggested another couple of approaches and we eventually agreed that we would instigate another, bottom-up budget review, this time looking for all possible savings. In many respects it was a discouraging meeting: having spent the morning discussing team working, there was no sense from those around the table that the financial problems were regarded as 'our' problems. Rather they were 'their' problems – 'their' in this case meaning me and Richard.

I spent some time thinking about the best way of dealing with the announcement, both internally and externally, regarding the appointment of a new Director of External Relations, and then went up to see Richard Hall. We talked about the budgets and deficits: we are both becoming increasingly worried about the whole state of the finances. There is so much that needs to be done in the finance department that will now have to be put off while we go through a full budget review. I was feeling tired and frustrated. I feel that I am wrestling with a miasma, a fog that I cannot define or pin down. The budget-making process is opaque, decision-making is incomprehensible, and I cannot yet see how I am ever going to gain any sort of control over this impossible organization.

Wednesday 10 September

Went in the morning to the Royal Ballet at Baron's Court.[27] Watched a number of classes and then watched rehearsals. I find dancers quite awe-inspiring: their physical capacities are so extraordinary, and dancers of this calibre make their movements look, even from very close up, effortless. I watched Anthony Dowell coach Belinda Hatley and Michael Nunn in *Giselle*; then I watched Viviana Durante and Irek Mukamedov dance the balcony *pas de deux* from *Romeo and Juliet.* Even in a rehearsal room, with the music being played on a piano and the dancers wearing rehearsal clothes, I was moved almost to tears. I could not quite believe that these artists were rehearsing this work in front of my eyes.

The ballet company is very straightforward: the people are friendly and the emphasis on physical exertion gives the impression that the

[27] The Royal Ballet was based in Baron's Court, in offices and studios rented from the Royal Ballet School. One of the purposes of the development was to enable the Royal Ballet to join the rest of the organization in Covent Garden.

whole group is just getting on with it.

I returned to the Royal Opera House offices at about 2.00. The afternoon comprised a meeting with Mike Morris, John Seekings, and Richard Hall about the operational aspects of planning for the new building. Although a long meeting it was a good one. All three are keen to work together as a group and want to get things moving.

Thursday 11 September

I spent most of the morning at the Barbican at the general rehearsal of *Giulio Cesare*: it is going to be good, with a design that is clean and arresting, excellent singers and – with just a few over-camp moments – entertaining direction.

Back to the office where I had lunch with Peter Katona (Artistic Administrator for the opera company). Many people have described him as the lynchpin of the opera company, since he is the person responsible for booking the singers, and for having quite a considerable input into the choice of conductors. Although we talked about the process of developing ideas for the repertory I still do not have any clear sense of how the programme as a whole emerges, or indeed who takes decisions about what it should be.

There was then a meeting of the Development Steering Committee, comprising Peter, Vivien, John Sainsbury, Kit McMahon (ex-Main Board Member and Chairman of the Development Steering Committee), Stuart Lipton (Chairman of Stanhope, the company that had constructed the new theatre at Glyndebourne), and the various professional teams. Discussion ranged between grave consideration of a half-million pound overrun on the tenders for the front-of-house fit-out, to a debate involving Vivien and myself as to whether or not there ought to be a tree on runners at the centre of a champagne bar in the Floral Hall. After the meeting I advised John Seekings and John Fairclough that if they wanted to get substantial business through a meeting of that kind they ought always to ensure that there was a tree, or its equivalent, on the agenda – steering committees find it easier and more entertaining to talk about such matters than about serious issues to do with the construction.

I went to the launch of the French Theatre Season at the French Embassy, where I saw Sue Robertson and Trevor Phillips.[28] I asked Trevor how he was enjoying being a member of the Arts Council and he said that all the Arts Council seemed to have done since he joined it was talk about the Royal Opera House. I spent some time talking to Nicholas Kent, Director of the Tricycle Theatre, who told me that he had received – through what means he did not make clear – a number of wardrobe covers from the Royal Opera House which had been dispensed with at the time the theatre had closed. Apparently these are worth quite a lot of money and he could not believe that any arts organization would be prepared to let such things go without either trying to sell them or making a gift of them.

While I was talking to Nicholas Kent, John Drummond[29] walked past. I stepped into his path so he could not escape short of actually running away or knocking me over and asked if he had received the letter I had written him the previous week. John is very knowledgeable about ballet and I had wanted to discuss the Royal Ballet programme with him. I had forgotten how tall he is: when he lifted his chin to one side he seemed to loom at least six and a half feet above me. He obviously did not want to talk, but I was determined that we should do so. He said that he was going away during the autumn and would not be able to meet me. I said well, perhaps we might meet at the Ballet Board.[30] He then exploded.

[28] Chief Executive and Chairman, respectively, of the London Arts Board. Trevor Phillips was also a member of the Arts Council.

[29] John Drummond had run, among other things, the Edinburgh Festival and The Proms. Although I had known him slightly when I had been at the Arts Council, he had not welcomed my appointment to the Royal Opera House, and had not spoken to me since.

[30] In addition to the Main Board there had for some years been two subsidiary Boards: the Opera Board and the Ballet Board. John Drummond had been a member of the Ballet Board. Peter had suspended these Boards for a time in order to rethink their role and their membership.

'Are there going to *be* any more meetings of the Ballet Board?' he asked in a tone of passionate disdain.

I said that was a matter for Peter.

'No it's not, it's a matter for *you*,' he shouted.

I said I did indeed have a strong view about the subject but it was Peter, as Chairman of the Board, who would take the decision.

'My view is that we should keep them,' I said.

I finally managed to elicit from him a very grudging agreement that perhaps he would be able to meet with me when he came back from Australia.

John Drummond has already written to Peter that I am 'openly hostile to classical dance'. I am not, although there are certain three-act classical ballets that I find somewhat artistically unexciting.

Friday 12 September

A series of meetings in the morning as I continue getting to know the staff.

Lunch with Ian Albery[31] at the Garrick Club, during which he told me that Sadler's Wells is now ten weeks late, and that there might well be financial problems at the end of October. I made a mental note to review the contract with Sadler's Wells on my return.

Returned to the Royal Opera House for yet more meetings culminating in a long session with Mike Morris at the end of the day. He is very good at his job, although sometimes rather fierce in his approach to staff difficulties.

[31] Chief Executive of the Sadler's Wells Theatre. Sadler's Wells was in the process of being redeveloped with the aid of an Arts Council lottery award; upon completion it was going to house the Royal Opera and Royal Ballet during the second part of their closure period.

Saturday 13 September

Went to the first night of *Cesare*. Afterwards I went backstage with Nicholas Payne and we greeted the cast as they came off and then went round to the dressing rooms. The singers were exuberant after the performance.

Sunday 14 September

Worked.

Monday 15 September

I woke up feeling listless. I was unable to do anything other than respond to the day rather than get on top of it, with the result that I sank into one of my *Cloud of Unknowing* states about the Royal Opera House.

I spent the morning walking around and continuing to meet new people. I finally found Nicki Spencer and Phillipa Rooke, the House Management team, hidden behind a door marked 'Lighting Consultant'.

I then had a meeting with Anthony and Nicholas about programming the new studio theatre.[32] It began rather awkwardly, with me setting out some possible approaches to artistic direction. After a while they both became more lively and Nicholas, in particular, started producing some excellent ideas.

Lunch with Bob Gavron (a senior Main Board Member) at The Ivy, during which we discussed a range of matters about the Royal Opera House: management, financial control and future planning. I went back for a meeting with Peter during which we covered much

[32] In addition to the main stage, the new building would also house a smaller, 400-seat theatre.

the same ground; then on to a meeting of the Remuneration Committee, during which – in the interstices of the other business – we yet again trotted around the same course. It is so easy to talk about bringing the Royal Opera House finances under control, but so very, very hard to do.

A call from the press office near the end of the day: apparently David Lister, arts correspondent of the *Independent*, has got on to the changes to Keith's role. I do not want to have to make any announcement until Keith is back from his holiday and we agreed that we would wait to see if David was bluffing before we took any action.

Home on the tube. Met Nigel walking out of Arsenal tube station and we walked home together. He is in ebullient form. I continue to feel gloomy. I am in one of my moods where I wish that I didn't have to work at all.

Tuesday 16 September

I bought the *Independent* on the way to the underground, and saw that David Lister had obviously received a leak since he set out the position vis à vis Keith Cooper and the new Director of External Relations with remarkable accuracy. Far more so, I suspect, than if he had been formally briefed. It was a good piece in that there was no positive or negative spin to it, merely a description of precisely what I was intending to do.

Went to the National Gallery for the Seurat breakfast and the first people we saw when we walked in were Carolyn Eady and Michael Portillo. Had an excellent breakfast with Michael who is looking more light-hearted than he has done for years. Carolyn said that, now he could finally stop watching the news every night or going into the House of Commons, they have spent virtually the whole time since 1 May going to parties. She also acknowledged that when you have been *that* busy, if you don't do something most of the time you can feel very depressed.

I saw Norman Lebrecht of the *Telegraph* across the room and, sure enough, when I stood up he came across and was charming – the charm of a journalist trying to extract information. The trouble with me is that I enjoy the company of many of them very much and am therefore too susceptible to their interest and flattery.

Went to the office. No one was in when I arrived and so I was able to do less than I had wanted in order to prepare for the announcement that afternoon about the changes to Keith's job and the new post.

Went up to the senior management meeting at 10.45. This one was the worst yet. We started off on the subject of complimentary tickets, with me remembering from the Arts Council just how grisly the whole question of ticket entitlements can be.[33] A large number of the comps go to staff: Nicholas Payne opined that as far as his staff were concerned 'they'll do what I tell them', while Mike Morris reminded him that most staff had a contractual entitlement to free tickets and they probably would not be prepared to 'do as they were told'. It has every appearance of being what I call a black hole project, in that an immense amount of energy will be poured into it without anything happening at all. I drew an inconclusive discussion to a close, having agreed that Richard Hall would prepare a note setting out the present position. Next week we'll discuss how we can rationalize it.

We then went on to budgets – a pessimistic account from Richard Hall about how he does not believe the budget review will yield substantial savings, and that we are likely still to be many millions adrift over the next two years. I commented that we seemed to have designed an organization[34] that cost considerably more than we

[33] In the old House, substantial amounts of money were being lost through excessive numbers of complimentary tickets being handed out in all directions. The closure period offered an opportunity to develop a more sensible and consistent approach.

[34] The original closure budgets had shown staff numbers considerably lower than those that had eventually been agreed: one of the reasons why the budgets now failed to balance was that the overhead costs were higher than had been allowed for. But the detail of that only came to light during the following weeks.

could afford to pay for it, and that, once we knew the final figures, we might have to take some very unpleasant decisions indeed.

The conversation drifted on to the question of budgets for the new theatre with Nicholas exclaiming that, 'Surely we could not be contemplating spending less on the opera and ballet in the new theatre, otherwise what was the point of having one?' I merely said that we could only spend the amount of money available and although he described the position as impossible it was, nonetheless, the position.

From there we progressed to financial procedures – yet more clashes, this time about who has the right to be involved in decision-making at various stages. First we talked on the pragmatic level of whether or not there was time to introduce any form of procedure for decisions about the main stage programme in the new House for 1999/2000. Then, on the level of principle, we discussed whether formal procedures of this kind were a good idea (thank God most people seemed to think that they were). Finally, on the more fundamental level, we began to talk about whether or not we were trying to run an integrated entity, or separate opera and ballet companies with additional services – such as technical and wardrobe – set off on one side.[35] I made my points; Nicholas made his points; the rest of the senior management group chipped in as they felt like it. The schism between the artistic heads and the other senior managers is becoming increasingly obvious. The former do not give the impression that they wish to be part of a collective management process. As far as they are concerned they are running their own companies and they want to be left to get on with it. Everyone else, in contrast, reckons that if they are left to get on with it they will rapidly – perhaps they already have – bankrupt us.

I concluded the discussion by asking Nicholas whether he thought the Chief Executive should have the right to approve the overall

[35] To my mind this remains the most fundamental issue about the Royal Opera House and its apparent resistance to any form of rational management. Sometimes it's regarded as one type of organization and sometimes another, with decision-making slipping down the cracks in between.

schedules. After a very long pause indeed he concluded that the Chief Executive should.

I moved on swiftly. The rest of the meeting comprised mainly an update from me on my thinking about senior management structures and a decision to commemorate Princess Diana somewhere in the development – we must get moving on that while the Diana momentum is still strong.

Lunch with Sally Greene and Joyce Hytner[36], where I met all kinds of people I had not seen for some time, including David Puttnam – on excellent form – and Mark Fisher, who was just about prepared to say he would meet me although he was sure he would not enjoy what I had to say. I said that it was better that someone should describe the problem to him, rather than him regarding it as a black hole of horror. He reluctantly agreed. Ed Victor, the literary agent, kissed me and said he would give me a few tips on running the Royal Opera House (I wish he would) and I sat next to John Mortimer at lunch.

Back at the Royal Opera House to see everybody who was affected by the announcement about Keith Cooper. Most people seemed OK, although it is hard to tell when a group of staff stand quietly and look at you.

After lunch I met with John Dowling, Grey Gowrie's personal assistant, in my office. John said that Grey wanted to leave the Arts Council now that I had gone – apparently it was no fun any longer. We have arranged that Grey and I will have supper together, if possible before my appearance in front of the Select Committee.

Then off to the meeting of the Governors of the Royal Ballet School, and an interesting discussion about recent reports of possible bullying at the school. Angela Bernstein, a Governor, forced the meeting to face the key issues – no one else appeared to have the stomach for it.

[36] Sally Greene is a theatre owner, who was trying to raise money to redevelop the Collins Theatre in Islington. The lunch was a fund-raising event, which had been organized by Joyce Hytner who was helping Sally to raise money.

To the Royal Academy for the preview of the Sensation show – and it was, in many respects. The Myra Hindley portrait was a powerful, shocking and haunting piece of work. Some of the more explicitly sexual pieces I disliked.

Wednesday 17 September

Spent the first part of the morning meeting more members of staff in the education department. I had been told that, during the last few years, the Royal Opera House had tended to boast publicly about its education department, as evidence of its commitment to accessibility, while privately slashing its budgets. If this was the case both heads of department were remarkably buoyant and optimistic. They were enthusiastic about their work and keen to develop it further once we move back into the new theatre.

I then went up to the wardrobe and spent some more time with Lorraine Ebdon, Head of Costume, whose company I am increasingly enjoying. She introduced me to various members of her staff, including the woman who was in charge of men's tailoring. I had not realized that when a designer sketches out a few rough scribbles to indicate what the costumes should look like, the staff then proceed to cut patterns from these sketches. It is an amazingly skilled and – at least for someone of my ignorance – complex business. I was shown how the pattern of one jacket was being adapted for a character who wore it habitually slung over one shoulder, with fullness being taken from the back and the front so that it hung properly. We then went down to the dye shop, where there were huge vats of bubbling black and indigo dye, and saw costumes being distressed with bleach and wax for *Billy Budd.* Then back to shoes, to see ballet boots being buffed and polished. Each one is made by Gamba for the individual dancer's feet.

Back to a meeting with Richard Hall, who told me he wanted to put a little more 'oomph' in the process of reviewing the budgets. He is worried that we will not meet the Arts Council's deadline of the end of the month. I said that there appeared to be little chance of eliminating the entire forecast deficit by the end of the month. Rather than dash towards a spurious deadline, therefore, I would like to use the budget review process to explore the Royal Opera House's budgeting procedures – if there were any, which was not immediately apparent – with a view to identifying how we might strengthen them. As far as the deficit itself is concerned we should aim to get it down as far as possible, then we would need to agree with the Board how we communicated with the Arts Council and the government. In the meantime I would deal, if necessary, with the Arts Council and the Department of Culture, Media and Sport (DCMS) as regards timing. He continued to look anxious but accepted my point. He said that so far the finance department had only managed to find £½ million from the overhead budgets, and he was still not confident that Nicholas and Anthony would find more than another £1 million between them. I reiterated that I wished the review to go forward as an orderly process – we mustn't panic.

Richard is also worried about the state of the finance department. Now all the staff are involved in the budget review he's had to delay the changes he wants to make.

Half an hour to myself and then lunch in my office with Gwynne Howell, a rumbly Welsh bass full of funny anecdotes. He first sang at the Royal Opera House thirty years ago and has been returning ever since. The way he describes the company gives me the sense of a long-lived, extended family. I can never hope to belong to it myself, but I don't mind. I just hope I can keep it together and move them all into their new home.

From there I went to a large meeting called the House Coordination Meeting. This comprises the middle management, those who I feel are the real movers and shakers of the organization. The interest lay not in the meeting itself, but rather in observing everybody and seeing how they interacted.

Back to my office to read some paperwork. Near the end of the day I received and read a memo from Nicholas on the budget cuts. Although it only covered a couple of pages, it was a long list of detailed, well-thought-through measures to create savings. And Richard is right: they only come to about £1 million or so. How on earth the original budgets were put together I cannot imagine, to allow such a large variance to emerge after only six months – it all seems to defy any logic. For the first time it started to sink in that we might really be facing a deficit of more than £10 million for the closure period. Given that we are already carrying an accumulated deficit of £5 million that was incurred in the years up to closure, it is hard to see how we can make the budgets balance without drastic measures.

Nigel collected me and we went over to see our friends Mary Gibson and David Barrie for dinner. Once we had found the street we realized that we couldn't remember the number – I was determined it was 42 but even I could see when we passed a semi-derelict house that I might be wrong. Nigel thought it was 14: I knocked on the door and an elderly man opened it, letting out a waft of chilly air. Then we tried 13, just for the hell of it, and got it right. The only other guests were Rick and Lizzie (Mary's twin sister) and we had a delightful evening, except that my hay fever, which had been brewing all day, exploded into action when I came into contact with the hair of their cats. Left as early as we could and I drove home sneezing all the way.

Thursday 18 September

Woke up at 5.00, worrying about the budgets. Every solution I can think of brings with it a greater problem. For example if we cancel the whole closure programme then the Arts Council might cut the grant. If we make large numbers of staff redundant then we won't be able to present the closure programme or enter the new House.

The day started with a meeting with Richard Hall, Nicholas Payne and Anthony Russell-Roberts. Richard and I had agreed that we would use the first part of the meeting to examine the budget cuts being proposed in Nicholas's memo, and that we would not get on to our larger fears until later. I managed to sustain this position until, after fifteen minutes' discussion between Nicholas and Anthony as to whether or not we should shift the ballet season in the Coliseum by one week, in order to make a saving of about £35,000, I said that since we were still many millions down perhaps we ought to be a little braver in our thinking. Nicholas seemed to understand what I was saying but Anthony gave me the impression that he had hardly taken in the scope of our financial problems. We then went on to explore, yet again, some of the implications of a £10 million deficit during the closure period, but without any suggestions being made that would materially alter the position.

To lunch with Melanie Leech, a senior civil servant at the DCMS with responsibility for the arts. We had worked together closely when I had been at the Arts Council. I was delighted to see her – a breath of sanity from the old world, rather than the madness of the new. I was quite close to telling her my fears about the Royal Opera House but implied them instead, agreeing with her that although she might hint to Hayden Phillips[37] that there could be trouble on the way, she would not be any more specific until I was able to give her further guidance.

From lunch I went, via a short meeting with John Seekings and John Fairclough, to a meeting of the Design Sub-Group. This committee comprises John Sainsbury, Vivien Duffield, Stuart Lipton, Peter and me, together with various professionals. We looked at elements of the architecture, and discussed the seats, signage, and the design of bars. Everyone had a different opinion; each had financial implications. In contrast to the Development Steering Committee the previous week, when we had all been concerned to save as much money as possible, this week we were deciding to upgrade the finishes and spend more money.

A few minutes back in the office and then on to the Appeal

[37] Sir Hayden Phillips was the Permanent Secretary in the DCMS. I had also worked closely with Hayden while I had been at the Arts Council, often on matters concerning the Royal Opera House.

Committee[38]. I said my piece, and Vivien remarked it was a delight that the new Chief Executive was so optimistic. I thought silently, 'If only you knew, and you will soon.'

Then over to the Tate Gallery to spend an hour and a half with Nick Serota, the Director of the Tate. He is so measured, calm and judicious. I enjoy spending time with such people because I find – or at least I like to think I find – that these qualities rub off a little on me. At any rate I was able to conduct most of the conversation in a tone of voice that matched his. We fenced somewhat, each giving away little, except I probably paused just a little too long when he asked about the future of the Royal Opera House.

I keep telling myself that I'm always the same when I start new jobs: the moment I spot problems I see them as being larger than they are. Though, come to think of it, it is difficult to imagine a problem that could be much larger than a deficit approaching £16 million.

Hey ho.

Friday 19 September

Woke up early in the morning after a nightmare: I had been walking up a hill that suddenly became very much steeper, so much so that I had to lie on the ground to avoid rolling all the way down to the bottom. Half-way down there was a flatter area with a fountain. I edged my way slowly back down towards this, and then suddenly found myself in a pond, neck deep in water. Beside the edge of the pond stood a tall woman, with a long blowpipe, rather like a bamboo, in her hand. She blew a dart into my chest and I felt as though I had become paralyzed. Nonetheless I managed to continue

[38] The Appeal Committee was part of the Royal Opera House Trust, an independent charitable trust established in order to raise money for the Royal Opera House. The purpose of the appeal was to raise funds for the development. Both the Trust and the Appeal Committee were chaired by Vivien Duffield, who had herself given several million pounds towards the Appeal.

edging my way down the mountain, and then suddenly I found myself beside the fountain. The woman was coming towards me; there was another woman there and I managed to leap into her arms – I was trying to explain what was wrong but the only sounds I could make were moans and groans, although I still had the strength to cling on around her neck.

At that point I woke up. I had been moaning and groaning in my sleep and I had also woken Nigel. I described the dream to him and he suggested that the mountain was the Royal Opera House, which had suddenly become far more difficult than I had anticipated.

I went to the office. Richard Hall came down at 8.30 and we started going through the budgets. This was the first time I had looked at the papers myself and the first task was to make sure we could actually understand them. The papers just about married, one sheet to another, although they are the most higgledy-piggledy sets of figures you could imagine. There were whole chunks of budgets for which there were no adequate back-up sheets at all. Richard said he would try and locate them – if they existed – and would let me have them by the end of the day. If the back-up sheets don't exist then how were the front sheets arrived at? I once again began to feel as though I was clambering around inside a bowl of mental treacle.

I asked Richard what progress we had made on comparing these budgets with those that had been produced in March, to see where the differences were and why they had occurred. Richard said that it would not be possible since the March budgets (prepared several months before his arrival) were in no order whatsoever. There were some files with heaps of papers in them, but nothing that resembled what we were now looking at. In that case, I said, I would like the auditors to pull together those papers into budgets using the same format as the most recent version, so that we could make that comparison. I wanted to know what had happened, the Board would want to know what had happened – and so, no doubt, would the Arts Council.

We then started looking at the possible solutions to our difficulties. Richard keeps saying that we are not going to be able really to tackle the larger numbers without also tackling the issue of head-count. By which, of course, he means redundancies. I pointed out to him that the credibility of the whole organization would be shattered if, having just gone through a substantial and painful round of redundancies,[39] we were suddenly to say the original decisions were wrong and a smaller organization should have been created. Because, of course, that is the problem: an organization has been created of a certain size, with not enough money to pay for it.

In any case it would not be possible to continue presenting the closure programme if we made substantial numbers of people redundant. Let's say we were really to tighten the screws in every direction, we might be able to continue with the closure programme and make up to twenty or so people redundant, without having to replace them with casuals. But the amount of money we would save, once we had netted off the cost of the redundancy payments, and once we had also factored in the need to begin staffing up in about eighteen months time to prepare ourselves to enter the new theatre, would be around 3 or 4 per cent of the deficit that we were trying to tackle. There is no sense in causing so much anxiety and insecurity for such a tiny gain. I think Richard agreed with me and I hope that we have now put that option firmly to bed.

We then looked at the rep, and whether or not we could make much more swingeing cuts than those envisaged at present. In other words, rather than distilling the existing artistic plans down into – as Nicholas describes it – the essence of what we need to do, we could start from a blank sheet of paper and work upwards, towards the minimum level of activity that would enable the companies to keep their creative muscles reasonably well-flexed. We agreed, however, that the two options would probably come to the same point, whereby reductions in the cost of activity began to be overtaken by reductions in the income from ticket sales. So we are probably embarked on the right course, via Nicholas's suggestions, to identify maximum savings from the rep.

[39] Around 300 members of staff had been made redundant when the Royal Opera House had closed in July 1997.

The only other approach we could think of was to squeeze every possible line of non-rep expenditure. I said that once Richard had given me the back sheets for all of the corporate budgets I would tackle them over the weekend.

I then went to the meeting of the opera company. There were a few people there who I hadn't yet met, and I sat and listened. An interesting exchange between Nicholas and some members of his staff. They are obviously worried about cost containment and seem to be more aware of the dangers of overspending than Nicholas himself, who became defensive when challenged.

Walked across Covent Garden to lunch. One of the things I love about this part of London is the sheer activity and bustle of it all, so different from the stuffiness of Westminster where I had been based when I was at the Arts Council. There are times when I walk through the streets around the office when I almost begin to feel happy.

After lunch an afternoon that was a mixture of walking around the offices and trying to wade through some paperwork. Fridays are good for meeting people. I spent some time in the ballet office talking to Anthony Russell-Roberts and getting to know Louise Shand-Brown, the ballet company manager.

Then another meeting with Richard Hall. This time we were looking more strategically at how the Board might react to our bad news. There are so few options: only one, really, which is that we gain access to the interest on the £10 million remaining in the Floral Trust,[40]

[40] The funds in the Floral Trust had been given for the purpose of supporting the development, although the terms of the Trust Deed were drawn more broadly than that, referring to general support of the Royal Opera House and the performing companies. Its funds had originally totalled £25 million, which had risen through interest accruing to £30 million. The trustees were George Magan, of Hambro Magan, Lord Carrington, Sir Jeremy Isaacs, Sir Angus Stirling and Lord Chadlington. At the time Richard, Peter and I began considering using some or all of the money to save the Royal Opera House, £20 million had already been given to the development and there was some £10 million remaining. We estimated that interest amounting to around £1.5 million would accrue on this during the next two years.

and add that to the interest on the proceeds of the property sales.[41] Even if we made many millions of further savings this would hardly bridge the gap. In any case, we both agreed that the likelihood of the Board endorsing any option that involved transferring funds out of the development and into the operating company was remote. Far more likely, we felt, would be that both Vivien Duffield and John Sainsbury would insist on talking to the Prime Minister and asking for more money. The Prime Minister's response would almost certainly be no.

After more discussion Richard and I gradually came to the conclusion that, in the event no funds were forthcoming from any source, we would have to advise the Board they could not any longer trade solvently, and the organization should be closed down. When we discuss these options it all seems absurdly melodramatic, but it is hard to see what the alternatives might be. I feel strangely cut off from the whole business, almost as though I am an observer to events that are happening to someone else. The sheer magnitude of the issues makes them seem unreal.

During the afternoon I had a phone call from Mike Wooley, the Finance Director at English National Opera (ENO), who told me that it had been announced today that Dennis Marks, the general Director of ENO, had resigned. Immediately I heard the news I rang Nicholas Payne, ostensibly to ensure that he knew, actually to drive home the message that ENO, as a company, are in an even worse position than we are since they have debts at an equivalent level[42] with no assets to set against them, and they do not have the political leverage of a large hole in the ground. Nicholas is quite bright enough to know what I was getting at, and I hope he will be reassured by evidence that I want him to stay.

[41] Although we were not allowed to use the proceeds from the sales to help shore up the revenue operation, it had been agreed that we could use the interest accruing on the proceeds, which it was calculated might be in the region of £1.5 million.
[42] Soon afterwards ENO received a stabilization award from the arts lottery funds, which reduced the deficit.

Saturday 20 September

Woke up around 9.00 after a really good – in fact surprisingly good in view of the circumstances – night's sleep. Went into Ipswich with Nigel, returned, looked around the garden, had lunch.

A desultory day until, at around 4.00, I began looking at the contracts. Most of them are reasonably standard, although it is surprising that we still have not signed the contract with the Shaftesbury Theatre given that it is only a month before our first performances there. Each contract appears to have been negotiated by either Nicholas or Anthony, depending on which company the theatre in question is for, with little evident involvement of the finance department.

I then read the Sadler's Wells contract, in conjunction with the many notes that had been made by Jenny (Genista McIntosh) and others during the period of its negotiation. Well, at least everyone involved seems to recognize what a dreadful contract it is. I cannot believe that the situation arose whereby the Royal Opera House was not in a position to insist that Sadler's Wells carried some liability for any failure to complete the building prior to the beginning of our run. The present position appears to be that we have paid a substantial amount of money into an escrow account, and if the Sadler's Wells management fails to complete the building before the final six weeks of our *third season*,[41] only then do we have access to that fund. I can understand why the Board were so agitated about the negotiation of this contract.

As far as I can see from the paperwork, what seems to have happened is that initially the responsibility for the negotiations was delegated by Jeremy Isaacs to Nicholas during the latter half of 1996. The negotiations were put on ice during the hand-over from Jeremy to Jenny, and then she took them on. Then half the Board seem to have become involved – it's hard to see who ended up negotiating the actual contract, but Sadler's Wells have done very well out of it.

[43] The Royal Opera and Royal Ballet were due to perform three seasons at Sadler's Wells: winter 1998/99, spring 1999 and autumn 1999.

I was moved when I read some notes written by Jenny, obviously to herself, in which she assessed the upside and downside to various courses of action. She sounded so isolated. I was interested to note that not only had she considered it possible that Bernard Haitink might resign if the companies did not go to Sadler's Wells but also Nicholas.

Sunday 21 September

Spent most of the morning reading Royal Opera House papers. By 1.00 was feeling my usual Sunday malaise when I have spent most of the weekend working. Why am I doing this? Why could I not be content with just a small amount of consultancy work, living simply in the country?

After lunch I tackled the budgets. Before I had got very far I contacted Richard Hall and we talked for an hour. He is now more sanguine about our ability to recover the position for 1998/99 and 1999/2000. I think he might be being slightly over-optimistic. In any case, even if we do manage to recover – and sustain – a break-even position for 1998/99 and 1999/2000, we are still facing an overall shortfall of £6 million on the closure period, including the budgeted £3.5 million overspend. But it is work worth doing – and we might just be able to scrabble together enough money to fill the gap, using interest from the Floral Trust and the property sales, together with some money from property rentals that has already accumulated in the Development Land Trust.[44]

Had a long conversation with Kathryn McDowell[45] about Dennis

[44] The Development Land Trust had been set up to receive the land, originally purchased by the government, to enable the redevelopment. It later transpired that it was not possible to use this money to help meet the operating deficit.

[45] Kathryn McDowell is the Music Director at the Arts Council, and during the period covered by this diary was the Arts Council's assessor, or responsible officer, for the Royal Opera House. Usually the assessor would have been the Deputy Secretary-General; Kathryn took on the role while Graham Devlin was Acting Secretary-General.

Marks's resignation and who she thinks might go for the job. She is less convinced than I am that Nicholas would be interested. I pointed out that Nicholas finds the lack of autonomy at the Royal Opera House irksome, in particular when that involves constant scrutiny by Richard and me of his plans and budgets.

Nigel has gone to evensong and I have been wandering around the darkening garden. It is so obviously now autumn. The leaves are beginning to turn yellow and there is a cold wind. Back to another six months of early nights, chill and darkness.

Monday 22 September

The day began with breakfast in the Connaught with Peter and Richard at which we discussed the forthcoming Finance and Audit Committee. Peter is alarmed at the scale of our financial problems, but Richard's recently-developed optimism calms us both. Plenty of questions, though, during the Committee itself, about how budgets presented to the Arts Council as being approximately break-even only six months ago could have deteriorated so far and so fast. Neither Richard nor I can give any answers, since we were not involved in drawing up the original budgets. The Committee members are frustrated that no one seems to be able to stabilize the problem and solve it. I said that we were conducting a fundamental review of all the budgets and that we would be presenting the most up-to-date figures to the Board meeting next week.

After lunch a large and painful budget meeting, convened by Richard Hall. Both Nicholas and Anthony – although the latter slightly less so – are reluctant to give up parts of their programme. Whenever the meeting threatens to degenerate into a protracted argument about whether a certain course of action will save us £30,000 I remind the assembled company that we are facing ruin. I cannot share Richard's confidence that he will be able to extract the full £6 million worth of deficit from the 1998/99 and 1999/2000 budgets, since there seem to be few additional savings over and above those we knew about on Friday. Richard and I will be meeting with every department to go through their budgets individually.

Off to the first night of *Platée.* It is a cruel and exuberant production, with Platée's self-delusion and rage at her subsequent downfall excellently portrayed by Jean-Paul Fouchecourt. Mark Morris's dancers drive the action forward with an ebullient indifference to the fortunes and misfortunes of the characters.

Tuesday 23 September

An hour with Nicholas during which we recapped some of the more painful aspects of the previous day's budget discussions. He suggested that we might try and find a way out of the Sadler's Wells contract. I reminded him that the contract tied us up in every direction, gave Sadler's Wells get-outs in every direction, and left us with no option but to perform there. We considered briefly the possibility that the theatre might not be ready, but even then there is no get-out. Why, oh why, did anyone sign such a dreadful contract?

Then the senior management meeting. It began with another black hole discussion about complimentary tickets. Even the note that Richard Hall had prepared setting out the interim position is, despite being based on discussions with several senior managers, apparently inaccurate. This subject is beginning to raise my blood pressure every time it is mentioned. I said I would talk to Andrew Stokes, the Marketing Director, as soon as he returned from his holiday, about clarifying the immediate position and developing a longer term policy.

Another trot through the budgets, with further discussion about the nature – or absence – of the existing financial controls.

I had lunch with Bernard Haitink, the Royal Opera House's Music Director. We walked to the restaurant together making small talk. Once we sat down he looked at me gloomily and said, 'Now tell me the bad news.' I described carefully the present financial position and he was appalled. How could such a thing happen? Why were the

March budgets so inaccurate? What were we going to do about it? I picked my way as delicately as I could through the minefield of our financial disaster. Unfortunately at one point I referred to the Edinburgh Festival (another loss-making programme, the highlight of which was to be *Don Carlos* conducted by Bernard) and he immediately looked even more gloomy. I tried again to emphasize that the most important thing was to keep the companies together, to enable us to get back into the new theatre with some semblance of a programme. He agreed but pointed out mournfully that instruments or tools which are not used grow rusty and he was worried about losing his best players. Having had Vivien on the phone yesterday, saying that it was out of the question to cut the new *Coppelia*, and now Bernard making similar comments about some aspects of the more expensive parts of the opera season, I can see that making any cuts at all is going to be a difficult business.

I returned to the office where I met with Michael Berkeley, who had joined the Board a year earlier. (He is a composer of operas and runs the Cheltenham Music Festival.) He expressed himself with some force about certain aspects of the companies' operations. Like Bernard – and indeed anyone else who hears about it – he is shocked by the financial position and worried stiff that we won't be able to recover ourselves.

Wednesday 24 September

The morning was filled with a succession of budget meetings with different departments. Disappointingly, there seems to be very little slack in anyone's budget. Most of the variances between March and now can be explained by simple error. For example, in one case the figure that appeared in the March budget was that on the bottom of the first of two pages and the total, on the bottom of the second page, had been omitted. I spent the morning feeling alternately aghast and depressed. We made a few minor savings and corrected any errors. The figures now go back to the finance department for them to draw up the next version of the budgets.

I then met Lorraine Ebdon, Head of Costume, and we went over to the running wardrobe in Paul Street. Only the opera running wardrobe staff were there, the ballet staff being over at the Labatt's Apollo. The opera running wardrobe is managed by a woman called Corinne, who joined the opera house at the age of 17 and has now been there for 27 years. She combined being lugubrious with being extremely good at her job and very funny indeed. She spoke at length about her dislike of the more modern productions, saying that she liked to manage proper costumes, by which she meant a good set of Elizabethan or Jacobean chorus costumes.

The whole running wardrobe is situated in a basement, and I was shown the laundry, which had only two days earlier been flooded with sewage. It was being deconstructed when I saw it, since during a recent re-fit the washing machines had been placed on a concrete plinth so high that it was impossible to put the soap powder in at the top.

Just before I left I met the opera shoes department, the door to which is decorated with a pair of ballet shoes. I asked why this was and Anne, an extremely large woman who runs opera shoes, said, 'Oh, because it's camp'. Opera shoes is less hectic than ballet shoes, where there are people all day long buffing, polishing, dyeing and generally reconstructing the boots and shoes that the dancers wear out.

I then went to the St Ermine's Hotel to meet Prue Skene from the Arts Council (and Chairman of its Lottery Advisory Panel). It is when I meet some of my oldest friends from the Arts Council that I miss it so badly. It will take me a long time before I can laugh with Royal Opera House staff and Board members in the same way I can with Arts Council members. Prue, once again, told me that I shouldn't have left and that the Arts Council has been more or less non-functioning since my departure. I said that the alternative would have been to allow the Royal Opera House to fall apart, and that in my view the Royal Opera House is, at the end of the day, more important than the Arts Council. Prue just about managed to agree.

Then caught the tube over to Hammersmith where I was greeted by a bone-crushing handshake from Paul Gregg who runs Apollo Leisure, the company that owns the Labatt's Apollo theatre. He ushered me up to a small room to meet Princess Margaret. She is very small – although the fact that I was wearing exceptionally high heels, which took me up to about six foot tall, might have contributed to this impression – and was dressed entirely in tangerine. She had that rather vague air that I associate with people who are either very rich, or who have had a very sheltered upbringing, inasmuch as they have not had to adapt their consciousness to the world around them. The result of this is that they free-associate from one subject to another expecting those to whom they are talking to follow them.

Then went down to the foyer and met Robin Woodhead, my first husband, and went into the show. Sylvie Guillem was not only at her most lithe and athletic but her interpretation of Juliet was soaring and passionate and I was moved to tears at several points. And so proud, too, that this was now a company for which I had some responsibility.

During the second interval we met Hayden and Laura Phillips. I was interested to notice that when Peter, talking to Hayden and to me, said with a certain degree of irony that he had expected to be offered the Chairmanship of the Arts Council, Hayden replied that of course they were going to ask him. Hayden did not deny that there was going to be a new Chairman. Grey really must be going.[46] Back for the remaining acts: all apparently enjoyed by a very mixed audience including many younger people who were crashing in and out during the show as if at a rock concert. I followed a group of them down the stairs at the end who were saying, 'Well, now we'd like to get the T-shirt'.

We went backstage afterwards and spoke to the dancers as well as to some of the orchestra. I failed to recognize several of the ballet

[46] Lord Gowrie left the Arts Council on 1 May 1998, and was succeeded by Gerry Robinson. He announced his resignation in early October.

company's administrative staff dressed up as Lord and Lady Montague, and the Nurse.

Robin and I went back on the tube. We encountered John and Anya Sainsbury beside the ticket machines, unable to work out how to purchase a ticket, John saying irritably that it was years since he had travelled on the tube and they hadn't had these machines then.

Supper with Robin. He is in a mellow mood and has several exciting job offers pending.

Thursday 25 September

Lunch with Jeremy Newton (the Arts Council Lottery Director). Afterwards I took him up Bow Street and showed him the development. I stood him at the point at which the surrounding hoardings had been removed, where we could see right over the huge area of space with the cranes, the pile-drivers and the scaffolding and said, 'Look, isn't that wonderful? Isn't it going to be magnificent?'

Friday 26 September

Spent two or three hours working on a staff briefing paper about the new theatre, and the working groups that I am establishing in order to take us forward on the various access initiatives.

I had a meeting about catering in the new House, which initially comprised staff, and then was joined by two catering specialists. Everyone has different ideas, different expectations and different demands, out of which I have to distill some kind of consensus pretty rapidly so that we don't interfere with the building programme.

After the meeting I had a brief chat with Ivell[47], who has been on

[47] Ivell Arnold had been the Commissionaire in the old House. He had featured prominently in the television documentary *The House*, and was known to all the Royal Opera House regulars.

reception since the House closed, and who is now leaving. I am sad from the point of view of the Royal Opera House, since he is such a well-known and loved figure, but it is the right move for him as he is going to the BBC where he will spend more time with people and less time on a switchboard. I was touched when he spoke warmly about my potential as Chief Executive, saying that he thought I was exactly what the House needed.

I talked with Andrew Stokes, who had just come back from Australia, about the continuing poor ticket sales at the Labatt's and a number of other marketing matters, and updated him on the senior management discussions about complimentary tickets.

Then another large meeting with a range of staff from different departments, this time about the daytime use of the new House. This went well, with people having all kinds of ideas about how we could get a broader public in and out of the building during the day.

Up to Ivell's leaving party where, to my deep embarrassment, he repeated all his comments about my potential as a Chief Executive to the company at large. At one point he said, 'She will be a terrific success,' in response to which somebody else near the back of the room growled out, 'She'd bloody better.'

Saturday 27 September

Nigel and I took in some pictures for the walls of my office and then walked around the perimeter of the building site. On the Piazza side the scaffolding has now been taken away from the new section of James Street, exposing the huge carving of the Royal Opera House crest. It looks magnificent.

A few phone calls in the evening, including one to Graham Devlin,[48] who was most agitated about the fact that the Royal Opera House cannot produce full and final balanced budgets by the end of

[48] Graham Devlin was the Deputy Secretary-General at the Arts Council, and had been acting Secretary-General since my departure just over four months earlier.

September. I said that surely the Arts Council was more interested in an organization that is well-managed financially and not going to go bust, than the production of imaginary budgets by a certain deadline. Graham said that he accepted my arguments, but was concerned that David Reid (the Chairman of the Arts Council's Audit Committee) and Hayden Phillips might not do so.

Pottered around until it was time to go out to the National Theatre for Richard Eyre's farewell party. There were many tributes from actors, writers and other colleagues, including a version of *Send in the Clowns* by Judi Dench. I was interested to hear, from Tom Stoppard who made a valedictory speech, that Richard hated every day of his first year at the National. There is hope yet.

I left the party at about 1.15, and had to walk all the way from Waterloo to the bottom of Rosebery Avenue before I found a taxi. Finally got to bed at around 3.00.

Sunday 28 September

Worked. And worked and worked.

For lunch I made a roast chicken with a stuffing pushed up under the skin comprising goats cheese, butter and many different kinds of herbs – it was delicious.

Monday 29 September

Walked around and met more of the staff, including Richard Sadler, the chorus manager, who is doing an MBA and who has interesting ideas about the culture of the Royal Opera House. He believes there is a tremendous amount of energy, aptitude and enthusiasm within the organization that just needs to be channelled in order to work together better. He agreed with my observations about lack of co-ordinated management and, in some instances, a lack of support on the part of the senior manangement for the desire of the middle management to cut costs.

The Board meeting began at 2.30. It was a brisk and well-managed affair, although there is a sense of disconnection between the Board and its discussions, and what is actually going on. I can't quite put my finger on it, but I feel that the Board is not in some way equipped, possibly because of the way it operates, really to engage with the issues being faced by the management. It is almost as though there are two groups of people acting in parallel, rather than a single group comprising people with different areas of responsibility, all functioning together as a coherent whole.

We went through the matters relating to the sale of the commercial property, and agreed to request the Arts Council and the DCMS to consent to an early sale of 95 per cent of it. I presented my ideas for tackling issues relating to accessibility, income generation and resource management in the new building. Richard and I talked through some preliminary proposals for establishing new financial controls, which were broadly endorsed. We then went through the present financial position, including the most up-to-date information on the budgets for the following two years.

The Board members were terrified – like rabbits in headlights. The prospect of a £3 million deficit during the current year, possibly compounded by a further deficit of up to £5 or £6 million in the next two years, and with no funds available for the £3.5 million budgeted overspend, would mean that if we could find no solution the organization would be unable to continue trading. We talked about the issue of insolvency, wrongful trading and everything else relating to this position. Peter said that he had decided – quite rightly – not to sign last year's accounts, since he could not confirm that the Royal Opera House was a going concern.[49] Rudi Mueller (a member of the Main Board and Chairman of UBS, the Swiss bank) queried with

[49] To be deemed to be trading properly, a company must be a 'going concern'. A company is not a going concern if it cannot pay its debts as they fall due. In the case of the Royal Opera House, the discovery of this massive gap between projected revenues and costs meant that the company would run out of cash well before the closure period was finished.

some vigour why the accounts had not already been signed and Peter had to take him through the 'going concern' aspects of the position. Rudi said that he had never been connected with an organization that was possibly not a going concern – I thought, 'Well you are now, mate,' – and that in any case he might not be fully familiar with all the relevant aspects of English law. We eventually managed to convince the Board that they were in no position to sign any accounts until we had finalized the budgets for the next two years and found a way of dealing with the problems. It was agreed we would bring the revised budgets to the meeting of the Finance and Audit Committee in mid-October.

I felt low after the Board meeting. I have noticed over these few weeks that my mood deflates after a meeting of the Board or a meeting of a subsidiary committee – the last time I felt really low was after the meeting of the Finance and Audit Committee. Either this means that I am not fully recognizing the seriousness of our position, and am only facing it in the context of a Board meeting or a Board committee meeting, or it means that the way in which the Board wants to face and handle these problems differs from the way in which I and colleagues such as Richard Hall wish to do so. I certainly do not feel that the staff and the Board are fully supportive of one another – not because there is any desire to create distance between the two groups, but because neither feel in control of any aspect of the management process. And the main reason for that is – as I am increasingly recognizing – because there *is* no management process of any kind.

If you look at each individual part of the organization, whether it be the technical department, the Friends, IT, you find an able and dedicated group of people performing their jobs very well. During the last three rounds of redundancies – in 1994, 1996 and 1997 – each departmental head has looked at issues relating to staffing and operational practices, with a view to creating a unit that works. And they have succeeded. However there are no means of connecting them. And any attempts to create those connections is viewed by the core of the organization – in other words the two performing companies – as encroaching upon their autonomy.

Tuesday 30 September

I woke up at about 5.00 worrying about my capacity – or indeed the capacity of anyone – to sort out the Royal Opera House. There are so many problems relating to the fundamental process of planning the artistic programme and budgeting that programme. I woke poor darling Nigel who had not gone to bed until 3.30, although I did not know that at the time, and he was, as usual, loving and comforting. I shouted a bit and said that I didn't want to continue working at the Royal Opera House, that the problems were far too large for any one individual to solve them.

However I know that that's not true. I have been here before. When I took over at the Arts Council in 1994 I took on an organization which was on the brink of collapse and turned it round. I also know that I have the personal resources to withstand the stress and the exhaustion. I just don't know whether I want to do it all again.

I went into the office and sorted out the papers from the Board meeting the previous day to make sure that I was tackling all of the Board's questions about the financial issues in the right order. Pippa kindly went out and bought me a double espresso – although I have not been drinking coffee recently – which I consumed and lifted myself on to a good caffeine high.

I went up to see Richard Hall and talked about a number of issues. One of the things I wanted to do was to test out some of the early conclusions I have been reaching about the absence of proper processes for planning and management, and changes I would like to introduce. I want to set up two new planning processes: one dealing with the operational aspects of the new House – a Planning Group – and the other tackling what I believe is the root of the problem: the absence of any collective effort in programming the organization. This latter will begin with a weekly Programming Meeting with Nicholas Payne, Anthony Dowell and Anthony Russell-Roberts to develop and agree a draft programme for the new House from December 1999 to summer 2001. If we brought these three people together as a group I am sure the quality of the ideas would improve.

Nicholas is excellent at planning a rep in a creative and innovative way and in bringing in good directors, designers, conductors and singers. If Anthony Dowell were to be involved in discussions with other people, he might take more artistic risks in relation to the ballet rep. Once we have some initial ideas for the programme we can then bring in the producton and sales departments, so that the artistic ideas and their financial implications can be explored in tandem. When I spoke to Anthony Russell-Roberts to say that I wished to institute collaborative Programming Meetings, he said that such a meeting had not been held for ten years. Apparently this was the approach Sir John Tooley used to take but it had lapsed under Jeremy's General Directorship.

I have yet to decide how I wish to use the existing senior management meeting. I am considering, at the senior management group meeting next week, just having one item on the agenda: 'What on earth are we all doing here? Why are we coming to these meetings?' The senior management group in its present form achieves little and makes a negligible contribution to the management of the organization. I could just abolish it, but people have already said it's the only forum in which they get to talk to each other. Later maybe.

I then had a meeting at 12.00 with John Seekings, Peter Morris and Phyllida Ritter[50] about taking forward all of the various projects designed to get us back into the new theatre, and told them about my ideas for a Planning Group, involving the three of them, to help me coordinate planning for the new House, particularly the working groups. It was an excellent meeting. I felt that we identified the need for various coordinating mechanisms, the need to become specific very quickly about what we were trying to achieve, and the deadline by which we had to complete the work. There was a positive atmos-

[50] Peter Morris was head of IT and Phyllida Ritter ran the Friends of Covent Garden. John, Peter and Phyllida were among the most able of the senior staff and wanted to help me prepare the organization to enter the new House. They had become an informal support group for me, and I was keen to recruit them to help with the working groups.

phere and everyone seemed to believe that what we were planning was possible. This is what I had hoped would be the main agenda for these few months. I certainly hadn't expected the ghastly financial context within which we would be doing this work.

Tony Hutt, from GJW, came in at 3.00 to talk about the Select Committee.[51] I am not allowing myself to become nervous about it although I know I will be, very, when the event actually takes place. I cannot believe that it continues to be interested in the process of my appointment: if I was a Committee member the first thing I would want to know is whether I was unhappy and whether I was about to leave. I still have no clear view as to how I might answer that question on the day.

Richard Hall, Liam Wall, the Financial Controller, and I then met with Keith Cooper and Andrew Stokes to have another look at the income forecasts. A short while into the discussion it was revealed that there was £1 million – or thereabouts – of forecast income which was an error. Apparently it is VAT, and should not have been included in the figures. I cannot believe it. Initially when I heard this I felt numb. I did not know how to respond: a few weeks ago I had had to accustom myself to the fact that the closure budgets, which I had been told several months ago were confidently projected on a near break-even basis, now showed a loss of over £10 million. We have done everything we can to try and reduce this deficit, although we are still not likely to be able to eliminate the entire amount. Now, very late in the day, I hear that the problem is £1 million worse than I had thought.

How can any organization be so utterly disorganized, have such a complete disregard for its own health, and be so irredeemably hopeless at communicating within itself, as to allow a further £1 million loss to lie around, undiscovered, unidentified, for four weeks during a budgeting process? I feel as though I want to burst into tears – not of grief but of rage. We have all been wasting our time.

[51] GJW is a government relations and lobbying organization, and had been helping the Royal Opera House prepare for its various Select Committee appearances.

Richard looked as winded as I felt – and that is the right word for it, winded. I couldn't react, I didn't know what to do or say. After Keith and Andrew had gone we discussed, for a while, what the implications of this were. I cannot conceive how any organization could have gone through such an incompetent budgeting process. The incompetence is not that of individuals, it is that of an organization which seems unable to function in any rational way whatsoever.

Then Liam left and Richard and I started to talk about insolvency. It is hard to see any circumstances under which we can continue trading. How can anyone be expected to manage an organization on this basis? I had no idea that running the Royal Opera House was going to be anything like as bad as this. Richard and I looked at whether or not we could continue with the operation until the staff received their October pay cheques but recognized that we would not be deemed to be trading properly if we kept going solely so that the staff got paid. I cannot believe this is happening. After Richard went I just put my head down on my desk for a while.

I eventually left the office at about 9.00 and went home. When I came out of the tube at Arsenal there was a match on and I could hear waves of sound rolling from the stadium. Suddenly, all I wanted to do was to go in there and watch the end of the match, and yell and scream and dance around.

Wednesday 1 October

It's 5.30 a.m. and I have been awake since 4.00. I still cannot believe that this is happening. Surely, once the figures have been reviewed yet again, it will be all right? Last night Richard said he had never encountered an organization with such a total absence of any financial procedures at all.

Got into the office around 9.00 feeling rather disconnected. Dug through the files looking for papers about financial discussions, and correspondence between the Royal Opera House and the Arts

Council: the files are horribly disorganized, with items missing, such as letters I know I sent to Jenny or to Peter when I was with the Arts Council.

Went up to see Richard Hall around 10.00. He was with Liam and they were discussing what we had discovered the night before. Richard told me not to get too hung up about an extra £1 million loss – the situation was so ghastly already. Despite Richard's optimism of ten days ago, it looks as though the re-budgeting exercise will have failed to cut costs or make savings to any significant degree. However Richard did agree with me that the fact an extra £1 million loss had just emerged during a meeting, and we might suddenly find another £1 million emerging – or demerging – from somewhere, rendered all of the budgets unreliable.

At one point during the meeting I told Richard that I felt like having a cigarette for the first time since I had given up smoking six years earlier.

Had a meeting with Mike Morris to talk about how I was intending to construct the new planning processes. It is odd simultaneously to be optimistic and excited about the new building and how we might work towards it, and to be alarmed at the prospect of imminent bankruptcy.

During the afternoon saw Anthony Russell-Roberts. He wants a new Cuban dancer who is apparently sensational, but who is asking for a lot of money. Since Irek will be leaving next summer, I suggested we use that money to pay for the Cuban. Anthony asked whether or not we shouldn't be saving money. I replied that of course we are saving money, but that there is no point in having a Royal Ballet if it is not a good Royal Ballet, and savings that damage the quality of the company itself are not worth making.

Also a meeting with John Seekings talking, yet again, about catering. This is definitely a black hole project. He is worried about how to deal with John Sainsbury and Vivien. He says they make him feel inferior and like a servant, by discussing issues in front of him as if he is not there. I said that one of the most interesting aspects of working in the arts was meeting types of people with whom one would not otherwise come into contact, in particular the very rich. I suggested that, rather than feel inferior, he adopt a more detached and quizzical eye. I also said that I would do the best I could to ensure that the meeting next week did not end up either indecisively, or with an unacceptable – because unworkable – decision. Compromise will be necessary and I must achieve it.

At 5.30 Lou Shand-Brown and I went down to the Labatt's Apollo and we spent an hour or so going round backstage while she introduced me to everyone. A photographer from *The Times* turned up. He had already phoned my office saying that there was going to be a large article about Lord Gowrie the following day and asking if he could take a photograph of me. Since *The Times* has a large number of photographs of me already this can only be a bad thing: in other words that they need a photograph of me at the Royal Opera House, to contrast with me at the Arts Council with Lord Gowrie. I sensed almost certain disadvantage for me, Grey and the Royal Opera House. I avoided the photographer.

The show was different from last week. Whereas Sylvie and Jonathan had been electrifying, sexy and passionate, Bruce and Leanne were tender, lyrical and romantic.

Bob Scott[52] took me for a drink during both intervals. He wanted to know whether we might reconsider coming to the Lyceum for the second closure year. I pointed out to Bob that the contract with Sadler's Wells was unbreakable. I also told him that the Sadler's Wells management – and the Arts Council – were virtually certain that the building would be completed by the time our contract begins. The photographer was still hanging round at the end of the show, so I slipped out at the side.

I am feeling exhausted. But more and more I want passionately to see it all work. Maybe I am being naïve, maybe there are things I will discover or know in two months time that will change my mind, but

[52] Sir Bob Scott works with Paul Gregg at Apollo Leisure. Apollo also owns the Lyceum, and had been very keen that the Royal Opera House should be resident at the Lyceum during its entire closure period.

right at this moment I feel I could love this job more than any job I've ever done. I want to make it work for me, for the staff and for the organization. I want to solve the financial problems, although I don't know how yet. However my determination is growing.

Thursday 2 October

This has not been a good day.

Got into the office at about 8.15 and dealt with some paperwork until Malcolm Warne Holland, the Orchestra Director, Richard Hall and Liam, came to see me at 8.45. We dealt with the orchestra budget. At 9.30 I had a meeting about broadcasting, with Nicholas, Anthony Russell-Roberts, Mike, John Seekings and Keith, which went well. We identified our main achievements to date and what we wanted to go for in the future.

Then I had a meeting with Richard Hall. Richard was due to have been on holiday next week, having already cancelled one holiday because of the Royal Opera House. We both agreed that there is no question of him going away at present, even for a week. The budgets are still millions short, and although there is still substantial and important work to be done on the figures, it is becoming obvious that there is no way we are going to be able to make the budgets balance. This means that we have to start taking the whole question of whether or not we are a going concern very seriously indeed over the next few days.

We phoned Peter in New York. He asked us to change the Audit Committee meeting on 20 October to a full Board meeting, and to invite the auditors to join us. The intention is that we will explore the scope of the problem at the Board meeting on 20 October, and then examine solutions to it at the Board meeting on 30 October. If we cannot find a solution by 30 October then we will have to close the company.

I went to the South Bank Centre and met Gavin Henderson (Chairman of the Arts Council's Music Advisory Panel) for lunch.

He talked about orchestras in a way that would, in any other circumstances, have been fascinating, but which today was merely distracting. Still it was good to see him. He is sensible and rises above all the Arts Council bickering about the Royal Opera House. At one point I said something about praying to God that I could sort out the finances. Gavin then said he had an anecdote about praying, and he told me about a time when he had been running Southill Park, an Arts centre in Bracknell, and had wanted to renovate the theatre. He required about £400,000 in order to do so and for reasons I cannot now remember that money was missing. He had prayed in a chapel and, quite extraordinarily, the money had become available. I need a cathedral.

I got back at around 2.45 and Nicholas came to see me at 3.00. We had an excellent meeting over the following two hours. We covered many issues about programming, controls and his own future. I made it clear that I admired his artistic vision and I very much wanted him to stay, but that if he felt now was the time to take on the leadership of a major national company, and wanted to apply for the General Directorship of the ENO I would support that as well, knowing he would be a prime candidate for the job. I went through my ideas for changing the planning processes of the Royal Opera House. Nicholas agreed with the notion of joint Programming Meetings in order to start establishing planning and management processes that are rooted in the artistic decision-making but which also involve all the other key departments at an early stage.

Then yet another budget meeting with Nicholas, Anthony and Richard Hall. Richard brought down the latest version of the budgets, produced by the finance department following the most recent set of departmental meetings. Even after all our work we have achieved very little. The £1 million that slithered out two days ago is indeed £1 million. We have saved only £2 million through our bottom-up budget review. The net result is that we are still facing a deficit of £5.8 million for 1998/99 and 1999/2000. Added to the £3.5 million that the Board agreed in June 1996 would be found through fund-raising, but which has since been unagreed, and the

£2.7 million we are forecasting to lose this year, that comes to a total of £12 million. *And* we already have a deficit of £5 million.

At several points today I have said to people, 'I think I am hallucinating.' How can any organization with an annual turnover of £40 million miscalculate by such a large amount?

Once I had finished my meeting with Richard, Anthony and Nicholas, I went to the Barbican to see *The Turn of the Screw*. It is a brilliant, extraordinary, almost shocking production, that explores the relationship between the children and the adults in a way that I have not seen before. I went backstage afterwards and saw Paul Daniel, ENO Music Director, and then went into the party. Had a long talk with Fiona Shaw and a shorter talk with Deborah Warner, the director, but I could not concentrate. I am facing a position that none of them know about.

I left the Barbican and walked half-way home before I found a taxi. No doubt tomorrow will bring new thoughts, new information and new possible plans of action. At the moment I cannot imagine what they might be.

Friday 3 October

More coverage of Lord Gowrie's impending departure from the Arts Council in the papers this morning. One good thing about the last few months is that I have managed to leave the Arts Council myself. I still have no regrets, and whatever happens to me I am grateful that I am not doing that grindingly impossible job.

The day began with a meeting of the Design Sub-group to discuss certain aspects of the design of the new building, with particular reference to signage. It all felt rather surreal, as I could not take seriously questions as to whether or not we had certain typefaces or words in the new building, given the dreadfulness of the financial position.

We talked a little about catering near the end of the meeting, and it seems that major decisions had been taken by management a couple of years earlier without reference to either the Board or the Development Steering Committee. Apparently there were originally plans for a substantial restaurant on the top floor alongside the staff canteen. These had been deleted before the main construction work had begun.

Then a meeting with Peter and Richard Hall to review the financial position. Peter was characteristically bullish, and is confident that we can raid the Floral Trust for sufficient funds to carry us through. I am not sure, yet, whether the figures stack up; I also find it hard to believe that Vivien will countenance such large sums of money – possibly more than £10 million – to be removed from a Trust that would otherwise have been giving these funds to the development. In any case, if these budgets are so shaky what is to guarantee that any future budgets won't be equally shaky?

I put in train arrangements for a day-long meeting on Monday, with all the departmental heads, to begin another fundamental review of the budgets.

Once Richard had gone, Peter talked for a while about the need to ensure this collapse doesn't take place, particularly in view of the criticism both he and I would attract through our former connections with the Arts Council. All of that has occurred to me already. My own position would be particularly difficult because, as Chief Executive of the body responsible for monitoring the Royal Opera House, I would be expected to have spotted any weaknesses in the plans and budgets. Quite apart from the budgets themselves, I find it hard to understand how the financial procedures could have deteriorated so spectacularly since Richard Pulford wrote his reports only a year ago saying they were OK. I now have Richard Hall telling me that there are no financial procedures, of any kind, able to control anything at all.

In this frame of mind went out to lunch with Graham Devlin at Orso. I wasn't quite clear in my own mind, at the beginning of the lunch, how much I was going to tell him about our financial position. It came out gradually, further hints of horror emerging with each glass of wine we drank. Even before I started outlining the nightmare of the Royal Opera House, Graham was looking grey with exhaustion. He is working over ninety hours a week. He could hardly believe what I was telling him. We started to punctuate our conversation with requests that what one of us was telling the other was off the record, since we wanted to be able to talk openly about the Royal Opera House's crisis without needing to convey everything we said back to our respective colleagues. Near the end we needn't have bothered: we were so mesmerized by the appalling possibility that the Royal Opera House might be about to collapse, so unable to believe that this could actually happen, and so horrified by what might follow if it did, that between us we drank two and a half litres of white wine, and I could remember very little of what we talked about at all.

I was in rather chipper form by the time I returned to the office. Later, I went out to the pub with Richard Hall and a couple of other people – the alcohol was having the desired effect of repressing my immediate awareness of our grisly problems – and then Nigel fetched me away. We drove down to Suffolk and I went for a walk at midnight, the fields just visible by the starlight.

Saturday 4 October

Woke up feeling hung-over; this rapidly degenerated into feelings of acute anxiety. We went to Southwold for lunch and then for a walk along Covehithe beach. The weather cleared and there was a cloudless sky and it was the most beautiful early October day, with no one else around at all. I was even insane enough to go swimming. I took off all my clothes and threw myself into the sea. I thought I was going to have a heart attack it was so cold. I came out immediately and we lay on the beach and Nigel put his arms around me and tried to tell me it would be all right. I don't know whether it will be yet, I still have this feeling of unreality, as a result of finding myself in a situation so far outside the bounds either of the expected or of common sense.

We eventually returned home at about 7.00 and went for another walk – another lovely evening. Spent the evening sitting by the fire and reading. There was quite a lot in the newspapers about Grey's resignation, including an interview with him by Valerie Grove. As part of that he said that a possible future project might be – and I quote – 'Writing about some of the fascinating women I have known'. He listed four, among whom was me. Well, I needed the laugh.

Sunday 5 October

Woke up at about 3.00 in a blind panic. One of the worst I have ever had – ice crawling up and down my arms and legs, my heart pounding, unable to do anything other than lie there frozen.

I now have regrets. I wish I had had the good sense to say no when Peter approached me about the job at the Royal Opera House. However difficult it would have been to stay at the Arts Council it could not have been worse than this nightmare. Though if the Royal Opera House had gone bankrupt and I had still been Secretary-General of the Arts Council I would have offered my resignation. So maybe the net result will be the same, I will have just gone through a different type of stress to get there.

After lunch I began to feel worse and worse. It is interesting how stress and tension manifest into physical symptoms. With me it is a very hard and fast heart-beat; a sense of prickling and movement in my upper body muscles, in particular the shoulders, chest and back; icy skin in the arms and legs; and an inability to sit or lie still.

Eventually I telephoned Peter and told him that I was finding things exceedingly difficult, that I thought the job was undoable, partly because of the number of silly decisions that had been taken during the last few years, and partly because of the scope of the Chief Executive's job. Add to that the present financial crisis, and the particular implications for me personally, given my previous role, and the stress level was bordering on the intolerable. He was calm and very sympathetic, talking as if to a child who had got themselves into a position of great danger and needed to be gently coaxed out of it. He says that he will find whatever money is needed to provide the necessary support.

He also said that he believes that I am the only person in this country who could get the Royal Opera House out of its present position. I said to myself, 'Yes, but at what personal cost?' I don't want to do a job that leaves everybody else with a nice opera house and me with nothing.

In the evening I talked through with Nigel Richard Hall's concept of profit-centre management and accounting. It seems to me that the trouble with the Royal Opera House at the moment is that structurally speaking it is neither one thing nor the other. On the one hand it could be a single integrated entity with shared artistic objectives being manifest through the work of the two companies. On the other hand it could be two companies quite clearly separate one from another, operating within a receiving house. The receiving house would then be able to bring in other companies as it chose, and the two performing companies would be able to go elsewhere if they so decided.

Monday 6 October

Arrived at the office at 7.00 in order to sort myself out before the day-long budget review meeting which began at 8.00.

We spent ten hours examining various ways in which the Royal Opera House administration, and the closure programme, could be restructured and reworked to save substantial sums of money. There were several interesting ideas put forward about how to restructure the production and technical departments so as to increase flexibility. Mike Morris reminded us of the controversy that would surround such proposals and the challenges that BECTU would mount. We discussed whether or not they would result in a strike, but agreed that if they did so this would be the least damaging time for a confrontation of this nature. We also recognized that, although there might be savings to be gained from such restructuring in the long term, any changes in the short term would have a minimal financial impact on the closure programme.

We looked at the possibility of a wage cut and agreed that staff would be most reluctant to accept being penalised for what they would perceive as the consequence of management incompetence.

We looked at redundancies and agreed that we could not have yet another round of *ad hoc* redundancies made on the basis of each department taking an equivalent cut. From now on it is essential that the Royal Opera House management takes strategic decisions about what the organization does, and makes reductions in staff numbers – if that should be necessary – as appropriate. We also agreed that we were too far into the closure period to begin redesigning the organization in the short term. We'd lose more money – through an inability to produce the shows and the resulting loss of box office income – than we'd gain.

We then went on, during the afternoon, to tackle the programme. This was a long and frustrating business involving many discussions and arguments between the ten or so people sitting around the table. Both Anthony and Nicholas are still trying to hang on to as much of their programme as possible, and are continuing to describe the financial issue as being my problem rather than a shared problem. There is no culture of team work, collaboration or shared responsibility, nor is there any sense of people working for a single entity.[53] Near the end of the day, when we were reviewing the progress we had made, someone – I forget who – said, 'Well, I suppose if we haven't saved enough money this time we'll have to sit down and start again.' I got as close as I have done during the last six weeks to losing my

[53] There had been several reports written during the previous fifteen years about the difficulties the Royal Opera House encountered in integrating its artistic planning with its budgeting. Not only had this contributed to the problems with the closure budgets but it also meant there was a culture in place that made it hard to address the problems.

temper. I said this had been the final exercise, that there should be no more savings to find, and that if there were we had been wasting the last ten hours. People do not seem to appreciate that we are genuinely staring bankruptcy in the face.

Anthony and I then left the meeting and went to *Giselle*, which was a good performance of one of the less exciting classical ballets. There was a distressing moment in the second act, when the dry ice failed to lift from the stage floor and formed an oily film over it, and the Queen of the Wilis slipped several times and finally fell. The audience gasped audibly and there was a wave of sympathy. I learnt subsequently that several people had gone to the box office and demanded their money back.

I went round backstage afterwards to see if I could find the dancer who had fallen over but she was in her dressing room and very upset. I talked briefly to Viviana Durante and then left.

Tuesday 7 October

Into the Royal Opera House by 8.30 for a brief meeting with Madeleine Watson, Jackie McDougall and Jane Kaufmann from the Royal Opera House Trust. I explained to them that, due to the financial problems, I was going to have to focus my attention on the present budget crisis, which meant that I would not be able to do as much as I would otherwise for the Trust. They said that sometimes there were problems about which they needed to consult me, and gave as an example the fact that Nicholas had recently told them that the *Figaro* sets were over budget by £40,000, and that he had suggested a Drogheda circle (a fund-raising device) to raise the money.[54]

I was, as I have been so many times in the last few weeks, literally struck dumb. I used to think that that was a figure of speech and, as such, an exaggeration. I have now experienced on a number of occa-

[54] It was not unusual at the Royal Opera House to try and raise additional funds from donors to cover cost overruns.

sions the sensation of wanting very powerfully to say something and simply not knowing what to say. Eventually I said that I felt impelled to one of two courses of action: either putting my fist through the wall or jumping out of the window. They asked apprehensively which I was proposing to follow.

How *can* anybody, within the present climate of financial desperation, even contemplate allowing a designer to go over budget to the extent it appears has happened with *Figaro*? Why were the designs not returned immediately with 'too much' scrawled across them? Why did he not discuss it with me before going to the Trust and asking them to raise the money?

After Jackie et al. had left, and I had strode around my office for a while, I called down Richard and asked Nicholas to come over and join us. We talked about what had happened, and Richard and I made it quite clear we were going to insist on the budget being adhered to. I am still staggered that an overrun of that kind could be contemplated, even for a second, by anyone in the organization.[55]

After lunch, another marathon meeting of the arts departments and the production, wardrobe and technical departments, to quantify more precisely the savings we had agreed the previous day. By the end of the afternoon I realized that, from the ten hours work yesterday, we have probably made savings of not more than £½ million. Even the agreements we had reached as to which seasons should be either reduced, eliminated or in some way altered, were being put forward by Anthony and Nicholas as 'possibilities', or 'perhaps we will', rather than the conclusive decisions that had yesterday been reached.[56] It was also obvious that the savings they had been airily envisaging were either based on slender evidence or had not taken into account other costs that would accrue as a result of the decisions.

By the time I returned to my office I was feeling angry: we had wasted a great deal of time to little effect. Richard and I agreed that

[55] The production did come in on budget.

[56] Yet again, the culture of dislocation between artistic excellence and financial accountability did not help in addressing these issues.

during the last few days we had done everything possible within our power to apply normal management techniques and budgeting procedures to this very difficult situation with virtually no effect.

I then had a discussion with John Seekings and Richard Hall about the three recovery scenarios that I now see shaping up.

The first is that we continue to operate through closure and at the same time bring in relevantly qualified specialists in order to help us plan every aspect of how we operate the new theatre. This option would have a bill attached to it of around £12 million for the closure period deficit (taking into account the savings we have made but allowing for some further deterioration) and a further £1 million or so for the specialists. I would want someone to help me review the overall structure of the organization: whether we are an integrated whole, or two companies and a receiving house. Once we have chosen a structural option, I would first restructure the senior management team and then the remainder of the staff as appropriate. My own preference would be for the integrated option, with both companies being run by a single, visionary artistic director-come-programmer, working alongside the Music Director and a resident choreographer. Richard wants help with controlling cash, putting in place budget and cost controls, and looking at more strategic issues relating to planning and budgeting. At the moment the demands of reviewing the budgets themselves mean that we have no staff time available to beef up the budgeting processes, or to strengthen the financial controls.

The second option is to cease all closure period operations immediately and effectively shut down the organization, retaining only a development team in order to complete the construction of the building and plan its operation. This would require us to pay all creditors, staff redundancies, contracted artists and theatre rentals, as well as the costs of staffing up for the new theatre. Whether or not this option would work would depend on the Arts Council being willing to continue making the annual grants available, to pay for these costs, even though the organization was not presenting any opera or ballet.

The third option is to put forward proposals as to how we might combine with ENO. This might produce savings over the longer term but will not help us with our immediate crisis. However it has to be included because so many of the Board members have been mentioning it as the solution to our problems.

The only alternative to these scenarios is to put the Royal Opera House into liquidation and I'm not sure, yet, whether the development could survive the liquidation of the operating company.

Having reached this point I am at present feeling – not optimistic, but excited that we could brainstorm the three scenarios and arrive at some concrete proposals that we could then put forward with dignity and competence.

Off to the Tate Gallery where, outside the entrance, I met Peter talking to Christopher Frayling, from the Arts Council, and Nicholas Snowman, the Chief Executive of the South Bank Centre. Lots of comment both humorous and serious about the Arts Council. A brief walk with Peter back to the entrance where I sketched out my thoughts about the three recovery scenarios and then back to the party.

During the course of the next two hours I spent most of my time with Nicholas Snowman, hearing about the South Bank Centre. There is no confidence that the Arts Council will ever produce a lottery award, and Nicholas says that the DCMS has effectively taken over the decision-making. I cannot believe this and warn Nicholas about the dangers attendant upon circumventing the Arts Council.

That reminds me, I had a dream about the Select Committee last night. I was facing it, and it was chaired by an elderly woman – the baroness of something or other. As the dream went on she thwarted all my attempts to try and account for my appointment by shushing me and offering me tea and sandwiches. Gradually it became a tea party, and she said that we had to meet for tea in the House of Lords. I felt frustrated, since the Select Committee had been the platform that I had been hoping to use to explain publicly the process of my appointment to the Royal Opera House. When I woke up I pondered the significance of this dream – perhaps the mention of the House of Lords has some connection with Lord Gowrie.

Wednesday 8 October

Peter joined me for sandwiches at lunch-time, and I took him through the position regarding the absence of proper budgeting processes and financial controls. I also described in more detail the three recovery options I had outlined to him outside the Tate Gallery the previous evening. He believes that we will succeed in obtaining £10 million from the Floral Trust, and agrees with me that any option that effectively disbands the performing companies, by closing down the organization, has to be seen as the most grave failure. Throughout the meeting I felt exhausted. It's not just physical exhaustion but a sense of mental – almost emotional – exhaustion as well.

We then went to the meeting about catering in the new House, which turned out to be quite fun. Talking about food and drink is light relief indeed. John Sainsbury and Vivien were both in excellent form, shouting away happily, and the rest of the meeting was laughing rather than being cowed. Back to my office to tidy things up, settle down, and start thinking in a more leisurely fashion about how to develop my three recovery options and how to begin setting them out in a paper for the 30 October Board meeting.

At around 6.00 Richard Hall came in looking white. Throughout the last few weeks he has been viewing with a certain amount of detachment the Royal Opera House's precarious finances. Not so this time. He told me that we were approaching a cash flow crisis to the tune of £600,000 and that we might collapse within the next few days. Apparently there should have been £400,000 in our bank account today, and it was at zero. And £600,000 worth of cheques have been issued.[57] This time it's my turn to feel detached – through utter disbelief. We managed to contact Peter and then I phoned Graham Devlin and asked him if he could accelerate some of the

[57] One of the inadequacies of the Royal Opera House's financial information that most concerned Richard related to the quality of the cash flow forecasting. His prognosis, that without adequate cash flow forecasting we were at risk of an unforeseen cash crisis, was coming true.

lottery payments. He will discuss this with Jeremy Newton tomorrow and they will do whatever they can within, of course, the constraints of the regulations.

Thursday 9 October

Richard Hall came to see me at 8.30, his eyes red with strain and lack of sleep, to tell me that he had now uncovered, over the previous twelve hours, a possible cash gap of £2 million in November – the position is far worse than he had thought last night. I spoke several times to Graham Devlin, then I rang the auditors and asked to speak to an insolvency practitioner.

'I have not been in this position before, but it seems to me that if we know we are going to run out of cash within a few weeks and be unable to pay our debts, that we are in danger of going into insolvent liquidation and we should close down the company,' I said.

'That's correct.'

'How long have I got to sort things out?'

'Oh, until about lunch-time.'

I told him I had no idea of the technicalities of closing down an insolvent company. He explained I would need to organize a Board meeting within the next two hours, and that the Board would need to take a formal decision as to whether or not the organization was solvent.

I then phoned Peter at his office and relayed this conversation to him. Peter went into the very calm, almost somnolent mode that is characteristic of him when there is a crisis and I start sounding anxious.

'Please can you speak to the Floral Trust?' I asked.

'I don't want to take any decisions without knowing the figures.'

'The figures won't be available until midday, and you will be leaving your office to go to Heathrow at 11.00.'

'Don't get so worked up.'

'We are literally hours from collapse and I think being worked up is an entirely appropriate response,' I said rather tersely.

He phoned George Magan, who said that we could have access to £2 million from the Floral Trust to carry us across the November cash gap. Peter wrote a letter to George confirming this, made a record note of the conversation and sent a copy of both to me. We are not about to go bankrupt immediately – at least not because of an imminent cash shortage. Without the Floral Trust £2 million we would not have been able to pay the wages in November.

I talked with Richard about how the position had arisen. Apparently the cash book has not been written up since the end of August.[58] That means we have had no record for six weeks of our cash position, and no way of establishing at reasonable speed what it might be. To say I am flabbergasted is to understate how I feel. And, of course, I can't get on with the work that I am meant to be doing to plan for the new House, and no doubt that will all come home to roost in April when we fail to produce the business plan required of us then. Added to which Richard and I have not been able to do any of the work we have been planning on the three recovery scenarios; those too have to be completed within the next couple of weeks.

Friday 10 October

A day of coming down from the acute anxiety of the previous day.[59] I continued with my Board paper about the recovery scenarios in the morning, and went to a meeting of the technical team leaders and

[58] The Royal Opera House's financial procedures were old-fashioned and time-consuming. During the previous eighteen months substantial numbers of staff had been made redundant in the finance department, but without financial processes being changed to make them more streamlined and less labour-intensive. The impact of two complete budget reviews, conducted in quick succession, had stretched the finance department almost to breaking point.

[59] The Arts Council confirmed that they were able to accelerate some of the lottery payments, without breaking the regulations, and the bank subsequently authorized limited borrowing facilities to cover any short term difficulties.

deputy leaders. They are all worried about the future of the organization and were able to tell me, succinctly and accurately, what they thought was wrong with it. The thought crossed my mind that perhaps if I replaced the senior management group with these people we might get ourselves sorted out more quickly.

I had lunch with David Puttnam and he confirmed my view that if the Royal Opera House were to be threatened with bankruptcy the present government would not bail it out. He said there are plenty of uses for a piece of real estate of that size in the centre of Covent Garden. He also said that the DCMS is having an away-day during the coming week and that one of the items on the agenda would be a proposal to privatize the Royal Opera House. I remarked that I hoped Chris Smith would discuss any such scheme with us before making an announcement about it, and that whatever way he might wish to restructure the Royal Opera House it would still need substantial subsidy, unless the character of its work was to change very radically. David gave me a phone number for John Newbigin, Chris Smith's policy adviser, and suggested I contact him.

Spent the afternoon going walkabout and covered just about all of the departments in the three buildings. The part I enjoyed most was when I finally made my way down to the basement and, having wandered around a labyrinth of storerooms, found the armory. I put my head round the door and saw a plumpish man sitting on a seat, staring at me.

'Hello, are you Rob?' I said.

'Yes.'

'I'm Mary.'

'I know.'

From this laconic beginning we went on to spend a fascinating hour as Rob Barham showed me the swords – some of them Napoleonic – pikes and guns. He also told me stories of requests from designers or directors for new guns to be made which, when brought on stage were either not used or used out of sight, wasting thousands of pounds.

In the evening I went to the last night of *Platée*, and to the

Drogheda Circle dinner afterwards. I was shaking with exhaustion. I was sitting between Sir George Russell, the Chairman of Camelot, on the one side – many trenchant observations about the Government and Camelot – and Tom Lynch, an Irish businessman in his mid-forties, whose parents had met at the Royal Opera House at a performance of *La Bohème*, on the other side.

I had forgotten what it was like to be this tired, and how I feel as though I am breaking apart from inside. It starts in my breastbone, and I feel that if someone were to put their finger on my breastbone I would just crumble into dust.

Saturday 11 October

I had been going to ask the AA to charge up the battery on my car and then drive down to Suffolk. However I discovered that the locks had been vandalized. After watching the AA man break into it – most ingeniously, the vandals should have tried his method – we had to drive the car to the garage and leave it there and then go on down to Suffolk in Nigel's car. I have rarely felt so tired. I was feeling that state of coldness you get when you are so exhausted that your body doesn't seem to be functioning properly.

When we arrived I took a duvet and lay on the sofa while Nigel lit a fire.

Sunday 12 October

Woke up early and worked all morning while sitting in bed. Spent the afternoon in a rather desultory fashion, wandering around the garden.

Monday 13 October

An early phone call with Graham Devlin, to talk him through the cash position. I also told him that I was finding it all rather daunting and dispiriting, particularly since I had more or less come to the conclusion that the organization was quite literally unmanageable. Not what Graham wanted to hear and he sounded low.

I spent the morning visiting the props, paint and carpentry workshops. Off to the props department first, which is located in Highbury, quite close to where I live. They were a warm and talkative group of people who were pretty on the ball as far as money was concerned. They had been prevented from buying some silver trays the previous week and asked me various questions about how the finances were, and whether they would receive their pay cheques at the end of the month. I said I certainly intended to receive mine and was giving the whole thing my best shot. They said, 'Well Jenny McIntosh stood where you are and said exactly what you're saying – how do we know that you won't leave too?' One woman was cutting out some pieces of some tough foam-like substance and curling them up using a blow torch and then fixing them on some polystyrene to resemble a Corinthian column. Once it had been painted it looked remarkably realistic.

Then on to the carpenters who were more phlegmatic. The workshop is a vast place, where entire sets can be assembled. From there to the paint workshop where I talked to a man painting a gigantic cloth using a tiny design and various reference books to create the back cloth for *Cinderella.* It is fascinating to see the way in which people both in the paint shop and in the wardrobe create designs using only a sketch from the designer, and then build them up from reference books giving detail of period decoration and costume. Also met the man who had been filmed in *The House* painting a cloth black and 'philosophizing'. He said that he had insisted on philosophizing in response to the demands by the film crew that he gossiped about colleagues. It was his attempt to get them to go away.

On the way back to the office I talked with David Pritchard, the Head of Production, about the feasibility or otherwise of contracting out the work of the production departments. As I thought, it would probably not be cost-effective since we are one of the – if not the – largest markets for all such work.

Lunch with Richard Pulford.[60] I told him what I had gone through during the last ten days, and that I was worried about our ability to continue in operation. I set out for him my theory of the two different modes of operation – an integrated whole, or two companies and a receiving house – saying that at present we were combining the weak points of each and that was why the organization was unmanageable. He agreed, but said that it would be much easier to become two companies and a receiving house, since that went with the grain of the organization at present. However he also agreed with me that the preferable route in the long term would be to integrate and have the whole thing led by a small team.

After lunch met with Michael Knight.[61] I described to him my vision for a single integrated operation, with both companies led by a single artistic director working within a small team under my leadership. He agreed that this would, in an ideal world, be the preferable option and said that I should have the courage to try and make it stick. He also said I should recognize that one outcome might be the failure of the organization because of a financial collapse that I can't stop; another might be that I have to resign because either the Board, or Peter, or the donors do not wish to accept my vision.

Then down to the Labatt's Apollo where I met Anthony Russell-Roberts at the stage door and we went briefly on stage. They had had a bad afternoon, with the transformation scene taking three hours to get right. They were still lighting the show and it was going to go up at least ten minutes late. *Sleeping Beauty* looks good on the wide stage. We sat in the stalls for about twenty minutes talking about

[60] I had asked Richard Pulford to review the income forecasts during the closure period and give me a view as to their likely achievability.

[61] The headhunter who had recruited me. Michael was also an organizational analyst, specializing in transforming dysfunctional organizations. It was in this latter role that I was now picking his brains.

various difficulties – of both the technical and the financial kind – and then went front of house for a drink.

Met Nigel amongst the crowds – everyone was being kept out of the auditorium while they finished the technical rehearsal – and then saw the show. In the interval we went to the retiring room with Peter and his guests, who included John and Jane Birt. John gave me some excellent advice about standing up to a tough press and about select committees. The key is to rehearse: bring together a group of people and make them be as nasty to you as possible. Bob and Kate Gavron were also there; Bob and I have agreed we shall have our lunch on Friday even though Peter now can't make it.

Home on the tube and I slept most of the way.

Tuesday 14 October

Arrived at work about 7.00 and continued writing my recovery scenario Board paper. Then went to Baron's Court and attended a staff meeting of the ballet company, following which I had a meeting with Anthony Dowell. The ballet company were friendly, although anxious. Everyone is aware that there is something very seriously wrong as the news has filtered down that we've temporarily had to stop issuing cheques. I talked about the development and the new House, which at least meant there was an upbeat tone to some of what I said. Anthony Dowell was, as usual, shy and self-effacing. He and I talked about my intention to have regular Programming Meetings, also about whether or not to agree a new contract with Sylvie Guillem, even though she is asking such high fees.

Back to the office for a couple of hours where I continued to write my Board paper, and talked with various people about sundry matters. I telephoned Michael Knight and we agreed that I would go and see him on Monday morning once I had my own thoughts about the organization's structure sorted out. One issue is whether I try and achieve change immediately, or whether I set out my objectives and then achieve change through consultation.

Wednesday 15 October

Felt quite light-hearted for most of the day. During the week when I am able to control – or at least attempt to control – the situation I feel much more relaxed than at weekends, when I just have to wait, and shiver, until I can get back into the office.

Started the day with a meeting with Peter and Richard Hall to review the budgets. Peter said that he felt trying to deal with this crisis was like trying to catch a falling sword: there was this sharp dangerous thing hurtling towards you and you had to catch it without having your fingers cut off. I told him about my lorry analogy: we were in a heavily laden lorry whose brakes had failed and which was tearing down a hill. We had to mend the brakes before we got to the bottom, while steering at the same time.

After lunch went to a meeting of the Royal Ballet Governors, chaired by John Sainsbury: a group of elderly people – many of them having been connected with the company up to twenty years ago – telling us what we ought to be doing about the rep and other matters. There is no obvious connection between this set of Governors and the Royal Opera House Board, although they seem to see themselves as having a similar role. John helpfully glossed over the changes to the upcoming programme. To have had the Royal Ballet Governors complaining about these alterations without being able to explain to them the nature of our financial predicament would just have provoked a row. And it is essential that, until we have found a solution, as few people know about it as possible. Lots of criticism of Anthony Dowell for not renewing Irek Mukamedov's contract – he stood up for himself surprisingly vigorously.

I was called out during the meeting to deal with a paper for the Select Committee, and took the opportunity to phone Richard Pulford who told me that his initial hunch about the income forecasts was that they were £1 million over-optimistic. My heart sank.

Thursday 16 October

Arrived at the office and had a meeting with Jim Butler[62] and Richard Hall to talk about the finances. Jim worried me. He was pushing Richard on a number of issues that they had obviously discussed before, and about which Jim appeared to be expecting more information than he was now being given. Richard looked exhausted and stressed; it is hard to know just how much to press someone under those circumstances – although one needs the information urgently, if you press too hard all you will do is decrease someone's capacity to produce it. The failure of the budgets, the absence of proper financial procedures, and the resulting weakness of the financial information available, make it very hard indeed to reach any concrete views on the finances.

Jim was suggesting that the reason there is a large hole in our cash flow is because the deficit is going to be considerably larger – perhaps to the tune of £2 million – than we were at present forecasting.[63] No one seems to have the slightest idea whether this might be the case.

Then Jim and I met with the lawyers in order to determine whether or not, in the event of liquidation, it would be possible to separate the development from the performing companies or whether the whole lot would go down together. My purpose in asking these questions was so that, if the end was reached and we had to go and ask the Government to bail us out, I had some idea of whether or not it would be possible to let the operating company go and keep the building site. The answer seemed broadly to be no, since the operating company – the Royal Opera House itself – is the vehicle through which money has to be channeled to the development[64]. According to the lawyers,

[62] Ex-KPMG and a member of the Royal Opera House Main Board. Although not formally Chairman of the Finance and Audit Committee, he played an important part in advising me and Richard Hall during this period.
[63] This was not the case.
[64] Although this was the initial advice we received, there were further reasons why, if there was any risk that the operating company might become insolvent, it would be difficult to split the two.

a very determined Government could rush through the necessary legislation to enable a replacement vehicle to be set up immediately, but even in that case Jim thinks there might be up to £50 to £60 million worth of donations withheld if the opera and ballet companies ceased to exist, and it would be an expensive option. So basically the point to make to Mr Blair, if we get that far, is that he either has a hole in the ground or he rescues the whole operation since it would be very much cheaper to do so.

Then out to lunch with Dennis Marks who'd just resigned as Director of the ENO. We talked about running opera houses and about his last days at ENO, and the difficulties he had had with the Arts Council at the end. Knowing, as I do, so much from the other side, it must have been tough going for everyone involved.

Back to the office for a meeting with Deborah MacMillan, the widow of Sir Kenneth MacMillan and Chairman of the Arts Council Dance Advisory Panel. She was delighted to see her painting on my wall. It looked good now that it was flanked by other pictures on a cream wall, and not just hanging by itself on the tatty old yellow paint that had been there when I arrived. She removed it because she wants to reframe it. Deborah and I covered a range of issues about the ballet company, including the need for more encouragement to young choreographers, a more imaginative use of the present rep and better management generally. She is obviously fond of everyone there and also of a whole range of people at the Royal Opera House, particularly in the making departments. She, too, gave me the sense of the company being a large family.

After I had seen Deborah, I had a brief meeting with Richard Hall and we talked again about the lack of financial controls. No management information has been produced for the last three months although that was, I thought, because the finance department has been preoccupied by repeated budget reviews, to the virtual exclusion of anything else. Richard now tells me that we do not even have the capacity to produce management accounts, because the way in which information is collected about expenditure does not correlate with the way in which the budgets are put together. The only financial information we are able to produce – although even that has not been produced during the last few months – are updated forecasts, and there is no way of reconciling forecast expenditure with the detail of actual expenditure.

Had a telephone conversation with Jonathan Skan, from Prince Charles's office, discussing arrangements for Prince Charles's visit in December to the building site. I went round and told John Seekings about the visit and said that I would have to start practising curtseying in wellies. Although I made a vow to myself when I accepted this job that I would curtsey to royalty – something I have never done before – I failed when meeting Princess Margaret on the first night of the Labatt's Apollo season. I wasn't helped by the fact that she is very small indeed. I managed a clumsy half bow – no doubt quite inappropriately – that was as much as anything else an attempt to hear what she was saying. However I will try and strut my stuff for Prince Charles on the building site.

More thoughts about the budgets, particularly in view of the telephone conversation with Richard Pulford yesterday. The figures drift inexorably downwards or, I suppose I should say, upwards since it is the size of the deficit which is growing. I am not 100 per cent confident we are going to get out of this. However I am considerably more than the 60 per cent or so confident that I should be to satisfy the test of proper trading. And so we will continue.

Friday 17 October

Before I went to the office I had a look at the building site, and the devastation we have wrought on the old theatre. I hadn't realized how much space was occupied by the portion of the building we were knocking down. I am rapidly revising my view as to whether or not Tony Blair would wish it to be in this state for the Millennium. It looks ghastly: a huge wound.

A meeting with Richard Hall, during which we determined that it will cost £26 million to close down the organization and pay all our debts, while allowing the development to continue. This would include a small team planning the operation of the new theatre and the cost of staffing up towards reopening, although this in itself would be a bit of a fantasy, since without the performing companies there wouldn't be anything to reopen for. It seems to me unlikely that the Arts Council would wish such a large sum of money to be spent on an arts organization *ceasing* to exist. So the alternative to securing money from the Floral Trust seems to be liquidation – unless, of course, the Government wanted to step in.

Every time we seem to be struggling towards a possible solution, something else happens to knock us back. The news from Richard Pulford about the income forecasts and the possibility, as suggested by Jim Butler yesterday, that the cash flow might conceal a much greater revenue deficit this year than anticipated, all make me feel as though I am a tired swimmer, trying to get out of a swimming pool, who is repeatedly pushed back in just as they have got to the top step. Each time I am metaphorically sitting back in the water, getting colder and tireder, thinking, 'Can I do this again?' It is terribly discouraging.

I walked over to the Folio Society in the middle of the day to have lunch with Bob Gavron. It was a lovely day, gentle, with the sun shining and a soft breeze. We talked about the Royal Opera House's financial position, its management, and the history of how it had arrived in this terrible mess. Bob still says the basic problem is underfunding by Government: no other international opera house in Europe has to run itself on this amount of subsidy. He is determined that we must have more money from the Government. I agreed with him, but I also said I thought it inconceivable the Government would give us any more money at the moment. We just have to accept the fact that we are underfunded and do whatever is necessary to stay within budget.

Walked back to the office and continued with my Board paper.

Saturday 18 October

Went in to the office at about 8.30 and worked through until about 6.00. It was a glorious day and I could hardly bear to look out of the window. Esther, my temp PA, was there too – she must be mad – as was Richard, the full finance department, and the wardrobe. They are working flat out to complete *The Merry Widow* before we go up on Thursday. Lorraine came down with her daughter around lunchtime and we had a good laugh. I managed to finish my Board paper and faxed it to Peter.

Went home and had a long and luxurious bath.

Sunday 19 October

Went into the office again, arriving by about 9.15, and had several long telephone conversations with Peter. He is pleased with my paper although he regards the tone as somewhat combative. I explained that this was partly because I was angry with the Board and partly because it was a way of releasing the stress I had been feeling. I reassured him that the final version would be written in emollient language.

Felt increasingly resentful at the lovely day outside, and returned home by lunchtime. Sat with Nigel in the garden, had lunch, and then went for a walk on Hampstead Heath. It was unbearably lovely. I cannot understand why I don't have the courage to give in my notice and live a different and more fulfilling lifestyle. Returned home and started doing some domestic admin. Spent the rest of the evening watching television, finishing with a long and very traumatic viewing of *Schindler's List.* Nigel and I were both crying and trying to conceal the fact from Nigel's children, Kate and Jamie.

Monday 20 October

Went over to see Michael Knight. He started off by using words like 'ludicrous' and 'grotesque' to describe the structure and operation of the Royal Opera House. I said that I had used many words like that but had found that my vocabulary quickly ran out. I needed words that were considerably beyond 'grotesque' in concept and strength in order to describe how I felt about the organization and the words did not exist. He agreed with my diagnosis and with my plans and I told him that I had decided to take a consultative approach to change, using Michael to work with the staff. He will let me have costings for the assignment over the next couple of days.

I then returned to the office for the Board meeting. It began with a presentation of the budgets, still showing a projected deficit in the region of £12 million, by Richard Hall. Within ten minutes I was at the point of losing my temper with several Board members, who were expressing the view that all arts organizations operate in the same way as the Royal Opera House, and that all of them lose money hand-over-fist the entire time.

One Board member then said that he thought that the present systems – the ones that I have described at the Royal Opera House – are common to all arts organizations and we should live with the systems we've got.

Someon else said that it was completely impossible for any business to budget two or three years ahead and be accurate, and that our business was tougher than most. Richard Hall responded robustly by saying that actually our business was easier to forecast than most, since so many of our contracts were let a long time in advance and we know the seating capacities – in other words we know our capacity to sell; the trouble was there were no feedback loops.

Richard then told the Board that the three main reasons for the failure of the budgets were errors and omissions (for example there had been no technical costs or orchestra variables included in the March version of the 1998/99 and 1999/2000 budgets at all); changes made during the summer without factoring the financial implications of those changes into the budgets; and the continuing under-performance of the box office.

Richard reminded the Board that, despite all of the many procedural inadequacies, we had got rid of our internal auditor during the most recent round of redundancies – at that point Vivien and I started laughing, through despair rather than anything else. There was one point when a slide was put up on the overhead projector that had the words 'Arts Council' on it. I stared wistfully at them and thought, 'I might have been there, rather than here.'

Vivien said, over and over again, that she thought that the best thing was for the company to go down. Clean sheet. Start again. I understand her frustration, but I was so frustrated myself that I felt like physically shaking her as I tried to explain clearly that the company could not go down without taking the development with it. The whole lot would collapse.

After the Board meeting, wrote my recovery scenario Board paper again for another hour and then went out with Grey. It was delightful to see him although he was in serious, rather than light-hearted mood. We discussed the Royal Opera House and its problems, and I told him we were £10 million in the red. He was horrified. He cannot bear the thought that the Royal Opera House might close during his Chairmanship of the Arts Council. I said that I was 75 per cent confident that we could sort out our present difficulties. I also said that if we couldn't we would not simply close but would, of course, come to the Arts Council first.

Tuesday 21 October

In the morning we had the first of our Programming Meetings, looking at the programme for the first season in the new House. Everyone was being constructive and I enjoyed being able to talk about the art rather than money. Nicholas had developed his ideas to quite a detailed degree; Anthony and Anthony were still talking about the type of work they might put in different slots, although when I go to

Baron's Court next week we will have a couple of hours in which I hope we will really be able to explore how we can best use the ballet rep. It's a good programme, although I am not keen on bringing back *Mathis der Maler*.

Peter and I met with George Magan at 11.15 in Peter's office, to ask whether the Floral Trust might be prepared to donate the remainder of their funds to the operating company – rather than the building – to enable us to continue. George didn't twig, initially, that he was being asked for the whole lot, and talked about the £2 million that he agreed a couple of weeks ago. Peter had to lead him gently towards the idea that this time we meant the full £10 million, plus any interest accruing. We made it clear that if the operating company went bust, so would the development. George was positive, and said he thought the Trustees would be prepared to be helpful. He also agreed with the conditions I suggested be attached to any donation: that a viable business plan for the reopened House should be prepared as a matter of priority;[65] that management systems and structures be overhauled; and that there should be improvements to financial procedures. Left the meeting almost dizzy with relief.

At lunchtime I met Kathryn McDowell (the Arts Council Music Director). She is so positive. She spent the whole time telling me to buck up, brace up and get on with it. But at the same time she was sympathetic – as we both agreed, she was well used to calming down frantic heads of opera houses.

Wednesday 22 October

Spent the morning continuing to work on the Board paper.

Walked over to The Ivy and had lunch with Cameron Mackintosh. He does not like the Royal Opera House. I was surprised by the vehemence of his comments about some of the Board

[65] This was the plan that was already in the process of preparation, through the Planning Group.

members and about the way in which the organization works. I told him that I was planning to restructure the entire organization, which would attract criticism, but would incidentally bring it more in line with the kind of organization he felt the Royal Opera House ought to be within five years' time. I also told him that I would need his support.

We talked about the Arts Council and his feeling that something needs to be done about it urgently. I said that the main thing that needed to be done about the Arts Council was that the Government should decide, finally, whether or not it wanted one and, if it did want one, fully to support it. After every single General Election during the last twenty years, an incoming Government has hummed and ha-ad over whether or not it wanted an Arts Council, considered whether or not to abolish it, decided in the end it wasn't worth the trouble, and then continued to support it in rather a half-hearted fashion, whilst the regional arts boards continued to whinge about it. I expressed all of this with some force to Cameron, who said he agreed with me.

John Newbigin (Chris Smith's policy adviser) came over at 5.00 and I took him round the development, lingering long opposite the massive hole we have created by knocking down the entire stage. I pointed to the proscenium arch and said that yes, the enormous destroyed space, leading back from the proscenium arch, was where the stage and backstage had been. He looked rather shaken and inwardly I cheered. Then round to the front, where I pointed out where all the new spaces were going to be, whipped hard hats off a couple of site workers, marched over to the edge of a deep hole and pointed out where the studio theatre was going to be, described how the scene docks would work with the wagon system, and then took him back into the office.

John said, rather dazedly, that I seemed to be very positive about the whole thing. I then went through my vision for the Royal Opera House, described how I wanted to increase accessibility, and gave him a graphic account of our problems. At last I felt I was talking to someone with political influence, who was listening to what I was saying, and who might be prepared to believe that the Royal Opera House could come through and could end up being the kind of organization that everybody wanted. I think it was a helpful meeting, although he also mentioned that the DCMS believes that the choice is for us to be like the Met[66] – in other words entirely privately funded and very grand – or become 'The People's Opera'. There is no chance of anywhere being able to be like the Met in this country: there is not enough money around. I'm not sure yet whether we will be able to bring the ticket prices down sufficiently to qualify as 'The People's Opera'.

I then spent a couple of hours working on my Select Committee memo and reached home at about 9.00. Read and listened to music. One of the pieces I played was the Grieg piano concerto, with the second movement that I had listened to on several occasions just before I had been interviewed to become Secretary-General of the Arts Council. It is a piece of music that reminds me of climbing mountains – or of accomplishments of some kind – and I had listened to it in order to psyche myself up. I don't think I have heard it since then. At any rate when the music came on I felt very melancholy. I realized how very much I missed the Arts Council, and all the people who work there. I was there for five years. I suppose it's like leaving a family. And gruellingly bureaucratic though much of the work there was, there wasn't the sense of nightmarish panic that has characterized my few weeks at the Royal Opera House.

I then put on *The Rite of Spring*. I must have been in a mad mood because I turned it up very loud indeed and sat directly between the speakers on the floor, letting the music flow through me with all the thumping and the pounding. And of course by that time it was after midnight so, yet again, I went to bed too late and had too little sleep.

[66] The Metropolitan Opera, in New York, has negligible public subsidy. It stays afloat by selling over 90 per cent of its 4,000 seats for each performance, and by means of a very substantial endowment, the funds for which have been raised from the private sector.

Thursday 23 October

Woke up at 7.00 feeling like the dead and went over to Shandwick[67] for the Select Committee rehearsal. I was not feeling very amused about it and so, when Peter started telling anecdotes about Gerald Kaufman saying to Lord Gowrie, 'I can't wait to get that Mary Allen in front of us,' I did not smile.

In the event I was surprised at how leniently the mock committee treated me. They, in turn, were surprised I said that, and felt that they'd given me a hard time. Well if that is all Kaufman is going to give me I'll be fine. In fact I am dreading it. I feel that the agenda of the Select Committee is going to be to trip me up and make me look foolish so they can criticize me. They were courteous to Lord Gowrie and accepted his evidence, equally so to Peter and accepted his, and particularly courteous to Jenny. By process of elimination, in Kaufman's mind I must be the villain of the piece.

Then I stayed to hear Vivien's rehearsal. I thought she was rather good and, when she lost her cool, extremely funny. If she strikes the right note she'll be very good indeed. Her fear will serve her well, because it will calm her down and stop her being over-assertive, but she needs to get angry once or twice because that's when she becomes amusing.

Walked back to the office. In the afternoon continued yet again to work on my Board paper, and then out to *The Merry Widow*. It was interesting to watch the Royal Opera try to come to terms with musical comedy. It is a different genre, requiring different vocal techniques and different styles of dramatic presentation. The first half was uncertain, apart from Tom Allen who seemed to be enjoying himself hugely and who has a great comic gift, but during the second act the company grew into the style of the show.

Took a taxi home and thought about the Select Committee all the way.

[67] Shandwick was the public relations company that Peter Chadlington had founded and now chaired. He had his main office there.

Friday 24 October

Quite a normal day really. Spent the morning finishing my Board paper and had some time to start thinking strategically about how I present it to the Board, and how we communicate the Board's decisions thereafter.

Saturday 25 October

Spent the morning reading material to help me prepare for the Select Committee and thinking about what I would say. Wandered around the garden for an hour at lunchtime with Nigel, had lunch, cooked dinner for twelve, and had our dinner party. I enjoyed it greatly – I hope the guests did too; we played charades after dinner which was great fun and I remember laughing almost uncontrollably at one point but cannot remember what I was laughing about. Everyone left at about 2.00.

Sunday 26 October

Spent the morning working – in other words reading more material for the Select Committee and thinking further thoughts about what I would say to Mr Kaufman and his colleagues. I interspersed my thinking and reading with wandering around the garden. It was still. The berries are looking very red: the season of mist and mellow fruitfulness is well under way. One slightly alarming moment when we found a hole in the rabbit fence where the individual strands of chicken wire had quite clearly been cut through. I do not believe that rabbits can gnaw through chicken wire with their teeth, otherwise rabbit fences would not be made of chicken wire. But something has got through there.

Drove home in the early afternoon in order to attend a concert by the Orchestra of the Royal Opera House Soloists, at 5.00 at Dulwich

College. The first piece was an exquisite display of Mozartian expertize. The second was a daring piece for double bass – it didn't quite work but it was the right decision to do it anyway. And the third piece was *Death and the Maiden.* I had a drink with members of the orchestra afterwards, and then returned home where I watched television before going to bed.

Peter had left a message on the answer phone saying that 75 per cent of the Board were now behind my paper. I bet he has not yet talked to Vivien. She is the one who will count. She and James Spooner.

Monday 27 October

Arrived at the office at 7.30 and began working on my statement to the Select Committee. Completed that by about 10.00 and then did some reading.

At 11.00 Peter Hemmings, from the Los Angeles Music Center came in to discuss a commitment he maintained Nicholas had made to him in the summer, that we would co-produce *Il trovatore* with him. He needs to know that we will give him £60,000 in the year 2002. I explained our various financial predicaments and that no one was in a position to make any commitments of that kind at the moment. He sort of understood, but his eyes started popping and his face grew red as he tried to persuade me to write a letter to him before Christmas saying that we would do exactly as he requested. I must ask John Harrison, who was with Nicholas at the point the alleged commitment was made, whether or not Nicholas actually said he would do it.

After lunch we had another Select Committee rehearsal. This time Peter led the questioning, and he was infinitely more unpleasant to me than the group had been last week. It lasted an hour and a half and was most stressful. I was pressed over and over again on why I had suggested Peter seek advice from the Department of National Heritage; and why I had not told Grey Gowrie as soon as I had found out that Jenny was trying to resign. I manfully – or womanfully – stuck to my guns, but I was told afterwards that I had appeared angry and exasperated. One of the more important aspects of the rehearsal was to work out ways in which I can respond to questions about the Royal Opera House's financial position *without* giving any indication we might be about to go bust. The press will be there and it is essential that the details of our appalling position are kept very quiet indeed until we know what we are going to do about it.

Once we had finished the rehearsal I spent the rest of the afternoon and early evening rewriting my statement for the Select Committee and practising conciliatory body langauge – hands loosely clasped on the desk in front of me, head slightly on one side, almost smiling but not quite and speaking in an even, gentle voice.

Richard Hall came down to my office shortly after 9.00 and we talked for about half an hour about the organization, its extraordinary nature, our frustration, and our anxiety that the Board will avoid grasping the various nettles that we are offering to them on Thursday. If the Board prevaricate in any way we will have no choice but to say that the place is insolvent. We also need to ensure that we end up with the support necessary to begin implementing the recovery strategy.

I had a letter today from a prisoner at HMP Durham. He said that there had been an occasion when he had been extremely frustrated in his cell and he had thrown his radio against the wall. As a result it was only able to receive Radio 3. He was therefore forced to listen to classical music and had come to love opera as a result. His reason for writing was to thank us for all the opera we produce.

Tuesday 28 October

Went to Baron's Court, where I had two hours with Anthony and Anthony, talking about the ballet rep over the next two years. No matter how anxious and stressed I feel about the rest of the business, I always feel soothed when we manage to talk about the art itself.

Their ideas were much more interesting than those which had been included in the original rep plans for the season 99/00, but I think we can go still further. We also covered a lot of management issues, including the sense of profound resentment and almost powerlessness that seems to be felt by the ballet management in relation to the Royal Opera House departments that are not to do with the art directly.

Back to the Arts Council for sandwiches with Jeremy Newton (the Arts Council Lottery Director). He took me through the whole process by which the Arts Council had assessed whether the Royal Opera House was meeting the conditions attached to its lottery award. We agreed that the Arts Council could not have monitored the Royal Opera House any more tightly than it did. It had its best project monitors working on the Royal Opera House; Richard Pulford was in there for a year; and professional advisers reviewed all the closure budgets. Most importantly, Richard Pulford had indicated that the problems of the Royal Opera House could be addressed with firm management and that, of course, is what the Arts Council had thought that Jenny would provide.

Back to the office to discover that, in addition to my own appearance in two days time, I am required to go before the Select Committee again, with Peter, on the afternoon of 4 November. Changed various meetings including the senior management group, the Joint Consultative Group, and the lunch I was due to have with the orchestra principals. I then called Colin Lee, the Clerk to the Committee, to see what we would be discussing and how long it would take. We are on at 4.15 with no guaranteed finish time; the evidence begins at 2.30, and we are advised to be there from the start.

When one looks at the line-up of the final day it is almost as if they are trying to create an opera out of the inquiry itself. First there is Chris Smith, presumably with Melanie Leech (his Assistant Secretary); then there is Lord Gowrie with Graham Devlin; and, to conclude the whole proceedings there is Lord Chadlington, accompanied by me, Richard Hall and Keith Cooper. I had earlier told Peter that it was an excellent thing that he was going last. He had sounded dubious. I spent some time working on the Select Committee papers, including re-reading all the previous evidence.

Peter rang to say that he had heard through a variety of sources that Kaufman's agenda would be to make me admit that I had told Grey Gowrie that Chris Smith had offered his approval to my appointment; to get Chris Smith to say he had never approved anything at all; and then to accuse Peter of failing to tell the truth, about Jenny and about the appointment process, so that – unbelievably – he could get me into the job. I listened, incredulously, and went home. After three quarters of an hour Peter phoned me again. He is exceedingly agitated and upset. The whole thing seems like a baroque fantasy. Although it was either Kaufman or one of his colleagues who said that there seemed to be more opera off-stage than on, if what Peter has told me is remotely true, Kaufman is attempting to create a drama of epic proportions. What really worries me now is that we have an enormously important Board meeting coming up and Peter will be entirely preoccupied by the possible events of next week. We are still £10 million down, and we still need to get the agreement of the Floral Trust to provide the necessary funds to stop us going bust.

I keep telling myself that this is all very interesting and how lucky I am to be in the middle of such an extraordinary situation. However I don't really feel like that at all. I wish I was doing some everyday job in a low-profile organization, where I could go in at a sensible time, leave at a sensible time and think about something else for at least some of my waking hours.

Wednesday 29 October

I woke up 4.45 and worked on tomorrow's presentation to the Board. It's now 6.30. It is hard to come to terms with everything that will be happening during the next few days. Not only are we going to be considering the future of the Royal Opera House – whether or not large sums of money can be made available to save us and the nature of the change programme that will have to be implemented in order to enable the organization to continue – but I will also be in front of the Select Committee, *and* there seems to be a possibility the Select Committee will try and make my chairman resign.

I feel exhausted *now.* The thought of having to go through a day that includes taking Princess Margaret round the building site leaves me feeling flattened. We are going out to dinner tonight; I hope I don't go to sleep half-way through. When I went to bed last night it was as though I had been hit with a hammer. I literally lost consciousness.

Met Peter and Richard in the office at 8.00. We all re-read my Board paper about the recovery scenarios. Peter sighed and said he wished the world was as ordered as I presented it. Then the telephone rang.

It was Vivien. She spoke to Peter for fifteen minutes: a continuous barrage of sound coming out of the receiver in which one could occasionally hear one's own name. Once Peter had come off the telephone we speculated about how to calm Vivien down, and what might be the consequences of her refusal to back the Floral Trust proposal. Peter said that she was determined the whole organization should go into liquidation.

We spent an hour and a half discussing how we could persuade her, during the next 24 hours, to support the Floral Trust proposal. Then Vivien, Tony Hutt (GJW), and Jim Butler arrived, together with Keith Cooper. We began discussing the Select Committee, and what Peter had told me last night. He seems even more pessimistic this morning. Half-way through the meeting he turned white and became quiet. I wasn't sure what was going on, but he then began talking about my and Vivien's appearances at the Select Committee, saying that please, could he just rely on us to support him. I have never seen Peter like that: tense and sad.

At 1.00, after five hours of continuous discussion, I was finally left alone for a few minutes. I am now facing the prospect of my own Select Committee appearance tomorrow, trying to stop the organization from going bankrupt, and the possibility of losing my Chairman and perhaps other Board members. I said to Richard that I had once again started feeling that sense of unreality – almost as if observing events through a pane of glass – I had experienced a few weeks ago when I had first recognized the budgets were totally out of balance.

Vivien had been calm all morning and we parted amicably. We had been dissuading her from wearing her scarlet suit for tomorrow. She said that instead she would wear the black and I suggested that she didn't wear too much gold jewellery. She and Keith then recounted that when they first met Vivien had noticed Keith looking at her jewels. So she said to him, 'I couldn't decide what to put on this morning so I just wore the lot.'

Then on with the wellies, hard hat and fluorescent coat, and over to the building site to meet Princess Margaret. It was an agreeable wander around the site. The day was beautiful and it was good to be out in the open air. Yet again, I was struck by how monumental the site is, and how much destruction we have wrought. If we go down, there is going to be a very large bill indeed for someone to pick up.

At one point we all went up to the top of the site in an outside hoist lift. I looked very hard at the notice in front of me and tried to stop the waves of vertigo and panic. When we reached the top and had got out, I said to Peter that I had found the journey difficult (Peter suffers as much from vertigo as I do) and I always found my vertigo was worse when I was feeling anxious anyway. And he said, 'Yes, the panic builds on other panic. Just feel my hands.' He brushed the palms of his hands across the backs of mine and they were wet with sweat. He is a much better actor than I am.

All the way round the site visit he and I were murmuring in corners. An hour earlier, he had received from the Select Committee a copy of a letter that Jenny McIntosh had written a month or so ago to Gerald Kaufman. In it she very courteously, but nonetheless clearly, says that Peter's comments about her illness had created the wrong impression, since she wasn't actually ill at the point she left, but only thought it possible she would become so if she stayed. She referred to a fax she had sent Peter, suggesting that perhaps they should use another reason for her departure in the press release. She also said she had been asked to leave immediately.[68] Peter had shown me the fax. He had also shown me her resignation letter, in which she had asked to be allowed to go as soon as possible. He is extremely angry. And he is determined to be as open as he can be with the Select Committee about what happened and how stressed Jenny was.

Once we returned from the site visit, I went into the House Coordination Group and talked for fifteen minutes about my plans for the future and how I wished to take them forward. I think it went well. At the end I said that I was going to the Select Committee tomorrow and that, however hard I tried, there would inevitably be bad press on Friday. Many people came up and wished me luck. When I returned to my office there was a card from Nicki and Phillipa. I was touched by the staff, and by their warmth.

Over to the model room to see the designs for *Il barbiere*. They are by Nigel Lowrey – who is also the director and was very nervous when presenting them – and are at the contemporary deconstructionist end of the artistic spectrum. The Royal Opera House departmental heads watched in silence. No one had any questions at the end, they just stared at what they obviously felt was going to be a pretty difficult prospect. I talked to Nigel afterwards and said that his Latin-American approach reminded me of Cuba, with the sense of heat, a rather sleazy ambience, and the surreal sense of different lifestyles, different cultures and even different eras being placed side by side.

Back to my office to sit quietly and tidy things up in preparation for tomorrow. Then off to dinner. I lasted for two hours – at 10.00 I suddenly felt a wave of exhaustion, almost to unconsciousness. Home by myself in a taxi and immediately to bed.

[68] This was an aside in a long paragraph dealing with the wording of the press release announcing her departure, and I believe it was a slip rather than a direct contradiction. However, much was made of it by Kaufman when I gave evidence the following day.

Thursday 30 October

I woke at 3.15. It is now 4.30 and I am very nervous. The Select Committee and then the Board meeting. I don't believe in God, but I do believe that if one prays it reaches something inside oneself and creates strength. I am praying hard at the moment.

Arrived at the office at 7.15. Re-worked my speech, looked at all the papers, got bored, became frightened and then went to the House of Commons. It was all as I remembered: long corridors with people standing in groups outside the Committee Rooms, looking as though they were in a medieval court and had been waiting for admission for several days to plead with some obscure advocate. We joined the crowd outside Committee Room 15. I spoke to several journalists. Witnesses were called and the crowds parted to allow Vivien and me, and those accompanying us, to walk in.

The committee was sitting round a large horseshoe table in one half of the room. Across the end of the horseshoe was a small table, with a placard with my name on it. I sat down, flanked by Richard and Keith. The press sat in the two rows of seats allocated to them on either side of the room, and the public filed into the fifty or so seats behind my chair. There were two television cameras, one facing me and one behind me. In the well of the horseshoe sat the two stenographers. Once the audience was seated I was asked if I wished to make a statement and I delivered my short speech. Kaufman shuffled papers and read notes while I was speaking. When the sound of my voice stopped he looked up as though he had only just noticed my presence and delivered a speech of his own, quite unrelated to anything I had said, littered with words like 'shambles' and 'crisis', all of which were written down by the journalists. And then we were off. It was not as bad as I had feared. It's like fencing – the most exhausting aspect of the questioning is maintaining 100 per cent concentration without allowing it to lapse for even a second.

The only point over which he really grilled me was why hadn't I told Gowrie, before Jenny resigned, that there was a possibility she might and that I might take over her job. I said that I had not believed she would resign until the point she did; that there was an enormous amount of anxiety and stress amongst arts managers anyway (remembering two similar incidents the year before); and I had thought that, with her professionalism, she would tough it out. He waved Jenny's letter around and made much of the fact that she had 'been asked to leave the Opera House immediately' as she had claimed, rather than saying that she could not carry on, and that it was perfectly obvious she could have carried on. I refrained from pointing out to Kaufman that his present view of her position was therefore identical to the one I had held at the time, thus vindicating my judgement – perhaps I should have done. Otherwise the most frustrating moments were when Kaufman seemed to be assuming I was asking for more money. I had emphasized in my introductory speech that I was not, but that the arts generally were in serious financial trouble. At one point Kaufman said that the Arts Council would be 'nuts' to give us another penny. I thought silently that he would be surprised if he knew how strongly I agreed with him. He is very clever though – he interjects these comments in such a manner that it is almost impossible to respond to them.

In response to all financial questions I hid behind the fact it was a condition of our lottery grant that we agreed all artistic and financial plans for the closure period with the Arts Council, and it would be inappropriate to speak publicly about that aspect of our business until we had done so. This was accepted without comment.

I felt I conducted myself reasonably well. Vivien was excellent, and at one point when they were asking her about the conduct of Board members, she shook her hands at them and said, 'For heaven's sake how could *you* run anything?' and the whole place dropped with laughter. We listened as a matter of courtesy to the evidence given by the Covent Garden Community Association – not wanting the headlines 'Covent Garden nobs walk out' – and then went back to my office.

A bit of dissection of how we had done, with both of us feeling that the Committee might be gunning for Peter. At one point during my evidence Kaufman had pushed me, trying to make me admit that

Peter should not have let the Royal Opera House operate without a Chief Executive during the summer.

Then, over sandwiches with Peter and Vivien, it emerged that Board members have been having discussions during the last few days. They have no intention of supporting the recovery option in my paper and instead wish to put the Royal Opera House into administrative receivership. I was angry that the Board should have reached a decision about my paper outside the meeting, before I had had a chance to present it or the Board to discuss it as a group. However, it then transpired that this was not the important piece of business at all: Peter believes that he will have to go as a result of the Select Committee, and the rest of the Board is determined to go with him.

The Board meeting began with a period of about forty-five minutes which was a 'non Board meeting'. Each Board member said they wished to resign, either in support of Peter or because they had failed to supervise the finances properly. Yet again I had this sensation of free-floating in a fantasy. Then the advisers came in and it was all discussed again in front of the lawyers and the auditors. Jane Murphy, our lawyer, pointed out that they could not just resign and hope to get away from the problem. The organization is on the brink of insolvency and they will be held responsible if it goes down. Particularly if, by resigning, they have precipitated the collapse. So then it was all discussed *again* for another hour.

Finally I presented my paper about the recovery scenarios, which I did with more than my usual brio, because of the frustration that had been building as a result of the fact we had spent two hours of the Board meeting without tackling the substantive issue of solvency. A debate ensued. They were all so hopelessly pessimistic, and seemingly determined not to rescue the organization. I know that most of them have probably been in this position countless times over the last few years, and that it probably seems like the last straw. Also they probably don't believe it can be saved. But they don't seem to recognize that if the company closes down – or melts down – the development will come to a halt indefinitely. Fund-raising prospects would plummet and the costs soar. It would be years – if ever – before the thing was completed. Vivien left the meeting early. Peter obtained an agreement from the Board that we could continue to explore the Floral Trust option, and that I could begin implementing the change programme set out in my paper. At least we don't have to close down the company yet.

Regarding the Board itself, it was agreed that all the Board members would write to Peter with their resignations, and that Peter would then go to Grey Gowrie and basically dump the whole lot back in the Arts Council's lap. Thank God I'm not at the Arts Council to be on the receiving end.

Had a drink with Richard Hall afterwards who was still reeling with the impossibility and implausibility of the whole situation, and then off to the Tate Gallery for the Prudential awards. It was a good party. Chris Smith came up and we had a brief word. At first I was hardly able to speak, I was so full of things that I knew I shouldn't say to him. I tried to indicate that I had plans, even if I wasn't able to implement them immediately. He said he was going to phone me on Monday. After the awards, when we were having pudding and coffee, I spoke to Hayden Phillips, who wanted to know that everything was all right, and to say that if I needed to speak to him to do so. Not yet.

Friday 31 October

Predictably the press coverage of my Select Committee session concentrates on the 'shambles' and 'crisis' at the Royal Opera House. Annoyingly much of it makes it sound as though Kaufman was attacking me personally for the mismanagement, although he himself had made it clear that he was not.

I had a meeting with Richard Hall and Jane Murphy about the prospects for our solvency and whether or not we were a going concern. She was positive.

Then over to the Arts Council to see Graham Devlin. I told him everything, including the potential resignation of the Directors,

Peter's difficulties with the Select Committee, and Jenny's letter. Graham listened with interest and asked a number of financial questions. We agreed that if it looks as though the Royal Opera House is about to go into liquidation I will first come to the Arts Council and see if we can close it down rather than allow it to melt down.

I walked back to the office. It was a fresh autumnal afternoon. The light was slanting, as in an Edward Hopper painting, and the buildings pink, lit from the side, with a pale blue sky above. As soon as I returned Peter Katona came to see me about his problems with booking artists for the 98/99 season. I told him that we were not intending to present any performances during the final three months in Sadler's Wells, and I suggested he get on with his thinking about *La Traviata.* He said that he had thought all he needed and he now required the ability to commit funds. I told him to hold it for a week. After Peter Katona had gone, Peter Chadlington rang and said that he had had a phone call from Chris Smith asking him to come in to see him, by himself, on Monday morning.

I am fascinated by what is going to happen. I cannot imagine how it will all turn out. I told Keith that I thought the Tuesday Select Committee would be rather like the culmination of an Agatha Christie murder story: after Poirot has interviewed each of the suspects separately he gathers them all together in a room and points the finger at one of them. What with Chris Smith, Grey Gowrie, Graham Devlin, Peter Chadlington, and Mary Allen, the only missing character is Genista McIntosh. The question is: at whom will he point the finger?

Later I commented to Keith that events have become so bizarre, with the involvement of a Select Committee, a Secretary of State, an organization that is about to go bust, and a Chairman who might be about to depart – that I feel that I am either literally in an opera plot or in the court of a Borgia Pope. Keith immediately shot back with, 'Well of course you could combine the two with Donizetti's *Lucretzia Borgia.*'

Saturday 1 November

During most of the day I felt a sort of free-floating anxiety: dizzy and light-headed. I went to the hairdresser and then met Nigel, Kate and Jamie for lunch at the People's Palace. They went on to the still-life exhibition at the Hayward Gallery, and I came home and went to bed. After a while I realized that my feelings were a version of panic about being out of control. So I started to plan how I was going to manage the organization through the next week.

Got up at 7.00 and prepared for John Sainsbury's seventieth birthday party. Wore my long black satin dress and Andrew Logan butterfly brooch and earrings. We had to park about fifteen minutes' walk away. The walk was exhilarating in the cold night air, along to the Sainsbury Wing of the National Gallery. One of the first people I encountered was Peter, who was looking ashen. I said that I wanted to talk to him tomorrow about how we would manage things during the following week, and he said that he thought it was all beyond our control – who knew what would happen. After he'd gone in Vivien came up looking magnificent in a long black velvet dress, wearing a necklace comprising several strands of huge pearls with a gigantic diamond clip, and many diamond brooches. She said that Dennis Stevenson[69] ought to be the next Chairman of the Royal Opera House, then that it should be Jocelyn Stevens, her partner, and that there should be no Floral money. This was all while we got rid of our coats and went upstairs.

We queued for a while and then greeted John Sainsbury and his wife Anya. Anya was looking glorious in a long, pink ball gown. I saw Grey and we talked about the Select Committee. He said that he had now read my evidence. He does not seem to be perturbed at the prospect of going before them again on Tuesday. When he introduced someone to me he said, 'This is Mary, she was my wonderful

[69] Sir Dennis Stevenson is a businessman and a member of the arts establishment. In 1995 he had produced, for the Arts Council, a report on large-scale opera and ballet in London. I knew him reasonably well.

Secretary-General but she left me and we had to get a divorce.' Oh, I do miss him.

On our way into dinner I saw Gillian Widdicombe, Jeremy Isaacs' wife, who said that she and Jeremy are worried about whether or not it might be appropriate to come to dinner with us next weekend. Who knows whether we will still be on speaking terms by then? What will have been said at the Select Committee by whom and about whom? I said that I would hope that we could keep friendship and professional involvement separate. I went up to Jeremy who likewise looked worried (a photographer took a picture of us both leaning against a pillar pondering this problem) and said that as far as I was concerned we were friends. He said immediately, 'Then we will come.' However I will suggest that Nigel phones Gillian next Saturday, once we know how things have panned out this week.[70]

Walked through to dinner with Hayden Phillips from the DCMS, and said that I would probably need to talk to him at some point. I am reluctant to let Hayden know exactly how bad things are, or to encourage him to become directly involved, following the Arts Council's rage over my appointment. Everything must be done through them.

After dinner, as we moved down to the restaurant for dancing, we talked to Kate Gavron, the Chadlingtons again, and Richard Eyre. I told Richard that I had been inspired by hearing that he had hated every day of his first year at the National Theatre. He said that, more than hating it, he had felt physically sick every time he had had to go into the office during the first eighteen months. I said well, since his time there had been so successful and since he had been there for ten years, it was reassuring to know that things could start off so badly and end up so well.

We then went down and danced. The music was rather reserved, but we enjoyed bobbing around. At one point I went out to catch my

[70] They didn't come to dinner – in the end we agreed it was all too difficult for the time being.

breath and was immediately collared by Bob Gavron and James Spooner, who hustled me into a corner and told me to get the receiver in.

Spent some time talking to Colin Nears (Chairman of Birmingham Royal Ballet and member of the Royal Opera House Main Board) and Peter Wright (Choreographer and previously Director of the Birmingham Royal Ballet). This immensely distinguished man was being very friendly and said he never knew whether I recognized him. I said it was me who didn't know whether he recognized me. Anyway, lots of hugs and kisses fuelled generously by alcohol.

Nigel went off to collect the car, as I had said I would not walk all the way back again, and I went down to the reception area with Luke Rittner.[71] Luke had just told me a joke and we were laughing and falling around rather when Nigel came in crossly and hoiked me out to the car, where he said he had been waiting for ten minutes.

We got home at about 2.00. I was pleased that we had had such a good evening.

Sunday 2 November

Woke up at 7.00. Worked in bed. Talked to Vivien on the telephone. Got up. Talked to Peter on the telephone.

Peter has now worked himself into a position where he believes that the meeting with Chris Smith on Monday is going to be an opportunity for Chris to square his evidence with Peter. I find this hard to believe. Nigel's view is that it is more likely it will be Chris telling Peter that he's going to take a hard line and out of courtesy letting him know beforehand. This would also accord with Chris

[71] Luke Rittner was Secretary-General of the Arts Council between 1983 and 1990 and I had known him earlier when he had been Director of the Association of Business Sponsorship of the Arts. I had worked with him there before he went to the Arts Council. Luke was now Director of Marketing and Communication at Sothebys.

saying he was going to phone me on Monday if he was going to tell me the same thing.

We talked about having a meeting with the Floral Trustees and another Board meeting. Peter said that it would be essential to arrange both. However I still feel that his priority – quite naturally – is the Select Committee meeting on Tuesday. It is extraordinarily unfortunate that the two should have coincided: Peter's appearance in front of the Select Committee and the need to have a Board that makes clear, immediate decisions. I hope we get through the next week.

Monday 3 November

Went to the opera company meeting and had to answer a number of questions about the Select Committee and about our future solvency. The members of the orchestra, in particular, are angry about newspaper reports that Jenny was asked to leave rather than having resigned. They said that Peter had made a big play of the necessity for her departure and they had given him strong support. Members of the opera company expressed equal disquiet. I said I had seen her resignation letter and that in it she had asked to be allowed to go as soon as possible.

Then a senior management group meeting, at which I gave them a briefing on the Select Committee meetings, and the failure of the Board to take a conclusive decision last week. A discussion on several issues including the Select Committee – the dancers are as angry and anxious as the orchestra about Jenny – and the Welsh National Opera box office income.[72] We are apparently hanging on to it in order to improve our cash flow, while Welsh National Opera are frightened that if we go down their box office takings will go down

[72] Welsh National Opera were performing in the Shaftesbury Theatre as part of the Royal Opera House's season there: WNO normally presented a short London season at the House, and it had been agreed to continue the association.

with us. I have said that I want it to be held in escrow. I could not bear to bankrupt two opera companies.

After the senior management meeting Peter came in and reported on his meeting with Chris Smith. Apparently Chris is about to launch an inquiry, led by Sir Richard Eyre, into the feasibility of ENO, the Royal Opera and the Royal Ballet all being resident at the Royal Opera House. Peter gave me a few details. I was so surprised that I hardly reacted.[73]

During the afternoon we had a rehearsal for tomorrow's Select Committee. For two hours we wandered to and fro and round and round the whole question of Jenny's resignation. I hope Peter is realizing that Kaufman will probably ask him other questions as well. It was eventually agreed that Peter would send the Select Committee a copy of Jenny's resignation letter, to arrive before tomorrow's session.

Near the end of the rehearsal Keith brought in the draft of a letter from Chris Smith to Richard Eyre setting out the terms of reference of his inquiry. I read it through and realized that what Richard has been asked to do is, in effect, the change programme that I was about to initiate. I felt so angry I could barely contribute to the rehearsal. I could only sit and look without expression. If an inquiry of this kind had been set up with the three broad objectives set out in Chris's letter, comprising a general brief to investigate the future relationship between, and best use of, the resources of ENO and Covent Garden then that would have allowed a much more open-minded study. But the way in which the briefing letter actually sets out the answers as well as the objectives, means that all those involved will not have a chance to work their way towards those or other answers, but instead

[73] It was unusual for an inquiry of this kind to be initiated by the Government since the Arts Council is responsible for funding the organizations in question and the Government would not – in theory anyway – have had the ability to implement any changes that were recommended. The timing of the announcement of the inquiry, coinciding as it did with Chris Smith's appearance at the Select Committee the following day, was seen by some as an attempt to divert attention away from the Committee's proceedings.

will be defending positions.

At one point I went through to my office and contacted Chris Smith's private office, asking if I could have some more details. Emma Cockell, his Private Secretary, took my call and then phoned back fifteen minutes later to say that all the information was given to the chairman and there was nothing more to say. I think she could hear in my voice that I was angry.

Went to a magnificent semi-staged production of *Pilgrim's Progress* at the Barbican. The singing was glorious, and the orchestra and the chorus and the soloists together really took my head off. Just what I needed. Went round afterwards and talked to a number of people including John Tooley (Jeremy Isaac's predecessor), who had heard the news about Richard Eyre. I went home and found several messages including one from Chris Smith. I phoned him. I said that I wished he had been more consultative and had gone through with me what ideas I had. It was not as if I had several years of mismanagement and inactivity behind me. I had been there for two months and had already drawn up plans covering several aspects of his letter. I also said that we would have to continue programming the new House, since it was out of the question to have to wait until May or possibly the summer before we programmed the year 99/00. Spoke to Kathryn McDowell and to Graham Devlin. They are both angry that the Government has stepped in over the head of the Arts Council. So much for the arms-length principle.

Tuesday 4 November

Arrived at the office early and prepared rapidly for what promised to be an exceedingly difficult day. Spoke to Peter about the Select Committee, and about my determination that we would continue planning for the new House, irrespective of the Richard Eyre inquiry. He agreed with me.

The Programming Meeting concentrated on the Chris Smith proposals. The ballet company is being surprisingly timid. I would have expected them to resent the fact that the number of their performances, or the amount of stage time to which they would have access, would drop from 50 per cent to 33 per cent. Anthony Russell-Roberts remarked that maybe it would be all right if they had an equivalent amount of time touring. I pointed out that it would cost me a fortune. Nicholas Payne said he thought it was all a very good idea but left me worried that he had not worked out what it would mean in any pragmatic sense. Once we started talking about the relationship between the two orchestras (Royal Opera House and ENO), the two choruses and the audiences for each company, we came to the conclusion that it would not be possible to allow the two opera companies to coexist without eventually amalgamating them. For a start, once you started performing regularly in the English language in the House, there would be a direct contrast between English-language performances, and original language performances with sur-titles. The latter are so much more euphonious and so much more comprehensible.

No time for the Planning Group meeting.

Sandwiches in the office and then off to the House of Commons. We arrived early and, although as I strode into the entrance there was a cry of, 'Hey, are you Mary Allen?' after me from a television crew, we were not filmed.

I found the first session of the Select Committee distasteful. Kaufman gave the impression that he wanted Chris Smith to implicate Peter in misleading statements as to whether Chris had said, or even implied, that he was 'happy' about my appointment. One of the other Committee members referred to dancing on a pin: whatever words were actually used, Peter was allowed to leave his meeting with Chris under the impression it was OK to appoint me, and no one tried to stop him when he proceeded to do so a few days later. Chris was careful in his answers, leavening them liberally with softening remarks, caveats, and even some nice remarks about me. I nearly fell off my chair when he made these last.

Grey was his usual funny self; he, too, made nice remarks about me.

Finally we were on. Near the beginning of our session Peter announced that we might be broke within a few days. I froze, staring at the Select Committee. I did not dare even swivel my eyeballs towards Richard Hall. This was going directly counter to everything we had been discussing and agreeing during the last two weeks. Presumably Peter's comments will be reported in the press and all our creditors will jump on us.

Otherwise the Committee focused on his session with the Secretary of State when they discussed my appointment. In fact they picked up on a piece of his evidence that he gave them himself, concerning whether or not he had told the Secretary of State that I would not be able to start until the beginning of September. They contended he had no evidence to support his assertion to Chris Smith that he would have 'a full team in place by the end of the summer', since at that stage he had not spoken either to Grey Gowrie or indeed properly to me. More angels on pinheads. At the end Peter tried to make a statement about Jenny's stress and her resignation letter but was stopped by Kaufman. He said that the Committee had decided that it did not wish to pursue this line of enquiry any further.

Back to the office for a couple of hours. There is a meeting tomorrow of the Floral Trust at 10.00, and then the Board at 2.00. I needed to prepare for both.

Peter rang from his gym: he thinks he has found me the additional £2 million I need to add to the Floral Trust £10 million. Hooray, that would make me a lot more comfortable about the next couple of years.

Walking from the office to the underground station, at about 8.30, I was once again hit, as I often am, by the sheer glorious pleasure of working in Covent Garden. I love the life, I love the business, I love the sense of excitement, I love the idea that when our theatre is completed everyone will be walking in and out of it, and that we will be part of that tremendous excitement of the centre of a city.

Wednesday 5 November

Senior management meeting at 8.00 where I briefed them on the comments made by Peter the day before about our solvency. It's all over the papers – front page headline in the *Guardian* is 'Going Broke – the Opera'. We expect a run on credit to begin. Also audiences will get jumpy and begin reclaiming money from the box office. We agreed a communications strategy for the day.

Richard Hall and I then went over to Shandwick in order to prepare for the meeting of the Floral Trust. Everyone was tense. Peter and I didn't exactly shout at each other but my response to tension, which is to become driving and assertive, clashed with his, which is to move towards lethargy.

The meeting of the Floral Trust was appalling. Half-way through I thought there was no chance at all of us getting the money. Angus Stirling was his usual cautious self, courteous to the last. Peter Carrington seemed detached and yet interested. George Magan – the man who was meant to be our firmest ally – said that now the Richard Eyre report was under way there was no point in rescuing anything. It took a very long time indeed to dig him away from this position. He also believed that the Government would bail us out. I said firmly that I had been a very close friend of Chris Smith's for many years, that he and I had had long conversations on this subject, and that they wouldn't. A very substantial exaggeration as to the extent of my acquaintance with Chris, but it served the purpose.

Jeremy Isaacs was there and made it plain he had been deeply hurt by Peter's assertions to the Select Committee that the financial information wasn't good enough during his time as General Director. He said he would be challenging Peter in public about this. I hope he doesn't. I have no idea what he left behind him, but what I found was inordinately muddled.

Finally we extracted a commitment from the Floral Trust Trustees that they would make the money available – we leapt into Peter's car and back to the Royal Opera House to interview two prospective Directors of External Relations. One of them said they were surprised we were carrying on with the interviews, given what was happening. I thought that, given what was happening, the thing that I needed most urgently of all was a Director of External Relations. I did point out, though, that if we were actually to go bankrupt we would not be making an appointment.

Then into the Board meeting – another grim one. The Board members did not seem to recognize that the *only* alternative to accepting the Floral Trust donation was liquidation. Vivien shouted and roared, I shouted and roared back at her (not directly about each other but about the situation in general) and we got there in the end. The Board approved the Floral Trust donation. Waves of relief – and a huge sense of achievement – that the company is solvent.

Back into my office to write the press release about the rescue package and make a few phone calls.

Then off to a staff meeting in the Chorus Rehearsal Room, another at Baron's Court in the main studio, and another on stage at the Shaftesbury Theatre. I told the staff we were solvent and described the rescue package. A few questions were asked about the finances more generally, and about management. I replied as best I could, talking about management reviews and the installation of new financial processes. By and large I think it went down reasonably well. Was interviewed for *News at Ten* before going briefly back to the office and then home. Nigel and I bought some champagne and drank it on the sofa, watching *News at Ten.*

Thursday 6 November

An excellent lunch with Charles Clarke, Labour MP for Norwich South. I dropped both knife and fork at one point when he said he had been talking to Gerald Kaufman and Gerald had expressed 'warm personal admiration' for me. I remarked that he had a funny way of showing it. We went through the Royal Opera House saga and talked about the Arts Council.

Back to the office where I had a meeting with Keith and Jackie

McDougall about the Royal Opera House Trust. Vivien is on the warpath about the Floral Trust deal. She has revised the appeal target downwards and is saying that we won't be able to raise enough money to complete the development. She seems to be blowing hot and cold about the Eyre Review. Then an hour with Stephen Fay from the *Independent on Sunday.* I enjoyed talking to him and it was a relief to be able to tell a journalist my side of the story. For the last six months I have read comments made by other people about me and my conduct and have felt almost invisible. To have someone listen to my version of what happened is cathartic.

Friday 7 November

In early to try and shift some of the paperwork that has been accumulating, and then a meeting with Normal Lebrecht of the *Telegraph* at 9.30. Norman is almost hypnotically sympathetic and I find myself telling him all kinds of things that I probably shouldn't. I admitted that I had had a serious wobbly after five weeks and contemplated resigning. I just want everyone to know what a dog of a job this is, and how natural it would be for anyone sane to want to leave it.

At 12.00 Richard Morrison, the Arts Editor of *The Times* came in and listened – with less sympathy but great alertness – to my views on the collaboration with ENO. The press has come out strongly against this idea and I am more than ever convinced that the Eyre review will be a version of the Hoffman report[74]: it has all the same hallmarks of autocracy, secrecy and, ultimately, lack of confidence.

[74] When, in 1993, the Arts Council had been considering whether to remove subsidy from two of the London orchestras, it had asked Lord Justice Hoffman to conduct an inquiry into the orchestras on its behalf and recommend to the Arts Council which should be subsidized. The Arts Council was widely criticized for not having the courage to conduct the inquiry itself, particularly when it failed to take any action in response to the eventual report.

Lunch with Christopher Nourse, who was the Assistant General Director until 1996, during which I almost offered him his old job back. Once he had described the way in which the Royal Opera House used to work, and the co-ordinating role he played, I was convinced that his departure was one of the reasons why the whole thing seems almost to have fallen apart. He said that he is committed to Rambert for the foreseeable future. I refrained from trying to persuade him otherwise.

Back to a model showing for *Figaro.* A sensible production that is now on budget, will look good and will be intellectually coherent.

Saturday 8 November

Got up and lit a fire immediately. Read the newspapers – yet more stuff about the Royal Opera House, but I'm almost too bored to read it now – and snuggled down on the sofa. Walked around the garden for a while around midday, and then went off to Aldeburgh. Jon, Helen, Janie and Douglas were in excellent form. A lovely lunch at the Lighthouse, very warm and convivial with Nancy and Polly, now four and three respectively, getting along well together.

Down to the beach where Jon and Helen swam. For one utterly mad moment I nearly took all my clothes off and went in too. Jon said afterwards that he felt very light-headed when he swam in winter.

Back home, where I slept in front of the fire, and then out to James and Tizy for supper. We ended the evening reading bits out of the Dictionary of Quotations to each other. I was particularly struck by the section that Nigel likes from *The Rubáiyát of Omar Khayyám* that starts:

The Moving Finger writes; and, having writ
Moves on: nor all thy Piety nor Wit
Shall lure it back to cancel half a Line,
Nor all thy Tears wash out a Word of it.

Once you have done something it cannot be reversed: you just have to live with the new present and the new future you have created for yourself.

Sunday 9 November

Got up and lit the fire again. Worked in the sitting-room all morning, just going out to get the papers. More nonsense about the Royal Opera House. My interview with Stephen Fay seems to have gone quite well, in that he interjects a few reasonably neutral comments from me. Wandered around the garden at lunchtime.

Peter rang at about 5.00 to say that Norman Lebrecht had been on the telephone to him saying that I had tried to resign, that he – Peter – had had to talk me out of it, and that Nicholas Payne had offered his resignation in the summer after the failure to stage *Macbeth*. I phoned Norman and said that it was not the case that I had tried to resign. I had gone through a major wobbly and Nigel had persuaded me to stick in there, but that I had only had a relatively short conversation with Peter just to let him know what a shitty job it was.

I am worried about Kaufman. When I had lunch with Charles Clarke on Thursday he said that, at the end of his conversation with Gerald, he – Gerald – had thrown out, 'I might recommend that both Chadlington and Allen go.' I cannot handle that.

Monday 10 November

Got up early and went over for a breakfast meeting with Graham Devlin at his house, to go through the closure period plans and budgets. It all seems to be OK. We talked briefly about the Richard Eyre review, but we will be meeting about that later in the day.

Shared a taxi into the Royal Opera House, stopping on the way to buy a copy of the *Daily Telegraph*. A huge picture of me, which was rather intimidating – the face was larger than life size – and an article which was rather melodramatic about me threatening to resign. Almost true, except that I never actually threatened to do it, I merely thought about it. Otherwise the article was excellent and got across points about me being in charge, confident, and knowing what the problems are. There was another piece in *The Times* – the result of my interview with Richard Morrison – which was excellent and very helpful.

Into the office and took a call from Vivien. She was sounding very, very strange. Sort of calm before the storm. I did not like it at all. We did two final interviews for the Director of External Relations, and everyone agreed that Judy Grahame was by far the best candidate. Mike Morris (Personnel Director) and I agreed how we will do the deal with Judy.

I then spoke to Mike about my lunch with Christopher Nourse and my thoughts about seconding someone from within the organization to be my assistant for the next couple of years. There will be co-ordination needed on the Eyre review, and a great deal of work on the business plan for the new House. Mike agreed that he would draft a staff notice requesting applications and put it up on the noticeboards before the end of the day.

Peter came through to my office and said that Richard Eyre had been on the telephone. I phoned Richard and we went through the composition of his working group and the timetable for its work. I told him that I was approaching this in a spirit of constructive optimism, which I think took him slightly by surprise. I also said I thought it had been unhelpful that Chris had announced the outcome of the review almost as a *fait accompli*. He did not quite agree with me but I sensed that he, too, wanted to take it more from first principles than the original announcement implied.

After I had spoken to Richard, Peter came back to my office. He was agitated about the Floral Trust and about Vivien. He was convinced that the deal was going to be unpicked. I was not quite sure, at that stage, whether to believe him. A couple of hours later Peter telephoned from his Shandwick office, this time much more agitated. We cannot get hold of the £2 million that we need to pay the staff's wages next week – the £2 million that George Magan had agreed three weeks ago – and no one can find George Magan or Angus Stirling. I put out a number of calls to Angus and we finally made contact at about 3.15. He, too, was worried that the deal was going to be unpicked. Apparently the Trustees were annoyed that Peter hadn't written or spoken to any of them to say 'thank you' after the last meeting, and Vivien has been talking to all of them. It was agreed that we would meet at 9.30 that evening.

Off to the Arts Council, where I was not particularly coherent. I was letting it sink in that we might – yet again – be about to become insolvent. It is a fantasy. At the Arts Council we talked about the agenda for the Richard Eyre working group meeting on Wednesday and what positions we are all going to take.

Back to office briefly and then up to the theatre, where I went round the dressing rooms. After going round backstage I went front of house and met Nigel, Prue Skene and her husband Brian. I explained I had to go to a meeting of the Floral Trustees at 9.30 and therefore could not watch the show. Back to the office for about half an hour and then picked up Peter's car. To the Connaught to collect Peter and Richard Hall, and then to Angus Stirling's house for the meeting of the Floral Trust.

As always, with Royal Opera House affairs, when extreme things happen I run out of vocabulary to express my views. The first part of the meeting dealt with whether or not the Trustees were prepared to advance us £2 million to deal with our immediate cash crisis. We circled round and round the issues concerning the Richard Eyre review, our viability, and the predicament in which we found ourselves. The Trustees seemed incapable of distinguishing between the Richard Eyre review – something that is happening, but with results that cannot be predicted at the moment – and the financial crisis, which has already happened and which cannot be averted.

After two hours of discussion we seemed to have reached a positive conclusion. Then George Magan began talking about whether or not this meant that the draw downs from the Floral Trust to the development should be frozen for the time being. I said that no, they should be frozen for good. He asked why that was. I said because we had agreed at the last meeting that all the Floral Trust money would be going to the Royal Opera House for its revenue operation. He looked most taken aback. He then said, 'But this is outrageous, we should have business plans, we should have audited figures.' I was becoming irritated by this time and commented that it would have been helpful for the trustees to have made these requests at its last meeting. Magan then pointed out that the situation at the last meeting had been very different. Although the Richard Eyre review had been announced, it had only been a day or so previously, and the Trustees had not had an opportunity to think through the implications. It now seemed to be the case that there was a serious danger to the House and its companies as a result of the Richard Eyre review and that it was incumbent upon the Floral Trust Trustees to ensure that any action by them did not further damage the House.

I could not believe I was hearing this, and I tried to point out that inaction by the Trustees would mean that the House and its companies would close down, probably for good. This point did not go down well. There was further conversation about the impact of the Eyre review on the development, and the likelihood that the review might discourage the donors from giving funds. I pointed out that they ought to bear in mind that the closure of the Royal Opera and Royal Ballet might also discourage donors from giving funds. Magan did not like hearing any of this; at one point he and I were eyeball to eyeball, arms folded, glaring at each other, neither of us blinking.

One of the most difficult things about the meeting was that out of the four Floral Trust Trustees present, one was Jeremy Isaacs and another was Angus Stirling. It is exceedingly difficult to talk about the management of an organization by one's predecessors when they are both sitting there.

We are required to provide a considerable amount of information to the Trustees as soon as possible. They will be sending in advisers to obtain the information and to interview Richard and me. We have a Board meeting next Monday and then there will be another meeting of the Floral Trust. But we really have reached the wire now: payday is on 21 November. The BACS[75] run has to be authorized on Wednesday next week, which is only ten days away, and we cannot make it without the Floral £2 million.

Tuesday 11 November

Into the office at 7.00, managed to clear up the piles on my desk so that at least there was a semblance of order, and then met Richard at 8.00. We went through everything that the Floral Trust Trustees had demanded, and everything in the Board minutes.

I telephoned Judy Grahame to offer her the job, explained our renewed financial problems, and said that I would not wish formally to appoint her – and that she should not leave her present job – until I am confident that I have a job to offer her. We agreed that I would keep her briefed on the position, and that I might want to ask her advice informally about contact with the media.

Had the Programming Meeting at 9.00 and we went through parts of the 99/00 programme. We finished after an hour, as I said that I needed to tackle various issues relating to the Floral Trust's conditions. I asked Anthony and Anthony to stay behind and apologized to them that I had done two newspaper interviews in which I said that decision-making took place deep in the bowels of the companies. I said that this was not a view based on the operation of the Royal Ballet, whom I had always found very co-operative and helpful.

Cancelled – again – the meeting of the Planning Group.

Angus Stirling rang and said that he regarded the previous evening's meeting as unfortunate in certain respects, but that he remained confident everything would work out all right. I said I was cheered by that, but the meeting last night had quite clearly reversed

[75] The automated clearing system through which money is transferred from one bank to another.

decisions taken at the meeting the previous week.

Out to lunch with Luke Rittner, which was my treat for the day. Luke is one of the most charming people I know, and always makes one feel one is having a good time. It is a tremendous gift. We talked mostly about the Royal Opera House, a little about Sotheby's.

At 3.00 I saw Phil Wallace, who is an insolvency practitioner. We rehearsed what would need to happen in the event the Board determined the Royal Opera House was insolvent and I had to take the company down. Near the end of the meeting I swore at him several times. Five minutes later I went up to see him in Richard's office and apologized.

'Don't worry,' he said, 'The language of insolvency is colourful.'

I felt anxious and depressed afterwards, presumably because I had had to face what might be the most difficult reality. Jim Butler came to see me at 5.00 and we talked at some length about Vivien, her motivation and her likely future actions. I know that she has put millions of her own money into the place over the years, and that to put in yet more funds must seem like throwing money into a black hole, but I cannot believe that the possibility of bankruptcy will persuade the government to give us more money. The only alternative then is liquidation and the complete collapse of everything. I am tired that we are having to retread this old ground. All the time I am letting down colleagues who want to look forward and work towards the new House and I am not there to offer them proper leadership.

Wednesday 12 November

Arrived early to prepare for a Royal Opera House Trust meeting at 8.00. Vivien chaired it well. The mood was anxious, but also bullish. The Floral Trust proposal was discussed, since it would have an effect on the amount of money that would now need to be raised through the Appeal. George Magan, also a Royal Opera House Trust Trustee, made a number of comments that indicated his caution about giving the Floral money. Vivien herself demonstrated that she was open-minded about the question of ENO being part of the Royal Opera House complex, and Peter Davis (Group Chief Executive of the Prudential and a member of the Royal Opera House Trust) spoke some stirring words about going to see the Prime Minister. There was still the faint sense that the Government would bail us out. However, there was more of a sense of purpose, energy and strategy than I have felt at Board meetings.

Vivien, Kit McMahon and I spoke for about ten minutes in my office afterwards and Vivien made it clear that she is not trying to pull down the companies, but that she is trying to secure a political advantage. I am not sure she will succeed in the latter, although she just may in the former.

I then spoke to Angus on the telephone. Far from the calm and cautiously optimistic mood he displayed yesterday, today he is full of anxious concern. He said that it was a moral issue whether or not he could allow the money in the Floral Trust to be used on revenue rather than on capital.

I pointed out that if he didn't use it on revenue there would be no capital to use it on. He immediately bridled and said I was blackmailing him. I said that I wasn't blackmailing him, since a blackmailer had the choice between exercising his threat or not, and that I had no choice whatsoever. I was merely stating what would happen in particular circumstances: in other words that if they did not give the full amount of money to the Royal Opera House we would close.

But he does not like to hear it.

Angus said that he might even have to resign if the Trust did give us the money. It was quite hard to see precisely what had changed his mood from twenty-four hours earlier. Half the time he was saying that it was against the purposes of the Trust for the money to be used to rescue the Royal Opera House, but when I asked whether the Richard Eyre review made any difference he said that it was infinitely more difficult now to think about giving us the cash than it would have been had the Eyre review not been commissioned. I said that it was important he knew that not only the operation of the companies but also the development would cease if we did not receive the money, and he again said that he felt as though he was being blackmailed and manipulated . . . I wanted to shake him.

At 5.00 I went to the DCMS for the first meeting of the Eyre working group. There were about twenty people around the table: sundry officers and council members from the Arts Council, various DCMS advisers and officials, and a selection of relevantly qualified artistic great and good. Relatively innocuous – although I seemed continually to be throwing spanners in the works – until Richard pressed me on whether we knew the cost of each production. He knows perfectly well that I don't know that. He eventually asked me when would I be able to let him know. I said that I was spending all my energy on keeping the company going. That in order to do so I had every one of our management accountants *and* a team from the auditor working flat out on solvency issues; that I was trying to extract proper financial information so that we could use it for planning purposes; and that the organization did not have the resources to accede to his request.

I also said at one stage that it would be very useful if Richard and Chris Smith could meet the donors and calm them. Richard became irritated and said that that was not his problem, and it was not his job to go round calming donors to the Royal Opera House. I pointed out somewhat tartly that I had £40 million or so sitting on the edge of a precipice,[76] and that without a building for the companies to perform in there was not much point in him doing any of this work.

The review is now exploring a range of options in addition to the proposal originally touted by Chris Smith that the Royal Opera, Royal Ballet and ENO ought all to occupy the Royal Opera House. Much was made by Richard of the need to have proper financial information about each of the possible options, in response to which various members of the group asked how we were going to find the

[76] At that stage there was a danger that a number of donors would withhold their funds if the Eyre review led to the Royal Opera House becoming a different type of organization from that to which they had made their donations.

necessary expertise. Richard said that we would need to have access to the appropriate financial modelling skills, and we discussed for a while whether we would use management consultants or accountants. The idea of testing four or five options, in detail, using financial modelling appalls me, in that it will either be very expensive, or it will be superficial and inaccurate. It is interesting that the Government has sufficient cash to do this kind of work but not to give more money to the arts. The options were discussed, various parcels of work were handed out and we are due to meet again on 28 November.

Back to the office where I found a letter from Graham Devlin, saying that the Arts Council couldn't make any more grant payments to the Royal Opera House until we had confirmed the Floral Trust donation. It also said that there was a cheque for £640,000 which was due to come through as part of the lottery award, which he could not sign. When I went to tell this to Richard, he said that we were due to receive another £3 million from the lottery for the development.

I feel sick. The situation is accelerating towards an uncontrollable point. Nigel came into the office and I told him what was happening. He said it has the smell of death. I feel so tired I can hardly function. Eventually we went to The Ivy for dinner with Janie and Douglas to celebrate Douglas's birthday. It was fun, and everyone was in an excellent mood, but near the end – after about 11.00 – I was literally falling asleep as I talked to people. I left before the end and then walked half-way through the West End trying to find a taxi home.

Thursday 13 November

Met Richard Hall at 8.00. He said that he was worried about the Arts Council letter in view of the fact that there was a Board meeting of Royal Opera House Development Limited (ROHDL – the company managing the development) that afternoon. He was concerned that the letter might prompt ROHDL to say that, without the prospect of the next slice of Arts Council lottery money, they could no longer call themselves a going concern.

By 9.00 both of us were convinced that liquidation would happen today. Jim Butler had the misfortune to stop by my office and was immediately pulled into a series of meetings. By 10.00 we had Jane Murphy, the House lawyer, round the table with us. By 11.00 the Arts Council had come over and we were all working together to see how we could manage the next ten days. We agreed there was no reason for the ROHDL Board to see the Arts Council letter, although Richard would quite properly refer to it if asked about the Arts Council's view. We also agreed that the issue for the ROHDL Board was the same as that for the Royal Opera House Main Board, namely: is there a reasonable prospect that the Floral Trust will decide to give us the cash. At present the answer has to be yes. We agreed that everything hinges upon getting £2 million of the Floral money by the middle of next week. Then the Arts Council can release the £640,000 that they are currently holding back from the lottery closure costs, and confirm our December grant payment. However that would not be sufficient to enable the Arts Council to release the £3 million that will be due from the lottery capital budget next Friday – that will require confirmation of the remaining £8.5 million from the Floral Trust. And without the Arts Council's £3 million, the development won't be able to pay the contractors the following Monday, who will then down tools and the development will stop, and restarting it would incur astronomical penalty payments. So we still need to sort everything out by the end of next week.

We then spent some time looking at whether, in the event the Floral Trust now refused to give us the money, it would be possible to close all or part of the company down, in other words paying all the debts rather than going into liquidation, thus enabling the development to keep going. Graham said that he thought it would be preferable to spend, say, £30 million on keeping the Royal Opera House in existence – even if only with the ballet company – and maintain the development, rather than watch the whole thing collapse. I said I would do a costing for ballet plus orchestra and ballet minus orchestra, to sit alongside the one we had done for closing everything as part of option two in my Board paper. I pointed out that if a proposal for using the Arts Council's cash in this way had to go to Council in December, it would probably collide with the allocation of the 1998/99 Grant-in-Aid.

During the afternoon I made various phone calls and tried to gain control of the rest of the day. Jim dropped by at 5.30, having had a meeting with the Floral Trust. He was cautiously optimistic.

Keith Cooper spoke to me sometime near the back end of the day to say that Dan Glaister from the *Guardian* was sniffing around. There had been banner headlines on the front page of the *Stage* earlier in the day saying, 'Payne rounds on Chadlington.' Nicholas had apparently spoken to a journalist and said it was 'bollocks' that the Royal Opera House was overspending rather than underfunding as Peter had told the Select Committee. I had had an uncomfortable session with Nicholas in which I pointed out that all press comment should be directed through the press office. Glaister in the meantime is trying to follow up the Nicholas Payne piece, and is speculating that the rescue package is falling apart. Keith dealt with it well – I said that I did not wish to speak to Glaister myself because I would either have to lie or be put in an impossible position.

Friday 14 November

Went into the office and met Richard Hall and Phil Wallace and talked for a while about the option of closing down the whole organization apart from the ballet company. I am opposed to this option: it would mean breaking up much of what is best about the Royal Opera House. I am also not sure that it would be workable. To impose something of this kind at short notice upon the staff might provoke an all-out strike, which would mean that we would probably go bust anyway.

If it had been planned carefully, over a long period of time then it might have been possible to do, even though it would have occasioned great distress and would have destroyed a great deal. But to do so as an emergency short-term measure is impossible. We all accepted the truth of this after a while and I left a message for Pippa to give to Peter in San Francisco that he must not tell anyone about this option, since it now proved unworkable.

Went up to see Mike and find out who had applied for the secondment. It is an interesting group of people, including some of the most influential in the organization: Ron Freeman, Richard Sadler, Carol Lingwood and Fiona Flint[77] among them.

Went to the Marketing Department to ask Andrew Stokes whether or not I was being paranoid, or was the box office in free fall. He was reluctant to be as pessimistic as I am, but he is worried. I asked him for ideas about how we could beef up our marketing strategy.

Back for a meeting with an accountant from Coopers and Lybrand, who is testing our figures for the Floral Trust. He asked a large number of questions about matters that went well beyond the budgets. However, mindful that the Floral Trust think we are reluctant to part with information, I answered all of them as best I could.

Bernard Haitink came in to see me at 12.30 and I did my best to reassure him. He was looking glum and said he hates the negative publicity. I told him that we were appointing an excellent new Director of External Relations, whose specialism was in conductors and orchestras. He still looked glum. He said he wanted me to be straightforward with him, so I told him that Edinburgh was still in the 1998/99 season, with *Don Carlos*, but that if it was going to lose a great deal of money I would have to take it out. I also warned him about the Select Committee report and the likelihood that that would generate still further negative publicity.

I banked my expenses cheque – might as well salvage what I could.

Up to King's Cross and on to the train, where I fell asleep and

[77] Carol and Fiona were Wardrobe Superviser and Assistant Wardrobe Co-ordinator respectively. Richard Sadler was Chorus Manager and Ron Freeman was Head of Wigs.

nearly missed the station. Out at Cambridge and off to the University Arms Hotel. Made a number of phone calls and then went to the first session of the British Spanish Tertulias, an annual conference between cultural, political and economic specialists from Britain and Spain.

Talked to Dennis Stevenson, who told me he thought that the Royal Opera House ought to close down. I tried – I felt unsuccessfully – to explain that if the companies collapsed the development would fold as well. He seemed impatient with this and repeated that the companies ought to close down in order to obtain a clean sweep.

By a stroke of luck Peter Mandelson sat down close beside me. At the end of the session I told him that we were very near the edge. After a minute I realized he didn't know what I was talking about, so I said, 'I am talking about the actual survival of the whole operation,' and he looked shocked. I said, 'If we are about to close permanently could I let you know beforehand?' and he said, 'Yes, please do so, at least a day or two beforehand.' And I said, 'Well, a day or two is probably all we would have.' But at least he knows – and that means that now Tony Blair will know. We then talked about the Chris Smith/Richard Eyre review, and I sensed that he was trying to draw me into criticizing it. I did not, although I said I felt it was unfortunate that it was announced so suddenly.

We had a glass of sherry before dinner, and I met the man who is running the Teatro Real in Madrid. Apparently it was due to cost six thousand million pesetas, and ended up costing twenty-one thousand million pesetas. It was also six years late. Anyway, they are very chipper about it now and we will be getting together when I go out in a couple of weeks' time to see the Royal Ballet.

Up to my room and to bed.

I have felt calm and relaxed for most of the day. I know that this is unrealistic, and that it just means my mental defences are strong today. Goddammit, I deserve a rest, so I am very happy to hide behind my defences. At the moment I think that things will work out. I believe that Coopers will confirm that our figures are good, and that the Floral Trust will give us the money. I hope I am not kidding myself.

Saturday 15 November

We have had a good day, with some interesting discussions at the Cultural Committee's sessions. The first session was about free university education and was introduced by Tessa Blackstone. I find the arguments in favour of paying quite compelling – on the grounds of encouraging the students to ascribe more value to their university education. I would certainly have worked harder myself, if I had known that I personally was going to have to pay for some of it. On the other hand most of the value I received from Cambridge was from the extramural activities, and anything that interfered with those would, in my view, damage the experience that university brings.

We then discussed rights of privacy versus freedom of expression, and both Virginia Bottomley and Chris Smith – who seemed to be in agreement with each other – spoke interestingly. I sat next to John Gummer at lunch and he told me about his campaign to challenge every planning permission under the new proposal to build thousands of new homes on green land.

A brief free period in the afternoon when I worked, and then back to the final session about fox-hunting and bullfighting. I felt strongly on the subject, particularly when other participants made comments that I regarded as foolish about animals; however trying to frame a comment of my own while at the same time being the rapporteur proved impossible.

At dinner I was sitting next to the Spanish Ambassador – an archetypal Castillian nobleman – and diagonally opposite the Master of Pembroke. Inevitably we talked about opera. I was virtually asleep in my seat by the time we left, even though it was still before 11.00. These days there is no intermediate state between sleeping and waking and the moment my body decides it has had enough it just wants to go unconscious.

Sunday 16 November

I spoke to Peter before the first session and he told me Vivien is trying to persuade each board member to vote against the Floral package. The Board had that discussion, took that vote, and decided in favour of the Floral package at the last meeting. It would be a most unusual way of doing business if it could just reverse the decision.

Completed my rapporteur notes. Outside my hotel window there was a black poodle, it must have been a puppy, galloping around on the grass in the park and every so often it jumped up into the air, all four feet leaving the ground. It was a wonderful picture of exuberance and joy.

I went over to the Old Library at Emmanuel, where I presented my report on the Cultural Committee's debate. Boris Johnson, from the *Telegraph*, gave a superb performance on behalf of the Political Committee, his presentation liberally laced with cod-Spanish phrases.

I had a quick word with Tessa Blackstone before the session began, to ask if I could use her as a hotline into Government if the worst happened and she said I could. (Tessa had been a member of the Royal Opera House Board until 1997.) She also said that she had had a long talk with Chris Smith, who had said that if we went down the Government would save the development. I said to Tessa that the most important thing for Chris to realize was that we had taken legal advice on that subject and had been told it was not possible to save one without the other. The two were not separable and any liquidator for the companies would take a charge over the theatre, so it would not be possible for the development to continue.

Monday 17 November

Into the office by 7.00 to plan what I was going to say to the Board meeting.

The meeting lasted for most of the day. In the morning we had three hours of figures, and comments about the figures. Vivien argued vehemently against the Floral Trust rescue package, saying we should not be taking on further obligations.

We then broke for lunch and Adrian Stanway, from Coopers and at the behest of the Floral Trust, came to see me. He introduced himself as being forthright, and said that he had heard that I, too, was forthright. In fact he occupied that rather grey territory between forthrightness and deliberate rudeness. He said he was an insolvency practitioner, that he knew all about running charities, but that he had no experience of the arts or of running opera and ballet houses. He banged through a list of questions including one about whether or not I would be prepared to accept what would be, in effect, a shadow Chief Executive. I told him I would not. We did not get on well, and it was an unpleasant meeting.

The Board meeting resumed. After an hour of general – and some quite vehement – discussion Vivien said she wanted Richard and me to leave, so that the Board could discuss whether or not we and Peter had misled them about the Floral Trust money. I asked to speak to that before I left. First I pointed out that I had manuscript notes of the discussions with the Floral Trust that demonstrated we had acted properly and in good faith. Then I made one final statement before leaving. All of the frustration of the past ten weeks was poured into a long speech about how it was not necessary to let the organization become insolvent, that there was a vision, and that with the rescue package there was the money to realize it. And, please, would they just give me and the staff a chance.

The Board meeting broke up about fifteen minutes later, with most of the Board members coming into my office to reassure me that they supported me. I don't want their support. I want them to conduct themselves in a responsible way, which will then provide a stable base from which I can lead the staff.

Graham Devlin rang me at 5.00. Adrian Stanway had been round to see him, and Graham had told him that the worst thing that could happen for the Royal Opera House would be to go into liquidation, and the second worst would be for me and Richard Hall to leave it.

Graham had directed Stanway's attention to the Edward Walker-Arnott report. Stanway had heard neither of this nor of the Select Committee – Graham said he must have been living on another continent or have adamantly refused to read any newspaper at all in order to escape knowing about these things.

I went over to the Royal Albert Hall where they were staging *Otello.* Went back stage and on to the stage for a while and then went up to see Patrick Deuchar, the Chief Executive of the Royal Albert Hall. *Otello* was spectacularly good in the Albert Hall. The sound effects, the set, the way in which the singers move around the stage, the sounds of their voices – it was wonderful. Afterwards Nigel and I went out to dinner with Patrick and Liz; it was delicious food and fun, though I was so tired by that stage I can hardly remember anything.

Tuesday 18 November

I arrived at the hotel where a meeting of the Floral Trust was taking place, twenty minutes before the meeting was due to start. I was put into an anteroom, which I realized after a few minutes connected through double doors to another room in which some of the Trustees were already meeting. I could hear Jeremy Isaacs, Angus Stirling and George Magan. I didn't think Peter Carrington was there. I sat on a sofa next to the double doors, pretended to read a newspaper, and tried to hear what they were saying. I heard one of them refer to a six hour Board meeting, and someone else say that, 'Mary Allen was upset.' Annoyingly I couldn't really hear enough, so I moved back to the other side of the room.

I was joined gradually by Peter, Richard Hall, Jim Butler and Phil Wallace, our insolvency adviser. Peter, as a Trustee, went into the meeting immediately and the rest of us waited to be invited to join. At about 10.00 Peter came out looking white and very tense, and said that the money might be available but there would be several conditions attached to it, including changes to the membership of the

Board, and he then went back into the meeting. The meeting finished around 11.00 with those of us outside most surprised that none of us had been asked to speak to the Trustees. No one came in to see us, but Jim went out and said that he had to talk to somebody.

Angus was alone in the other room and Jim spent some time with him.

Then Peter went in.

I put my head round the door at one point and said that I wished to see Angus before he left.

Jim and Peter came out and I went in with Richard Hall. I asked Angus what the conditions were. He said one was that the Arts Council produces all of the money due to the Royal Opera House within the next week or so, and that they made an absolute commitment to the future funding of the Royal Opera House in every respect. The other was that there would be some form of management intervention, undertaken by a professional support adviser, appointed by the Floral Trust, which the Board would have to accept. I asked what form it would take. He said that one role would be to review the closure budgets, another role would be to review the structure and composition of the Board – although he went to some lengths to emphasize that there would be no changes to the membership of the Board – and a third role would be to help draw up the business plan for the new House.

I asked whether the third role would include any executive decision-making, or whether it was just figure work. Angus said the two were inseparable. I disagreed and pressed for a clearer answer. He said that he was unable to give one.

I said that I wished to receive a clear, detailed and comprehensive description of what this person would be doing. Once I had received that, I would think about it in relation to my own position and then I would tell the Board what I intended to do.

I went back into the other room and told Jim and Peter that if a professional support adviser was appointed with decision-making powers that superseded my own – in effect a shadow Chief Executive – I would resign. Either I'm to be allowed to do the job properly, or not at all.

I rang up Graham and told him I wanted to come and see him. He said come right over. Peter took Richard and I off to the Connaught and bought us a bottle of champagne. We talked. Richard and I were like a broken record: not believing what was going on, not accepting the failure of the Board and other interest groups to allow the organization to be managed properly, and saying how inappropriate it was that the Floral money will only be given to us on condition the new management is – in effect – monitored by the old.

I went over to the Arts Council and I lay on the sofa in what had been my old office and told Graham what had happened. He was most sceptical about the Arts Council's capacity to be able to meet the condition relating to its money.

Then I went back to the office. I tried to get through the paperwork on my desk. I spent twenty minutes lying on the sofa with my eyes closed and the lights out. I spoke to both Melanie Leech and Graham Devlin several times during the afternoon.

Richard confirmed that we have to press the button on the BACS payroll run by 7.00 tomorrow evening (Wednesday). If we delayed, even by a day, the wages would not be paid and the creditors would come in. I told Jim Butler and he was appalled, as apparently the Floral Trustees are meeting again on Thursday morning, and there was no question of any money being put into our bank account by 7.00 tomorrow night. I told this to Graham Devlin. There was a silence. I asked him if he would give us the money. He said, 'Mary, you can't ask that.' I said to him I was not trying to put pressure on him, that I had not pressured him and would not pressure him, that I respected the limitations of his role, and the constraints on the Arts Council. It was just a question for information.

What I did not say was that I think it is an outside possibility, at a final desperate moment, that the Arts Council might put £1.2 million into our bank account, as an advance on our December grant payment, so that we can pay the staff and not go bust.

I went briefly to a meeting of the Royal Ballet Governors, who were debating the Eyre review. I returned to my office and after a few minutes John Sainsbury came in. He told me of his concern that there weren't enough ballet practitioners on the Eyre review group. I agreed and we discussed who should join it. Just before he left my office I said, 'John, we have twenty-six hours before we go bust.' He didn't appear to engage with what I was saying. He looked sad – perhaps he thought I was about to ask him for money – and left quite quickly.

Peter telephoned around about 7.00 and said he was sorry for having brought me into all of this. I told him he had nothing to be sorry for, that when he had offered me the job and I had accepted it, I had done so with my eyes open. There was nothing he had concealed from me. Apart from, I suppose, the difficulties with budgets, which he didn't appear to know about.

Went home. Nigel helped me draft a resignation letter.

Wednesday 19 November

There is another Board meeting today, when we will be able to add our insolvency practitioner to the banks of advisers already surrounding us. Jim is going to talk to one of the Coutts directors to see if it is possible to do something about the BACS run. Apparently you can't stop the run once it has been started, all you can do is to try and retrieve the money from the individual bank accounts, and – not surprisingly – banks don't like doing that.

I arrived at around 8.00. Jim came into my office an hour or two later and we talked for a long time. Poor man: he is having to handle Vivien, me, Peter, no doubt other Board members, and the Floral Trust. I told Jim that I had drafted my resignation letter the night before. He looked alarmed and said, 'For God's sake don't sign it.'

Later in the morning Richard Hall came in, looking shocked. He said, 'We have £1.2 million sitting in the Royal Opera House Trust bank account, specifically for supporting the companies, which is due to be fed in instalments to us during the next few months, and the Trust will not let us have it now. This is the amount that would pay the wages.'

I went in to see Peter and Jim and they confirmed this.

Jim then told me that Peter had spoken to Graham Devlin the night before and had introduced the idea of bringing forward some of the grant-in-aid payments.

I said to Peter, 'You should have told me this.' It is not helpful if the Chairman starts behaving like an executive and not informing me and Richard of what is going on.

Then one of them produced a piece of paper on which was drafted the terms of reference for the professional support adviser. The adviser will be Adrian Stanway and he will be cutting straight across my remit. His first task is to do whatever is necessary to bring the budgets within the original estimates: in other words to reduce them by £10 million. Not possible. The second is to restructure the Board and management. The third relates to preparing the business plan.

I can't remember who said what to whom and in what order, and who was in the room at the time, but there was one exchange between me and Peter when he started to pretend that it wasn't as it seemed, and that everything would be all right, and I told him that if the 'adviser' was appointed with an executive remit that overrode mine I would resign.

He said, 'No you won't.'

I stood up and shouted at him, 'It is entirely within my power to do what I wish with my life, and I can assure you I would resign.'

By that stage there was also a standoff developing between the Arts Council and the Floral Trust, each one wanting the other to budge first. The Arts Council said it would not advance any money until the Floral Trust had given adequate assurances. The Floral Trust said it would only give adequate assurances if the Arts Council guaranteed to supply all the money.[78]

[78] The idea was to persuade the Arts Council to advance a sufficient sum from the December grant payment to cover the wages. Since the Arts Council cannot give public funds to an insolvent organization, it could only advance the money if the immediate solvency of the Royal Opera House was assured, and the immediate solvency of the Royal Opera House depended on it receiving £2 million from the Floral Trust.

We arrived at the Board meeting, and Peter briefed the Board about the negotiations with the Floral Trust. The moment he had described the condition relating to the professional support adviser Rudi Mueller stopped him, although Peter tried to continue. Rudi said, 'Wait, we must discuss this, it is completely out of order, it is utterly unacceptable, and puts Mary in an impossible position.'

Michael Berkeley said, 'This is deeply undermining for Mary – it must not be allowed.'

Peter carried on reciting the position as it was. Soon they returned to the issue of the professional support adviser. Michael said he couldn't comment on it further until he had heard about how I felt about it. I said that I couldn't comment yet, because I did not have sufficiently precise information about what was going to be involved, or what authority the adviser would have, but that once that was available I would seek my own independent advice and come to a view as to what action I would take.

Bob Gavron said, 'Quite right too,' and then addressed the Board saying, 'If Mary takes us for constructive dismissal she would win substantial compensation.'

The Board meeting did not last for very much longer. I called Judy Grahame and took her through what was going on, and she confirmed my view that resignation was the only option if there was any condition introduced that would interfere with my capacity to lead the organization.

Jane Murphy stayed in the Boardroom, working with Jim on the wording of an agreement with the Floral Trust that would allow the Arts Council to guarantee the BACS run. Peter joined them intermittently, otherwise he wandered in and out of my office – I can't remember what we talked about. We had made up from our row of the morning but Peter said that I reminded him of a girlfriend he had once had who shouted when she was angry, which made him go quieter and quieter. They had eventually broken up. I remarked that his behaviour reminded me of Robin's – my first husband – and we too had broken up. I also remarked that maybe we should ensure that he – Peter – and I do not break up. Although I am beginning to wonder whether, in one way or another, we inevitably will. My resignation is one possibility. His departure is another, although he is now determined to stay.

I whiled away the late afternoon. Peter was negotiating with the Arts Council and the Floral Trust, and Richard was putting in place the preparations for the BACS run at its 7.00 deadline. By 6.20, alarmingly, nothing seemed to be progressing. Richard said that he had to leave at 6.30 in order to go to *Otello*. Peter had already left – also for *Otello*. I asked Richard to come down to my office while I made a few final calls to Graham and the bank.

The moment I spoke to Graham it was apparent that all was not nearly as well as Richard seemed to think. Graham was still having serious difficulties with the Floral Trust and they were not giving him the assurances he needed in order to be able to release the money. Richard said he was going to go to *Otello* whatever happened, particularly if this might be the last night the opera company ever performed it. I let him go – there was nothing he could do that I couldn't do myself. He left at 6.30.

At 6.40 Graham rang and told me that he was quite definitely not able to guarantee the BACS run.

Complete panic.

I phoned Rob Sher, the man at Coutts who was responsible for authorizing the run, and asked him for a time extension, from 7.00 to 7.30.[79] He said it might be possible for there to be a few minutes extra.

I phoned Peter on his mobile and told him what was going on.

I tried to phone the Chief Executive of Coutts, and the Chairman of Coutts, but they were both out at parties.

I phoned Graham again and said that we were just about to go bust. I told him we had four minutes – it was four minutes to seven at this stage – and for Christ's sake do something. He got on the

[79] The window of time open is the period allocated for access to the electronic network through which the transfer of cash from one bank to another is expedited. Generally speaking, once that window is past the transfer cannot be done.

phone to Hayden Phillips and then to Angus Stirling.

I tried to phone Jane Murphy but someone answered the phone and said, 'She is on the other line.' I said, 'This is terribly urgent, please could you ask her if she could take my call.' The person sounded most put out and said, 'She is on the other side of the hall – I'll have to go and talk to her.' After five minutes she returned to the phone saying that she couldn't get hold of her.

I phoned Graham once more. It was now 7.00. He was still negotiating with Angus.

I phoned Rob Sher again and begged for the extension to 7.30. He said he would get back to me.

Peter was phoning me about once every three minutes.

At one point I yelled at him, 'You're a millionaire – you pay for it.' Wisely he demurred.

At another point I had Graham on one line and Peter on another, both wanting to speak to one another. I thought about putting the two telephones together and telling them to shout, but I told Peter to phone Graham and then put both telephones down.

Rob Sher phoned to say that he had extended our window to 7.30, and to ask whether or not I had people in place ready to do the transfer.

I went upstairs and found Liam and he said we had someone in IT and someone in payroll, ready to do the actual processing. (It sounds fascinating – I have no idea what they actually do. I must go and find out when this is all over.)

Back down to my office and at 7.25 Graham rang again. He said, 'You can do it, you can do it, I've got the guarantee I need from Angus.' He read out what the condition was – I was shaking so much I could hardly get the words down on paper. He then said, 'Christ, I'm shaking all over.' So that made two of us.

I went upstairs to Liam and told him to press the button, and then I phoned Rob Sher and gave him the authorization.

This is complete madness. We were within – I was going to say we were within minutes of going bankrupt, but technically we were twenty-five minutes after going bankrupt. And what is so unspeakably grim is that we will have to go through the whole question of the professional support adviser again tomorrow, as we have to extract a commitment from the Floral Trust to pay us the remaining £8.5 million, in order for the Arts Council to release the £3 million by Friday so that we can pay the site contractors on Monday.

This episode has proved conclusively that the Government will not bail us out. They knew, through Hayden Phillips, that we went to the brink, and they showed no inclination to do anything about it.

I walked over to The Lexington in Lexington Street, where I had dinner with Michael Waldman, a close friend of many years who had directed *The House.* He knew something had gone badly wrong, as I was three quarters of an hour late, but I managed not to tell him what it was. I told him that one day, well into the future, I would tell him why I had been late for dinner. It was a good evening but I can hardly remember what we said.

Went home feeling exhausted. Fell asleep on the platform waiting for the train. Fell asleep between each station. Unfortunately the only station at which I was asleep while the train stopped was my own.

Woke up at Finsbury Park, got off, went through the passage and on to the platform at the other side and got on to the train there.

After it had been travelling rather fast for a long time I thought this couldn't possibly be just going back down the Piccadilly line to Arsenal. I looked up at the underground map opposite and saw that I was on the Victoria line, although I didn't know whether I was going north to Seven Sisters or south to Highbury and Islington.

Seven Sisters.

Went across to another platform, and got on a train. A man came past and said, 'I wouldn't stay on there if I were you love – this is going to Walthamstow depot.'

Got off the train, went up stairs, found another platform, got on to another Victoria line train back to Finsbury Park; found the right platform at Finsbury for Arsenal; got off at Arsenal and walked up the road to find my car.

It was gone.

I walked all the way up the road on one side, all the way down on the other, all the way round the corner, all the way back up the road.

No, it was quite definitely gone.

I walked home. I told Nigel that my car had been stolen. He said no, there had been a match and it would have been towed away. I pointed out that I had not parked it in a restricted area. Anyway, he says he'll sort it out.

During my walk I had been formulating in my mind the idea of possibly making a statement, with Richard Hall, at the next Board meeting. It is not acceptable for an organization to lurch from one appalling crisis to another appalling crisis with quite such frequency and lack of control as the Royal Opera House does at present. It is no good for the Board to say that it's all the Arts Council's fault that the Royal Opera House can't balance its books – the Board has to decide what it's going to do about it and then stick to its decisions. I will discuss this with Richard.

Thursday 20 November

When I arrived at the office and spoke to Richard I found that his thoughts had been travelling in an identical direction. We considered what we might do and agreed that we would both draft a letter, to go either to Peter or to the Board as a whole. We talked about all these matters for some time.

During the morning Peter, Rudi, Bob and Jim were with the Floral Trust Trustees negotiating a letter of agreement between the Floral Trust and the Royal Opera House, covering the initial £2 million, and the conditions necessary to be met before the Royal Opera House could have access to the remaining £8.5 million. Peter phoned me mid-morning to say that he had had to leave the meeting in order to go and deal with some other business, and the negotiations were continuing. Also during the morning Graham phoned. His thoughts, too, have been running along the same lines as mine and Richard's about the Board. I told him we were planning to write a letter to either Peter or the Board as a whole.

Jim Butler phoned me around about midday and said that he would like to take me out to lunch. Ominous, I thought: that is what one normally does if one is about to impart unpleasant information and wants to stop the recipient making a scene. Jim met me at 1.30. We went to the *Palais du Jardin* in Long Acre. I was open with Jim about my concerns about the Board, and I told him that I would be bringing them up with Peter before the Board meeting on Monday.

We then talked about the letter of agreement between the Floral Trust and the Royal Opera House. Jim said that he was not able to remember very much about the role of the professional support adviser but what he did tell me left my concerns unaddressed. He said I should knuckle down and tolerate it and not do anything silly. I said I needed information about the role of the adviser and issues such as whom they report to.

The letter of agreement – still in draft form – was faxed over to me at 5.30. It included the terms of reference of the professional support adviser, acceptance of which was one of the key conditions. Despite all the efforts of Rudi, Bob and Jim, they had not been modified at all from what I had seen the day before.

Rudi phoned to try and persuade me that it was tolerable. I said I did not think it was.

Carolyn Newbigging, Chairman of the Friends of the Royal Opera House and their representative on the Board, phoned later and was extremely supportive and warm. She said that above all I must stay with the organization.

None of them seem to recognize that the fundamental problem is one of organizational integrity. How can the organization function properly if the authority of the Board and Chief Executive is being overridden by someone reporting to another body?

Went home early and spent the first part of the evening drafting a letter to Peter about the Floral Trust letter of agreement. In it I asked a number of questions about the authority of the support adviser, who would appoint them, and to whom would they report. I also made it quite clear that Peter must sign the Floral Trust agreement, and do so quickly, because only that will ensure the solvency of the

Royal Opera House. My future with the organization should be a secondary concern.

The second part of the evening I spent drafting a much more difficult letter to Peter about the Board.

Friday 21 November

Arrived around about 9.30 – demotivation is making me spend less and less time in the office – and gave a copy of my letter about the Board to Richard. He gave me one that he has drafted. The two letters exemplify our characters: mine clear, emphatic and asking for an immediate resolution; his prudent, cautious and suggesting a review. I told him that I thought a review would not get us very far – it would just be another opportunity for more fudge and whitewash.

I had already faxed Peter a copy of my letter about the Floral Trust agreement, and faxed a copy to Graham. When I arrived at the office I faxed further copies to Jim, Rudi, Bob and Melanie Leech.

In the middle of the morning Peter phoned. He said that it wouldn't be possible to sort this out within the next few days. I said that, on the contrary, it was important that it *was* sorted out within the next few days, as both our positions and that of the Board were unacceptably compromised until the questions in my letter had been answered. I suggested he phone Angus immediately and ask him for the information I had requested.

He said it wouldn't be available.

I said in that case the Floral Trust letter of agreement shouldn't have been written if the answers to some basic questions about authority and power to act weren't known.

He made it clear he did not propose to phone Angus today.

I pointed out to him that this was an issue of governance and affected the Board as seriously as it affected me, and that as the Chairman of the Board he had a duty to clear up these outstanding issues and ambiguities as soon as possible. I also suggested that he return to the DCMS and ask whether they might reconsider their refusal to allow us to use the proceeds from property sales for revenue purposes. At the end of the day, all the money is going into the same place, and at least we wouldn't have a comprising deal governing some of its use.

He said he would not.

He talked about my position, saying that it would be all right. I talked about his position, saying that this was a fundamental issue of governance and what was being proposed compromised the Board and the whole organization. We did not finish the call on good terms.

An hour later he rang me asking about the ticket sales for the 'Night of the Stars' the previous evening. I was brisk and explained why they had been poor. We did not refer to our earlier conversation.

I phoned Melanie Leech and asked her about the use of money from property sales. She confirmed – as I had known she would, I just wanted the question to have been asked – that it was not possible to use this money for revenue purposes. She came over to see me at 12.30 and was warm and sympathetic. There is no doubt in her mind that I will resign if matters are not satisfactorily resolved.

Lunch with Norman Rosenthal, who had been a member of the Opera Board, and then on to a meeting with a donor.

I returned and went up to see Richard to continue our discussion about how we tackle issues relating to the Board.

I then went home to redraft my letter to Peter about the Board. Calmed it down and included many of Richard's more cautious phrases. We then drove down to Suffolk: we arrived at about 10.00 and I sat staring into a fire for a long time.

Saturday 22 November

Walked around the garden for a long time – the sky was cloudless, there was dew on the grass.

Sunday 23 November

Got up at 7.00 and started working immediately. Revised my letter to Peter. Walked around the garden several times between 8.00 and 9.00 and looked at the berries and the grass under the dew, silent, still, as the fog began to lift and the blue sky shine through. Spoke to Graham and Melanie. They both said they wished me not to go, but both recognized that I would, if this agreement transfers control of the Royal Opera House out of the hands of the Board and management.

I had a long and helpful conversation with Paul Richards, a merchant banker friend, about how banks manage this kind of situation. He confirmed that they don't put in a shadow Chief Executive but rather either work with the one that's there or replace them. Exactly as it should be.

After lunch I slept by the fire for a while. When I woke up I was in one of the deepest depressions I have known. I could barely move or do anything. Judy rang and I could hardly talk to her, let alone react to the suggestions she made as to how we might respond to the Kaufman report. Rumours vary as to when it is going to come out, but it is now virtually certain that it will be during the first week of December. Everything else has been so grim that I've hardly thought about it.

Jeremy Isaacs rang and offered support. We talked about the Floral Trust deal and I felt he began to see the whole issue of the professional support adviser in a different light, except that it is far too late to do any good.

Monday 24 November

Arrived at the office around 9.00 and almost immediately began a series of telephone conversations with Peter. He is now of the view that he is compromised in the negotiations with the Floral Trust – being one of the Trustees himself – and was asking me to give the advice that I had given to him on Friday, to the three members of the Board negotiating committee.

I spoke to Jim, who didn't really offer a view.

I spoke to Bob, who told me that I was talking nonsense. There was no question of the Floral Trust wanting to intervene in the management of the Royal Opera House and once the deal had been clinched all I should do is put the agreement in the bottom drawer and forget about it. I remarked that this approach was inconsistent with that taken by the Floral Trust to date, who had given every impression that they wished to implement the terms of the agreement in full. Bob laughed and told me I was being silly. He was an experienced businessman and had done many of these deals. Just put the agreement in the bottom drawer. I wish I could believe he might be right.

I couldn't get hold of Rudi.

Peter rang and asked me to go over to Shandwick for a meeting. I arrived and went in to his office and began to talk business. He cut across me and said that we needed to have a conversation about our working relationship, which seemed to be deteriorating rapidly. It was extremely difficult. I like him very much as a person, and I believe that he is working hard in the best interests of the Royal Opera House. However, I also believe that some of our problems are due to the fact that he is occasionally reluctant to face conflict or confrontation and tries to find a way to side-step it. When the issues are so enormous, as they are with the Royal Opera House, this just leads to avoidance and confusion rather than resolution.

I told him that he was as compromised as I am by the way in which the Board runs itself, and he is effectively barred from doing a proper job. I tried to give him the letter that Richard and I had written about the Board, but he refused to accept it. He asked that we wait until after the Kaufman report. I said I would have to discuss that with Richard.

Back in the office I spoke to Richard about the fact that Peter had refused to accept our letter about the Board. We both thought that we should nonetheless give it to him now. I went into Peter's office and placed it on his desk, saying that both Richard and I wanted him to have it before the Board meeting. He accepted it in silence.

At the Board meeting, the Floral Trust agreement was dealt with, and Peter was authorized to sign it. Finally we are irrevocably solvent, although much remains to be clarified about the control of the organization. It was agreed that Rudi, Jim, Bob and I should meet in a couple of days' time to begin discussing the exact remit of the professional support adviser. We would also ask Graham Devlin to join us to ensure the relationship between the Arts Council and the Royal Opera House wasn't compromised.

Then we discussed the Eyre review. The Board members had no suggestions to make other than the most important thing that Richard Eyre could do was to ask for more money for the Royal Opera House. I suggested that perhaps, instead of being reactive, they might want to think now about what they would like to get out of it – in other words to take an active stance and start having a bit of vision of their own. I said this with a certain amount of emphasis, in response to which Rudi Mueller said that in his business that was the job of the management, who brought business plans to the Board. I reminded him that I had already told the Board on two occasions that business plans were being prepared, and when they would come to the Board, but that was also the role of the Board to have a bit of vision to kick the whole process off, unless they were happy to delegate in its entirety the process of participating in the Eyre review to the executive. I then commented that since Chris Smith had made it absolutely clear that there was going to be no more money, and Richard Eyre had said that there was going to be no more money, and what's more if he were to ask for money he would not be asking just for opera and ballet but also for drama, in other words all the performing arts, any contribution by Richard would be more likely to take the form of a general arts lobby. Although they might wish to continue thinking about how to lobby the government for more money, it was important that they also thought how they wanted the whole thing to operate on the basis of the same amount of money as they had now. This was not well received.

At the end of the meeting I left, to allow them to discuss my request to Peter that the Royal Opera House pay for a lawyer to support me through the coming negotiations with the Floral Trust. Peter came out after about fifteen minutes, once the Board had finished, and told me that they had decided against this. They say I can have support of whatever kind I like – so long as it is not a lawyer.

John Seekings came to see me and his common sense began to cheer me up. He said that I should on no account leave.

I then went up to the Shaftesbury Theatre with Thelma Holt and saw *Il barbiere.* It is a wonderful production – pure stand-up comedy while at the same time giving an intelligent interpretation of the piece.

Tuesday 25 November

Went into the office for the Programming Meeting, and we went through the 99/00 season again. There is a complicated section in February/March/April 2000 where we are trying to present too much ballet, and therefore overstretching the rehearsal resources, without enough opera rep to enable the ballet programme to be spread out a little more.

Lunch with Ian McGarry and Peter Finch from Equity. They wanted reassurance about the Eyre review and the possible implications for their members. I told them the general buzz coming out of the DCMS was that the proposal announced by Chris Smith a few weeks ago about combining with ENO was the least likely to happen.

Back to the office to see Michael Knight and his colleague Philip Heatherington at 2.00 to discuss the restructuring assignment that I had agreed with Michael several weeks earlier; then into the senior management team at 2.30 with the first hour comprising a discussion with Michael and Philip. They explained the basic issue, that we were trying to run two organizational structures simultaneously with the result there were very few co-ordinating mechanisms between different departments, and no real sense of accountability for decision-making. They said that they would be wishing to talk individually to each member of the senior management, and to groups of staff.

After they had left we went on to talk about how I wished the senior management group to focus on managing the organization during the closure period, the first and most important aspect of which would be finalizing the closure programme. We began to discuss it. At one point Anthony Russell-Roberts said to me that next week he would be wanting to discuss changes to the rep, which would carry additional costs that would be offset by extra income.[80] I could not believe my ears. I advised Anthony to be very cautious indeed about proposals for extra income, since experience suggested that we were pretty useless at accurate income forecasting. If he wished to increase the costs in one part of his programme he would need to demonstrate how he was going to cut costs by an equivalent amount in another part of the programme. I didn't think he quite believed what I was saying. So I said it again very slowly and eventually he said, 'I really do hear what you say.' Good. We'll see what he does now.

Keith told us that we had had the bailiffs in last week. Richard said to Keith that we must stop the *Stage* writing about it. Keith pointed out that, since it was true, we couldn't stop anyone writing about it. What he, Keith, had to do was to try and prevent it from being given a high profile in the national press.

After the senior management team, talked with Mike about a number of issues, including the appointment of my secondment. We have had some very good applicants, and I will be interviewing on Thursday.

Bob Boas from the ENO Board came round for a drink. The ENO Board sounds like a haven of common sense.

Off to the Connaught, where I met Peter, Lucy – Peter's wife –

[80] Adjusting income forecasts in order to balance increased costs had been established practice at the Royal Opera House. In this instance the programme was eventually changed in such a way that there were no cost increases.

and Nigel for dinner. We talked mainly about the Board and the Select Committee. At one point Peter said that he had had intelligence from the Select Committee that the report was going to recommend his resignation. His face got that grey look that I have seen it take on several times now, when there is a possibility that he might have to step down from the Chairmanship. He did not mention any similar recommendation regarding myself, but that might simply have been that he was so worried about himself he was not really able to focus on anything else.

Wednesday 26 November

The day began with a meeting with Graham Devlin, Rudi and Jim (Bob had been unable to attend) about the Floral Trust adviser, which was predictably difficult. Rudi took the approach that all of this should just be regarded in a positive light and that we should not anticipate problems. He talked vaguely about providing information, until I pointed out that since the man who had been appointed[81] by the Floral Trust was a company turnaround director, it was unlikely that he would take as passive a role as Rudi anticipated. Rudi paused for a minute and then launched back into his exhortations that we should think positively. Jim contorted himself as he tried to tread a fine line between optimism and pragmatism. I asked a number of questions, such as to whom this person would report and the status of their recommendations. In each case we all knew the proper answer – me and advisory – and the likely answer – the Floral Trust and overriding the Board. I tried to conduct myself softly and gently with a smile on my face; inside I felt as though I was falling apart.

Lunch with Nick Brett, my first proper boyfriend, whom I had not

[81] Everyone who had met me and Adrian Stanway had agreed that there was not the slightest possibility we could work together, and therefore Pelham Allen had been appointed in his place. He was a self-employed accountant who worked in close association with Coopers and Lybrand as a turnaround director.

seen for twenty-eight years. As I walked across the restaurant, he stood up and said, 'Age shall not wither us.' Nick has been a journalist for most of his life, and is now head of a BBC publishing outfit. I talked animatedly with the surface of myself, the rest of me aching and wishing we could have met under different circumstances.

Back to the office. Ron Freeman, Head of Wigs, took me for tea at the Savoy. We talked over the tea, scones and sandwiches, listening to a pianist. I acted being light-hearted, while inside I felt as though my heart was being eaten away.

Back to the office and went up to see Lorraine and Fay in wardrobe. Lorraine gave me a huge hug, and then asked me how I was, and I had to pause before replying, otherwise my voice would have shaken. Why do I feel so depressed? I think it is because I fear that a company doctor will come in and dismantle the organization. I am being put in an impossible position: asked to remain leader in name of the Royal Opera House, but without the authority to bring about the changes I believe are necessary for the organization to survive, while at the same time possibly having to implement changes that I believe are wrong and damaging.

Returned to my office and plodded through some paperwork.

Peter phoned and asked me how the meeting about the adviser had gone. I said that I was not optimistic and I asked for his support.

He said that he did not think he would be here; I said that I knew he was away for part of next week, but did that mean he was going to be in San Francisco for all of it? He said no, that he had not meant that, but it was now general speculation among his political contacts that his resignation would be required by the Kaufman report. He said that he hadn't received any information about mine and he did not think that would be part of Kaufman's agenda. When he had brought it up last night I had thought it was just Peter being pessimistic. He now said that he could not see any way in which he could resist it.

Shortly afterwards Judy telephoned to tell me that two journalists were now actively pursuing the rumour that Peter and I were having an affair. I put the telephone down and put my head in my hands.

Later, in the car on the way to friends, Nigel asked me whether Peter and I had ever done anything that could be construed badly. I said that, far from it, we had spent very little time in each other's company. We had never accompanied each other to an opera or ballet; we saw little of each other in the office (apart from the last couple of weeks of incessant meetings) and that we would have appeared distant rather than close. I told Nigel that Judy had said the journalists would only write about it if they could find some proof, and that I had told her there wasn't any proof – how could there be for something that didn't exist?

When we got to Joe and Sally's I phoned Judy and we had a long conversation about her determination now to give in her notice, announce her appointment, and join the Royal Opera House as soon as possible. I told her that she was insane. I was still not at all confident about my own position and if, as she said, she was coming to the Royal Opera House to work with me she might find herself with one of the shortest jobs in history. She said she would take the risk because she felt it was so critically important that the Royal Opera House received as much guidance as possible, as far as the press is concerned, over the publication of the Select Committee report.

I was *compos mentis*, communicating and awake for about an hour at Joe and Sally's. It was 9.30 by the time I came off the telephone; we had dinner and by 10.30 I was asleep in my chair. They put me on a little sofa beside the dining table with an armchair pulled up for my legs, and let me sleep for half an hour and then Nigel took me home. He carried me out of the car and into the house and I went to bed, probably by about 11.45.

Thursday 27 November

Spoke with Peter at 6.30 to tell him about wishing to announce Judy's appointment; spoke to Judy when I arrived at the office and made all the necessary arrangements. At least this gives me the feeling that we are doing something positive, and the very fact that Judy is prepared to take such a high risk with her own career makes me feel more confident. Although she won't be starting properly until the beginning of January, she will come in for the next week or so to help us through the Kaufman report. She has already suggested that we organize a press breakfast for the morning of 2 December, which is when we know the report will be coming out. At least we can try and give some positive news about the Royal Opera House, and next year's programme, at the same time.

Spent the morning interviewing for my secondment. All the candidates are impressive in different ways. Richard Sadler has the most appropriate mix of skills for the tasks I need done, in particular writing the business plan, and I decided to appoint him.

Had a meeting with the chorus in the afternoon. The groups of performers feel disempowered at the Royal Opera House: they give the impression that they see the Board and senior management at the centre of the organization, then there is an administrative circle and they, who should be the heart, are on the outside. Given the underlying sense of anxiety and resentment, they were surprisingly positive.

I walked over to the Lyric Theatre in Shaftesbury Avenue. I enjoyed the Royal Shakespeare Company's production of *Cyrano* although I was feeling tired and sick. We spent a few minutes at the party and then went home. As we were leaving the party I encountered Chris Smith and told him that he had been right: I had been mad, after all, to take on the job.[82]

I went to sleep on the tube, but at least Nigel was there to stop me going on to Finsbury Park.

[82] I had had a meeting with Chris Smith on the morning my appointment to the Royal Opera House was announced. He had congratulated me and then asked me why on earth I wanted to do the job. I told him I liked taking on difficult arts organizations.

Friday 28 November

Began the day with a quick half hour with Judy when we went over some of the things we might discuss at the press breakfast next Tuesday.

Then an hour with the Arts Council/Royal Opera House Liaison Group, which was positive and constructive.

Then, at about 10.15, Peter rang from his car and said that he had heard from a 'triple A star' source that the Select Committee report would be recommending that the Board disband itself, that he and I leave, and the whole operation pass to the hands of the DCMS. All I feel is tired. Almost too tired to care.

I made a few phone calls before going off to the airport to catch a flight to Madrid where the ballet company was performing. Nigel came in briefly – I had left my passport and ticket at home – and I told him what Peter had said. He put his arms around me. I told him he seemed even more upset than I was. I suspect the truth is that he is more immediately upset and it will grow on me.

On the tube I nearly went to sleep. At the airport I nearly went to sleep. On the plane I nearly went to sleep. I just felt this profound sense of exhaustion. Then Lou Shand-Brown met me at the airport, and she was so nice and bright and friendly on the way to the hotel that I began to feel better. Changed and then went to the Teatro Real.

Sleeping Beauty looked marvellous. I spent one interval in a state room with the British Ambassador and some Spanish grandees; the company had a party afterwards that I would love to have stayed at – however I had to have dinner with more grandees. But how wonderful it is to be here, with the ballet company, rather than in London.

Saturday 29 November

Woke and read in bed for a couple of hours. Went down to breakfast at around 11.00 and then took a taxi up to the Prado. It contains a remarkable collection of paintings by Velasquez, Goya and El Greco displaying each aspect of the artists' talents. I also saw the Italian rooms that contained equally impressive collections of paintings by Raphael and Titian. I don't think I have ever been in a museum – with the possible exception of the Uffizi – where great artists have been represented by quite so many of their works. I wasn't able to lose myself entirely in the gallery though, and thoughts of the Kaufman report kept sliding around the edge of my mind.

I walked back into town and to the hotel where I was due to meet John Seekings and John Harrison, and we walked over to the Teatro Real. We first went round the front of house, including the restaurant, which has dark red walls, wooden finishes, and hundreds of tiny lights set into the ceiling. Certainly there is nothing of 'The People's Opera' about the Teatro Real, despite having been built entirely with public money. The building materials are more expensive, the audiences more chic, and the ticket prices higher than anything we will ever have at the Royal Opera House.

We then went backstage and down into the deep basements. I had hoped to see evidence of the wagons in use but since they do not yet house a producing opera company there are no sets to be stored on them. The subterranean storage space, which is the size of several tennis courts, was most impressive. We then went further down and I saw the machinery that raises and lowers the various wagons and stage floors. It comprises eight or more complex spiral springs with a vertical section and a horizontal section so that they can either be raised into strong columns, or flattened into cylinders the size of a hatbox. The Johns explained to me how they worked and I think I understood it after a while, but it still seemed to me to defy any practical application of solid materials.

We then went back upstairs and looked at the backstage facilities, including the canteen, the orchestra rest room, and the ballet and chorus rehearsal rooms. I went round the dressing rooms and talked to some of the dancers, and then went on stage. Anthony Russell-Roberts and I had a long conversation in the semi-darkness while the dancers gradually gathered on stage, the girls in their first-act tutus and leg warmers, practising steps and parts of the routines, while lit low down and from the side in pink and yellow. I then left the theatre and went back to my hotel, where I tried to read but fell asleep for a couple of hours.

I met John Seekings in the foyer. We had a drink at my hotel and then one at his, and then found a Spanish restaurant. We had some kind of local stew, which you ate first by pouring the liquid over some noodles and eating it as soup and then eating the remaining chick-peas and meat. Delicious but filling. During the course of the evening we talked about every aspect of the Royal Opera House. He is a remarkable man: able, ambitious, modest, and one of those people – rather like Kathryn McDowell – who seems able to do three jobs simultaneously while giving the impression they are lazing around with their feet up. We are lucky to have him.

Back to the hotel and crashed out.

Sunday 30 November

Spent the first two hours of the day in bed reading. Off to the airport and spent an hour talking to Bruce Sansom and drinking coffee while we waited to go through to the plane. Uneventful flight.

Returned to the house, having to wade through a football crowd, by about 3.30.

Made a number of telephone calls to Peter and others, including my parents and my sister, Liz. I warned them about the Select Committee report, and said I would let them know as soon as it was out how bad the damage might be. They sounded alarmed but I told them on no account must they worry. I will be all right, and since the worst possible outcome is that I am forced to leave, the worst possible outcome is not that bad.

Spoke to Peter Davis in the early evening, and he made some positive comments about the need to ensure that the Coopers support adviser does not in any way cut across my authority. He also indicated that there are some serious worries among the Royal Opera House Trust members about the Board.

Monday 1 December

Started with a meeting of the Royal Opera House Trust at 8.00, at which various Trustees expressed their disquiet about the Royal Opera House's financial position and the need for them, too, to appoint an independent adviser to assure them that they were not giving money to an insolvent organization. They said that if possible they would like to use the same Coopers adviser as the Floral Trust. I mentioned to one of them afterwards that it might take some time to agree the terms of reference for the Floral Trust adviser.

I spent an hour afterwards with Vivien, trying to re-establish a relationship that has deteriorated through four or five tense Board meetings. She is always more difficult to talk to than I think she is going to be, since she shares with other very rich people I have met the characteristic of pursuing her own train of thought and expecting others to follow. She still believes that if we threaten the Government enough they will give us more money. I cannot imagine they will. I know she wants the best for the Royal Opera House, but I cannot agree with the way she is going about achieving it. I came away from the meeting worrying about further incidents of possible bankruptcy.

Lunch with Michael Morris, from Artangel. We talked about the possibility of William Tuckett working with him to do a major installation in the Piazza, involving the projection of huge images on to the wall of the Royal Opera House.

Back to the office, where I continued clearing the desk for tomorrow onwards. We have no idea what we might have to do in response to the report.

Then a long-ish conversation with Peter about how we are going to handle the media tomorrow, although we can't make any decisions until we know what the report actually says. Conversations with Judy about the same subject. A conversation with Michael Knight about the Coopers support adviser. I said that I have a profound sense of distaste about a lot of what is happening at the Royal Opera House at the moment. He said he had had the impression that Jenny had felt the same thing.

Off to dinner at the BBC; initially sat between John Humphrys and Barry Norman and talked at length to John Humphrys about farming and bananas. After everyone moved round I was between John Birt and the political editor of the *Financial Times.* John Birt advised me to tread a very careful line tomorrow when talking about my predecessors. On the one hand it appears ungracious to slag off those who have gone before you; on the other hand if you don't, you end up being blamed for their mistakes.

Earlier in the evening I had gone up to Damien Green, a member of the Select Committee also at the dinner and noticed that he could not meet my eyes. I said, 'I do not know what is in your report tomorrow, but my priority is to protect the companies.' He could barely talk to me.

Tuesday 2 December

The alarm rang at 5.00. I awoke, full of apprehension and foreboding, and later than I'd anticipated.

I went into the Royal Opera House and planned the afternoon's senior management meeting – which was inevitably going to take place without me – and then Judy came in at 8.00 and we discussed the press briefing. The press arrived around 9.00 and we had a pleasant breakfast. I was photographed in the wardrobe department.

Over to Keith's office at around 2.00. The report arrived at around 2.30. Although it is embargoed until tomorrow the press has already had it. This means that the journalists will have two cracks at it: first 'speculating' tomorrow what might be in the report, and then reporting its contents the following day.

I read it. There was nothing in the summary of conclusions about Peter either in relation to Jenny's departure or my appointment – the main criticism of him is that he took too long to appoint a Finance Director. Nonetheless there is still a recommendation he should resign. I could not properly take in the comments and recommendations about me,[83] except that they were personal, damaging, and expressed in intemperate language. The Select Committee has recommended that I resign immediately, along with the entire Board. I was aware that my heart was starting to beat very fast and very strongly as I read the report, but initially I had no real emotional reaction to what was being said about me.

I cannot really remember the events of most of the afternoon. I phoned Nigel immediately and he came over.

Judy got on the telephone to all the journalists and phoned round relentlessly discovering what they thought, trying to influence what they wrote – she is a real professional.

I spoke to Melanie Leech a couple of times, who was warm and supportive.

I spoke to Graham, who sounded harassed and embattled.

In the middle of the afternoon I took a photocopy of the summary and conclusions over to the senior management and talked them through what had happened and asked their advice on how to communicate to staff. At one point I was overcome and could barely continue. They were very supportive.

Nigel and I came home at around 6.30. We watched some television and then I went to sleep on the sofa. I remember him saying to me that I must go upstairs and me refusing; I wished to do nothing but lie and relax.

I woke up at around midnight. Nigel had brought down a duvet and had put it over me, and had brought down another duvet and had lain down on the floor beside me. We both went to bed.

[83] The report said that I had given the wrong advice to Lord Chadlington in suggesting that he should discuss the process of appointing Genista McIntosh's successor with the Department of National Heritage, and that I should instead have referred him to my deputy at the Arts Council; and that I had not given Lord Gowrie adequate notice of the possibility that I might be asked to do the job. In the final summary I was accused of disloyalty towards my then employer, the Arts Council.

Wednesday 3 December

We went out early to get the papers; the initial coverage wasn't too bad. I went into the office and all was quiet. Judy said that she did not want me to be visible at all, and that she had arranged for Michael Berkeley to do all of the radio and television interviews as he was an experienced broadcaster and an excellent communicator. I resisted initially, saying that throughout the last six months, and particularly during the summer, other people had spoken on my behalf, had usually failed to convince, and more often than not had been inaccurate. Judy insisted and I gave in.

There was a senior management meeting at 8.00 that morning – it had been planned in order to discuss the Richard Eyre review. We did discuss it, since one of the things that makes me most angry about recent events is that they have prevented me from managing the organization and keeping the day-to-day business going. Once we had covered the business of the Eyre review, we also reviewed what has happened thus far re Kaufman, and talked again about how we should communicate with staff. We had agreed that there would be another senior management meeting at 5.30.

Bob and Jim came in for another meeting to discuss the role of the Floral Trust adviser, but none of us felt in the mood: we agreed it would be simpler for me and Pelham Allen to try and sort it out between us. The conversation drifted towards the Kaufman report and the intention, now, of the Board to resign *en masse*.

Kaufman held his press conference at 10.30; it didn't finish until about midday. Then the activity began. I stayed in my office while Michael Berkeley did interviews inside and outside the building. It was a strange feeling, almost as though I was in a prison, with time suspended, while frenetic activity went on outside. At one point I slipped out through a side door to go to lunch.

Judy had arranged for Nick Higham to interview me for the BBC news and that was set up for around 4.00.

I received a fax from James Spooner saying it was essential I stayed and did not resign.

At the 5.30 senior management meeting the directors produced a letter, which they had sent to all of the newspapers, setting out their support for me and saying they wanted me to stay. I was deeply touched. After the meeting I watched the news on the television in Peter's office and saw the item on the Royal Opera House, which comprised first of all an excerpt from *The House* showing me; then Kaufman and me at the Select Committee; and then an extract from my interview that afternoon. I winced when I saw the change in my appearance between early 1994 – just before I became Secretary-General of the Arts Council – and now.

We went out to dinner with our friends Bill and Sarah at their new house in Camberwell. Delightful though the house is, nothing could induce me to return to live in that part of the world. Travelling down the Walworth Road, towards the bleakness of Camberwell Green and the sense of smart enclaves tucked away among dispirited streets, reminded me of how much I had disliked the area when I had lived there myself. Bill and Sarah were in good form; their children impressed that I was going to be on television. We talked, ate, watched the television, talked a little longer and then, as with Joe and Sally the week before, I began to fall asleep. And as with Joe and Sally the week before, they tucked me up on a little sofa, adjacent to the kitchen, and I went into a deep sleep until Nigel took me home.

Thursday 4 December

I had two and a half hours sleep before waking up. I sat in bed and thought until around 5.30 when Nigel went out to get the newspapers.

They were appalling. The *Guardian*, in particular, had a two-page spread with my name written in large letters all over it. All of the nastiest comments made by the Select Committee about me were extracted and printed in highlighted boxes. I felt humiliated. There were some nice comments, notably in the first leader in *The Times*, but they were overwhelmed by the sheer volume of material about me and the repetitions of the critical comments in the report.

I wept for a long time on the bedroom floor. I then phoned Judy and shouted down the telephone at her that I could not possibly do the Today Programme as I was far too upset. She allowed me to think that I wouldn't do the Today Programme until she judged I was calm enough to hear her tell me that I should now really start pulling myself together; that she would meet me at Broadcasting House at 6.45; and that I must do this because the programme was the most effective form of response.

I went to Broadcasting House and made the mistake of checking in about twenty minutes before I was due to go up to the studio. They tried to take me up immediately and I insisted that I was meeting someone there. They remonstrated, so I waited outside, reckoning that they could hardly drag me in off the streets to be taken up to the studio. Judy arrived at about 6.50 and we went up together. She calmed me, giving me good lines to say. Jim Naughtie came out and we talked through the issues and how we were going to tackle them on the programme.

The programme went – to my ears anyway – reasonably well, although I flinched somewhat as I heard myself declare with great confidence that I could sort out the Royal Opera House relatively quickly. The best moment for me was when Jim Naughtie repeated some of the Kaufman criticisms and metaphorically flung them in front of me saying, in effect, 'So what do you say to that then, eh?' Which gave me the opportunity that I had waited six months for and never dreamed that I would be able to take in front of several million Radio 4 listeners. I talked about the Edward Walker-Arnott report and then quoted from the Arts Council's press release announcing my appointment to the Royal Opera House, in which Lord Gowrie had said that he had been consulted throughout and that the Royal Opera House could not have made a better appointment. I don't know whether it had any effect, but at least I felt, finally and at long last, that my own voice had been heard.

We went to Shandwick, where I went up to Peter's office and waited while he dealt with a draft letter to Hayden Phillips. Just before 8.30 Peter went down to the Board meeting. Five minutes after it had begun I realized that I would need to get a note down to ask if I could go in immediately, otherwise they might disband themselves before I had offered them my resignation. I sent down the note and was asked to join them. When I went in the mood was quiet. I sat next to Peter at the end of the table and offered them my resignation. I had barely finished speaking when they said that they refused to accept it, and that it was essential I continue in office.

When I left the Board meeting I joined Jane Murphy in the adjacent room. I remarked that she must be becoming rather used to sitting outside meetings connected with the Royal Opera House and she and I spoke for some while. I then went up to Peter's office, retrieved my coat and left.

I returned to the office and took a warm call from John Birt, who said stick in there, public life is bloody, and you must continue to do the job.

By that stage I had started to receive flowers and numerous messages of support, including a fax from Bernard Haitink. Bernard had rung immediately after the fax had come through to check that I had received it and to reiterate his message, which was that I must stay.

Once I had begun to read the press coverage in a slightly less emotional frame of mind I was able to see that most of the press were saying the same thing. I remarked rather tartly to one person that I seemed to have been given two booby prizes this week: I had had my name dragged through the mud, and I was *still* going to be the Chief Executive of the Royal Opera House.

Keith phoned me and said that he was on his way to Shandwick. Then Peter phoned me; he read out a press release, which started with 'Lord Chadlington has resigned.' I interjected and said, 'But surely the whole Board has resigned', and he told me to be quiet while he read on. It became clear that he had resigned immediately and that the rest of the Board would carry on in a caretaker position, although they too had declared their intention to resign to make way for a new Board. An hour later, the donor whom Peter had found, and who had offered the additional £2 million, telephoned to say that the offer was withdrawn, now that Lord Chadlington was no longer Chairman.

Several meetings had been arranged at the DCMS during the afternoon. John Seekings agreed to take Prince Charles around the building site – we felt it was important that no one connected with the Select Committee report should be involved.

My first meeting at the DCMS was with James Spooner, who had been appointed Acting Chairman of the Board, and Vivien at 2.30. I walked over, in order to give myself the exercise and get rid of some of the adrenaline, and met Vivien in the lobby. I just missed the journalists. James came in having brushed his way through them. We were taken up to the waiting room, and then into Hayden's office. Vivien was in vintage form, bouncing Hayden off the walls. Melanie went from compressing her mouth into a thin line, to sucking in her cheeks, to putting her hands over her mouth, to shaking her shoulders, to cracking up completely with laughter. We covered, in a rather informal fashion, many of the issues that have been discussed during the last few Board meetings, namely the need for the Government to give extra funds to the Royal Opera House, and the difficulties of our financial position, although without reaching any conclusions. I suspect that the main purpose of the meeting was to make sure none of us was going to say anything too spectacularly silly in front of Chris Smith later.

On our way out, James and Vivien went first and while the cameras were preoccupied by them I tried to slip out unobserved behind them. No such luck – I was pursued all the way around Trafalgar Square with photographers running on all sides. I walked back to the office and took some more calls of support while waiting for the second meeting, which was due to begin at 4.15. James came up to my office and we walked to the DCMS together. We skirted round the back of the building and came up from behind. Nick Higham from the BBC was out there by that stage and was far too beady to let us get past unobserved. He shouted after us that he hadn't expected to see us walking – I suppose he thought we would swish up in a Bentley – but we got in without making any comment.

We went up to the waiting room where Vivien joined us five minutes later.

Grey and Graham came into the waiting room briefly, on the way out of a meeting they had just had with Chris Smith about the Royal Opera House. Grey said that the press wasn't too bad. I said that if your name was Mary Allen reading the *Guardian* that morning had not been a pleasant experience.

We then went into the meeting with Chris Smith, Hayden and a squad of civil servants. We spent some time discussing the position of the Board and what should happen next. At one point I remarked that someone would need to be insane to accept a place on the Board of the Royal Opera House, given its financial position. Hayden asked me what I meant. Could he and Chris really be unaware we are virtually bankrupt? We have been telling the DCMS on an almost daily basis about our difficulties. Anyway, it is likely that there will be an announcement about the Board in the middle of the week.

Near the end of the meeting I pointed out that the Board was only one half of the issue and that my own position was the other half. I remarked to Chris that since he had made it very clear to the Select Committee that he had 'no locus' in the question of my appointment, he would presumably have 'no locus' in the question of my possible resignation. This provoked an uneasy laugh from the DCMS side, with Hayden muttering, 'I think she is being ironic.' I said that I had offered my resignation to the Board, who had refused to accept it, but it would also be helpful if Chris had some kind of view about my position, since I was inevitably going to be questioned by journalists – beginning with the cluster that were waiting, as we spoke, outside the DCMS. After a lot of umming and ahhing Chris said that since he had declared that his priority was to stabilize the situation, and since my departure would destabilize the situation, he thought it was best I should stay.

The meeting finished and we went down to face the media. We had decided to take a direct approach. We walked through the doors and I went straight over to Rosie Millard, from the BBC and she interviewed me. I let James deal with the issues about me and the

Board, although when Rosie asked me directly why I hadn't resigned I told her that I had, to the Board that morning, but that they had refused to accept it.

Walked back to the office again and went through a range of telephone interviews with the main arts correspondents, with Judy pushing me hard. We then had another senior management meeting, where I briefed them on the discussions. I continued talking to more arts journalists, including a long session with *Music Matters.* Things then began to calm down. I dealt with some paperwork before going out to meet Melanie for a drink.

We spent a long evening together, covering what had happened and each talking about how we felt about our jobs. At around 11.00 we walked up to Covent Garden underground station, which was solid with tourists, and so I took her down to see the development. I positioned her opposite my favourite lobbying spot, which looks right into the heart of the destruction – lit up at this time of night by orange floodlights – and did my usual line about the excitement of it, allowing her to absorb the horrific consequences of it not being completed.

On the way back we met a group of staff who stopped me and said on no account must I leave. When they left Melanie looked at me and said, 'Not even you could have set that up.' But I am glad she saw it.

I managed to get back without falling asleep and missing my tube stop. Home by midnight.

Friday 5 December

I got up very slowly, moving like an old woman, and went to the office.

A relatively uneventful morning. I saw various people, such as Richard Hall and Richard Sadler, before leaving to go to Aldeburgh. More flowers arrived. The press wasn't too bad although there were some unattractive photographs of me striding through Trafalgar

Square, looking jowly.

Nigel collected me at midday and we returned to Highbury, where we had lunch at the local Italian restaurant, and then went to Suffolk. It was a long drive, with many traffic jams, and we did not arrive at the house until 5.30. There was barely time to get ready before going to Aldeburgh.

I went round backstage, wished the cast good luck, and talked to people such as Peter Katona and Terry Edwards, the Chorus Master. Everyone was greatly supportive. I then went to the Britten Room for a drink before the show and again received much support.

Paul Bunyan is a magnificent piece, both funny and moving. The chorus were superlatively good. Whereas they had looked uncomfortable with the dance routines in *The Merry Widow*, Francesca Zambello, the director of *Paul Bunyan*, made them look as though they had been performing in musicals all their lives. Afterwards we went to the cast party at the Wentworth Hotel, where I spent some time talking to various members of the orchestra and chorus, and to Francesca Zambello. I was impressed by her. We then went to the house that Pat Pursey, the technical team leader, had rented for the week, to another party at which there were about twenty people from the show. It felt as though I was in a haven. When we left Pat put his arms round me and told me that I must on no account leave.

It was 3.00 by the time we got back, but I was very glad we had done it. The only way I can get through this period is by taking strength from the desire of other people I should stay at the Royal Opera House.

Saturday 6 December

Felt even more like an old woman in the depth of my tiredness. Hung around in the morning and made a few phone calls, and then went to Woodbridge and Ipswich where I completed my Christmas shopping. It just shows what lack of time and a bit of determination can achieve.

Before going out I had spoken to my parents who were interested to hear about everything that was going on. They both said that Thursday had been most unpleasant for them, and that they had found it extremely painful imagining how upset I must have been. But they were encouraging about my performances on the *Today Programme* and later on the BBC television news.

When we got back from Ipswich I just lay on the sofa and read a trashy novel. Nigel lit the fire and put on a CD of some Bach flute sonatas. At about 9.00 I made a squid casserole. I wish I could spend more time here doing things like that.

Sunday 7 December

A day dedicated to phone calls, sorting out papers, writing letters and paying bills. Mostly Royal Opera House admin, but some domestic admin too.

Tomorrow it will be back to the maelstrom. Only two more weeks – please God – before my holiday. I have already told James Spooner that the Royal Opera House must not have a financial crisis between 20 December and 4 January.

There is a sense of the aftermath of the storm. I wrote a personal letter to Chris Smith saying how sorry I was that all this had happened during his first year in office, and that I would now do the best I could to sort things out at the Royal Opera House, and put it through his letterbox once we returned to London. I then wrote a letter to Peter, in which I said I was very sad that all the great hopes we had had when we started out together at the Royal Opera House had been laid so low.

Monday 8 December

In early, to do more sorting, and then a meeting with the senior management at 9.00. We talked about how we might ask the staff to give us names for a new Board, which I would then feed through to the Arts Council, the DCMS and the remaining Board members.

To the Arts Council to attend a meeting of their Audit Committee. I was completely open about the budgets, and why they so dramatically failed to balance in any direction, and how there was nothing we could do about it. I told them about the Floral Trust and the adviser, and the extent to which that adviser might undermine the Royal Opera House's relationship with the Arts Council. Because of the constraints upon intervention, they weren't able to do anything, apart from listen and say that we were in a terrible position.

Back to the Royal Opera House where I had a long meeting with Richard Hall to talk about the finances. During the last few weeks, every time something dreadful has happened we have said to each other that things couldn't get any worse. However such observations generally turned out to be the preface to some fresh catastrophe. This time, though, we both said that we felt the situation had finally reached its nadir – we have now reached the bottom of the pit and can start planning how to climb out of it.

Ron Freeman came down with the words of the final lines of the first act of *Paul Bunyan*, about the need for dissolution, discontinuity and confusion on the way to healing. He said I should think of them when things are at their worst. He hugged me and told me that everyone wants me to stay.

Tuesday 9 December

An excellent day, most of which I spent actually doing my job.

Programming Meeting in the morning, during which we continued programming the main stage for 99/00. We are nearly there. We also began looking at 00/01, for which the ballet company is setting the pace. Advance planning of this kind makes me feel that I am beginning to get things under control.

Then two hours with the Planning Group, which has now been joined by Richard Sadler, going through each segment of the plans for the new House, looking at progress and checking the timetable for the working groups.

Three hours in the afternoon with the senior management, looking at the closure programme. We completed the review of the schedule, and I am alarmed at how many of the practical details of the Sadler's Wells opera seasons have not yet been sorted out. I will need to have a separate session with Nicholas Payne to go through the detail, since it is time-consuming, unproductive and ultimately uncomfortable for us to hammer out these issues in front of so many other people.

Wednesday 10 December

It's all beginning again.

James Spooner came in for a meeting at 8.00, which went reasonably well. We discussed a range of options for Board members. We were joined at 9.00 by Vivien, Jim Butler and Richard Hall to talk about finance. We had two hours of discussions, with a substantial amount of arm-waving and hand-wringing, and got nowhere. I talked about the need to be calm and restore confidence, but the likelihood of being able to move forward in an orderly fashion begins to look increasingly remote.

Met the conductor Richard Hickox at Joe Allen at 12.30. We talked about future planning, and about *Paul Bunyan* and *Pilgrim's Progress.* He was encouraging, both about my own position and about the future of the Royal Opera in general.

At 4.00 went to the Waldorf to meet Pelham Allen, the Floral Trust professional support adviser. Pelham and I spent two hours talking in a reasonably courteous fashion. I encouraged him to tell me about his background. I am concerned that he has no experience in the public sector, with charities, or with the arts. During our conversation we laid all of our cards – or at least he seemed to lay all of his and I laid nearly all of mine – on the table and I made it clear that, skilled though he might be, I had not invited his participation, and that I would not choose to appoint him, given the very substantial expense of employing a senior person from Coopers and Lybrand for six months or more.

I asked him how he saw his role. He tried to avoid being specific but what little he said did not encourage me. We agreed that he would meet Richard Hall tomorrow, and that he and I would then meet again on Friday. I am deeply concerned about the implications of his appointment, particularly in view of the fact that we have a holding Board, rather than one with any status or authority. He seems nice enough; he is obviously bright; but the role he describes would make him, in effect, a shadow Chief Executive. If I *am* to continue doing my job it will not be helped by being possibly undermined by the involvement of an externally imposed 'adviser' with executive authority.

Back to the office briefly and then to *Paul Bunyan.* I was marginally less tired than when I saw it on Friday and the acoustics of the Shaftesbury Theatre are so dry that I managed to hear many more of the words. I had tears in my eyes at the end of the first act.

Thursday 11 December

Met with Sheila Forbes at 8.30, who was helping me develop a staffing structure for the new theatre. (She had helped me restructure the Arts Council the previous year.) I am hoping she will work with the staff to rebuild the workforce in preparation for moving back into the new House. I said I wanted to take an approach similar to that we adopted at the Arts Council: first setting out the ground rules for the exercise, then identifying the outputs we wanted from each department, then working with the staff to identify the most efficient and cost-effective way of delivering those outputs.

I also told her about my difficulties with the Floral Trust adviser. She was sympathetic.

Lunch at Joe Allen with Sean Magee, an old friend and Mercutio to my Juliet at Cambridge in 1971. He lives in the village of

Chadlington, after which Peter took the name of his title; apparently the local residents are not pleased at being so visibly and repeatedly linked to the goings-on at the Royal Opera House.

I went to the Development Steering Group to show my face and try and give some confidence, and then back to my office.

Peter Davis met me at 5.00 and we had a comforting discussion. He is a sensible and solid man, and agreed that he would think about the best way to reassure Vivien and contain her anxieties.

Christmas drinks at the BBC and a tremendous party. Kathryn McDowell was there and we sorted out some Royal Opera House business. Dennis Marks looked ten years younger than when he had been at ENO and seems to have lost quite a lot of weight. I was talking to Simon Brett and gesticulated, catching the bottom of someone's glass with my hand and sending white wine flying over about four people. One of them was the Oflot Peter Davis who commiserated with the hell of being in the press. Saw Nicholas Kenyon, Alan Yentob and others, before leaving.

My sister Liz arrived soon after I returned home and we had a brief supper. She talked about Joseph, my nephew, and I yearned to be able to spend more time and energy with friends and family.

Friday 12 December

Met Pelham Allen at the Waldorf Hotel at 7.00 and had a discussion that was considerably more gloves-off this time. I asked him to try and define his role more clearly, and he said that would depend on what he found when he arrived. It sounds as though the work will be determined by what he perceives to be the priorities, rather than what I perceive to be the priorities. I made my own position very clear indeed. He said that George Magan had told him he had to be in the Royal Opera House by the end of that day. I said in that case I would be out of it. He put his head in his hands at that point. Near the end of the meeting he said he felt he was between a rock and a hard place, to which I said, 'Now you are experiencing what it is like to work at the Royal Opera House.'

He confirmed that Vivien thought it would be the best thing to close down the operation, although George Magan feels it's important to keep it open. The sense that events are being dictated by people and forces entirely beyond my control increases all the time.

We also talked about the finances. Pelham Allen has discussed the position with Richard Hall and believes that we need to reconstruct our financial processes over a very short time scale. I agreed with him, and said that the problem for the finance department had been to stabilize the position for a sufficient length of time so that they can start beefing up the controls. I also told him we had had a team from the auditors in for over two months. I authorized Pelham Allen to do a check on the solvency of the organization, to be ready by Tuesday lunchtime, so that we could present it to the Board that afternoon. We agreed that he would report the rest of our conversation to George Magan.

Then up to the BBC to do a Radio 5 Live interview with David Mellor. He was helpful, feeding me useful lines and cracking some good jokes. He also gave an excellent plug for *Paul Bunyan.*

Back to the office to be rung by Bob Gavron from a car phone. He was returning, with Michael Berkeley, from a meeting they had had at the DCMS with Vivien and Hayden Phillips. He said he thought it would be necessary to put the Royal Opera House into administrative receivership on Tuesday. I said I thought we should have this conversation face to face rather than over a car phone so Michael came to see me. It transpired that the meeting had begun by talking about how to reconstitute the Board, at which Vivien's lawyer, who had accompanied her, said he had advised Vivien that, since the organization was almost certainly insolvent, she should not accept a place on the Board, and more generally that no one should be invited to join the new Board until solvency had been assured. There was a sufficient level of doubt in the minds of the Board members present for them to believe that perhaps administration would be the preferred route. I said to Michael that I still did not believe it would be right to go into administration, but if the Board decided that was what they wished to do I would, of course, do everything necessary to support that decision.

I then went over to the Arts Council to meet Graham for a lunch, most of which was conducted by what we now describe as 'Orso's rules'. In other words you forget as much as possible of everything that has been told to you. It was a desperate lunch – we are both so exhausted.

Returned to the Royal Opera House and talked with Richard Hall about solvency. Pelham Allen rang me and said that it was not going to be possible to complete the solvency check in the time available, that things were OK in the short term, that the solvency of the organization actually depended more on the donors than on other aspects of the business, and that what was needed now was a very rapid action plan to sort out the finances and the financial controls. I asked him to write that to me in a letter.

Caught a train to Cambridge where I was going to the annual Selwyn dinner. Christopher Frayling, Rector of the Royal College of Art and Richard Cork, Arts critic for *The Times* (and both members of the Arts Council) were there, and no sooner had I arrived in the pre-dinner reception than I saw them and David Harrison, the Master of Selwyn (and Chairman of the Eastern Arts Board and member of the Arts Council) huddled in a corner. I walked over and remarked that, even at events like this, the Arts Council seemed incapable of separating itself.

The dinner was fun. I talked a great deal to all those on either side of me and opposite me and ended up at 1.00 drinking port and talking about the arts and opera.

Saturday 13 December

Woke up after five hours sleep. Staggered around the room and eventually worked out how to turn on the gas fire – it had been a freezing night in a narrow, too short, single bed – and arrived at breakfast by

8.30 where I attempted conversation with Christopher and other guests from the night before. Christopher and I talked on the train back to London. For one wild moment he had the idea that the best solution would be for the Arts Council to take over the Royal Opera House – then I reminded him about the debts and he rapidly changed his mind.

Talked everything through with Nigel for what seemed like hours when I got back. Ate. Slept. Went down to see my parents in the early evening. Told them everything that was going on. Just about managed to keep my stress level to below that which would send me screaming round the bend, and went to bed at 10.30.

Sunday 14 December

I am beginning to wonder whether or not going into administration would be a better option.[84] When I look at the Sadler's Wells plans, in particular the number of decisions that still need to be taken about various practical aspects of them, and the extent to which these could have cost consequences; when I look at the way the box office continues to be almost in free-fall, with no new ideas from the marketing department; when I think about the difficulties being experienced by the finance department and their continuing inability to produce any reliable financial information; I cannot feel confident that I am able to account to the Board for an organization that will remain viable for the next two years.

The Floral Trust professional support adviser is also upsetting me deeply. I am being asked to agree to something which will compromise my ability to run the organization, while at the same time will release the necessary money to allow it to stay afloat. I spoke to my

[84] Our insolvency adviser had warned me about what he described as 'the seduction of administration'. The anxiety of managing a company that is continually on the brink of insolvency is so great, and the process so exhausting that it is apparently quite usual for those in charge to end up welcoming the thought of administration just so that someone else can come in and take over.

father and he agreed it was probably better to be insubordinate and let them sack me rather than to resign. I feel trapped. We had lunch, and afterwards I curled up in front of the fire.

We went home relatively early and I felt a little better once I was able to start working. I spoke to Graham. I spoke to Melanie. I spoke to James Spooner and others. I worked until quite late.

Monday 15 December

To work early. As I walked into the office my left leg gave way beneath me. My knee felt simultaneously very painful and as though it wouldn't support me. I could not believe that, on top of everything else, I was now going to have problems with my knee. I managed to drag myself across my office and take off my coat.

I had a meeting with Judy, Keith and Andrew in order to discuss marketing. Having spent the first half of the meeting ventilating their feelings about those who programmed the art, they then addressed issues of pricing and how we sell the shows. It was only a beginning but I think we could get somewhere.

Then Richard Sadler, my new assistant, came to see me. I said that if he was going to be working closely with me he needed to know, in detail, about the difficulties we were presently facing. I told him the whole story about the organization, its solvency, the Floral Trust adviser, and the possibility that I might leave. He was calm. He had already presented me with a report on the Richard Eyre review, which was excellent, and which he had prepared over a very short time. I said I wanted him to move into Peter Chadlington's office immediately – I might as well establish that there is no Chairman's office before another Chairman arrives.

By the time we had finished that meeting, I couldn't tolerate the pain in my knee any longer and Andy, from the Occupational Health Unit, came up to look at it. If one has to have a problem with one's knee, an organization that incorporates a ballet company is the best possible place to do so. Andy had my trousers off, tights down and was spraying cold things on to my leg in an instant. She then rubbed in some cream, gave me a tubigrip and some pills to take. She also gave me a stick – I think it is called an elbow crutch – with which I practised for the following ten minutes. She thinks it is something to do with my cartilage.

The senior management meeting concentrated on the closure programme and whether we were likely to be able to complete the closure period without going bust. Richard and I wanted as detailed information as possible to present to the Board tomorrow. Once we had discussed the programme in some detail, I asked the senior management group whether or not they would put their own money on our viability. In other words, if we agreed now that we would go ahead with the programme, and it failed, they would have to lay out £10,000 of their own money; alternatively they could decide now that they wouldn't take the risk. Talk about shaking a tree and the apples falling out – the moment I had finished speaking all kinds of other risks tumbled out on to the table. For example, Jackie revealed that she was worried about achieving her fund-raising targets. Once we had dealt with these new issues I repeated my challenge. I did not receive a conclusive reply.

I did not tell them about the Floral Trust support adviser – I am not yet ready to tell them and I don't think they yet need to hear.

James Spooner phoned after the senior management meeting to say that George Magan, Adrian Stanway and Pelham Allen had gone to see Chris Smith that morning with a proposal as to how the Floral Trust adviser might work in the Royal Opera House. There was due to be another meeting at the DCMS that night to discuss new Board members. I phoned Hayden. He confirmed that there had been a meeting, but with him rather than with Chris. I made it clear that I was not prepared to carry on trying to be Chief Executive of the Royal Opera House – I described it as the most difficult job in the arts and possibly one of the nastiest jobs in the country – unless I was able to do the job properly. He agreed with me.

Two people from Coutts – one of them Rob Sher – came in to see me and Richard and we discussed the possibility of a £9 million borrowing facility to tide us across the next few months on the development, bridging any gap before we receive the proceeds from the property sales. They were taken aback at the size of the loan we required and were not able to provide any reassurances about being able to help us. We agreed that a new Chairman would be the most useful signal that the Royal Opera House was beginning to develop a more confident base.

When I then asked them for £1 million borrowing facility, to tide the operating company across a few weeks at the year-end, they seemed relieved that I wanted such a comparatively small sum of money and agreed almost immediately.

Tuesday 16 December

I phoned James Spooner at 7.00. He said that the discussion at the DCMS the night before had not been about Board members but about an extremely intrusive proposal that had been put forward by Coopers suggesting that Pelham Allen should either come in as an executive deputy chairman, or as a non-executive member of the senior management. It seemed to me that the former was unallowable, and the latter a contradiction in terms. Apparently the DCMS and the Arts Council had both expressed reservations at the meeting.

Anthony Dowell and Anthony Russell-Roberts turned up at 9.00 for the Programming Meeting. Nicholas was caught in traffic and did not arrive until 9.45. Anthony Dowell told me some gory stories about knee operations he had had.

Once we had given up waiting for Nicholas, and the Anthonys had returned to Baron's Court, I had a telephone conversation with Graham Devlin that was surprisingly harsh in tone. He was telling me to stop making difficulties and agree terms with the Floral Trust, whereas I was saying that I would only agree terms that were compatible with my role as Chief Executive. Graham was emphatic that everything had to be agreed now.

I put the phone down, thought, and then phoned back ten minutes later and said I would have another go with Pelham Allen. I then spoke to Peter Davis who said he would try to ensure that George Magan did not push me into an impossible position.

Half-way through the morning Jim phoned to say that he was the only one on the Board who thought that going into administration would be irresponsible. This did not augur well for the Board meeting that afternoon.

The meeting began with Board members discussing how long they were prepared to stay. There was a general consensus that 10 January was the outside limit. That did not seem to me compatible with their apparently simultaneous point of view that the Government will not find people to serve on the new Board until at least mid-March. They then discussed the financial position. Richard and I, having realized that all our attempts to reassure the Board about solvency tended to precipitate them towards administration like lemmings towards a cliff, took the opposite approach this time and were as pessimistic as possible. There was a restrained discussion about our solvency and a moderate conclusion that we just had to continue hoping for the best.

Some brisk discussion about the Floral Trust support adviser and the fact that terms have not yet been agreed. I repeated that I was bending over backwards to do everything that I could, that I had already had two discussions with Pelham Allen, and that I was going to be having another one the following day. I sensed a combination of anxiety about my possible departure, anxiety about my possible resistance to the Floral Trust conditions and something from Vivien I couldn't quite pinpoint; not quite hostility but perhaps a determination to push things as far as she possibly could. There is still the sense that we should be trying to find a way of forcing the Government to give us more money. I remain convinced that there is no chance of that until after – and probably quite a long time after – we have properly sorted ourselves out.

I tabled a letter Richard Hall had drafted from me to Pelham Allen, asking him to undertake some work on the finance department and the financial processes immediately. The Board endorsed it, subject to an amendment allowing the Floral Trust to have sight of any material produced by Pelham Allen.

Because of my leg, I didn't go to any of the Christmas parties I had been invited to and returned home at 6.30. Although Nigel and I spoke for some time, I couldn't stop myself from going to sleep, and by 8.30 was unable to talk properly: sentences kept trailing off into gibberish as I started dreaming. Nigel put me to bed. I woke up at 1.00 with my heart beating hard. After two hours of alternately dreaming and waking I went back to sleep and woke up at 8.00.

Wednesday 17 December

Went to the doctor: he felt my knee and then sent me off to the Lister Hospital for an X-ray. He said that I should spend the next fortnight with my knee up – applying packets of frozen peas at fifteen minute intervals – so as to see whether or not it would recover of its own accord. If not I might have to have an operation, although he is reluctant to recommend that since, apparently, once a joint has been opened up at my age it tends to lead to arthritis later on.

Back to the office to draft my own terms of reference for the Floral Trust adviser.

Over to the Arts Council at about 4.00 to meet with Pelham Allen. The meeting went well: we were both trying to accommodate each other's positions. He made clear what was expected of him by the Floral Trust, and I made clear what I needed if I were to continue as Chief Executive of the Royal Opera House. I had taken Michael Knight with me, who was helpful in identifying those parts of the assignment that undermined my position. The three of us spent two hours together, and at the end of it I felt more optimistic than I have for weeks. We agreed to allow the more intrusive aspects of the adviser to rest over the Christmas period and that I would write to

George Magan setting out the immediate priorities for the next few weeks. Michael and I walked down towards the House of Commons in the rain, with me limping along on my crutch, and Michael telling me about the concert he was going to at which one of his daughters was playing.

I went into the House of Commons and met Charles Clarke for a drink. He saw me to a taxi, and – predictably – I fell asleep instantly even though it was only 9.30. To bed and slept for seven hours. I am feeling triumphant.

Thursday 18 December

I arrived early and began drafting the letter to George Magan that Pelham and I had agreed would be helpful.

Pelham rang at 8.00 and we discussed his draft note of the meeting the previous evening. I carried on drafting the letter. He rang later to say that Magan was not quite as comfortable as we were with the position that had been reached but after some toing and froing with draft letters all seemed well.

Went out to have lunch with Sue Robertson. She has had almost as hellish a time as I have, with changes to the lottery regulations, the establishment of the Greater London Authority, and general uncertainty about arts funding. She has also completed her two-year-long review, as a result of which she is now cutting grants to several arts organizations in London. She talked about the difficulty of doing so, and my heart went out to her, remembering what it was like to refuse a grant to someone, let alone cut a grant.

I returned to the office to prepare for the Royal Opera House Trust meeting, which began at 5.30. All went well until we reached the item about continuing financial support. The Trust needed to be reassured that the Royal Opera House was going to be viable throughout the closure period and for a year into the new House before they could continue to give their money.

Up until that point, Peter Davis had chaired the meeting with great courtesy. When the question of financial viability arose, David Davies took over the lead. He asked me how progress was going on the Floral Trust agreement. I told him that I had issued a letter of instruction to Coopers the previous evening about the financial aspects of the assignment; that I had proposed draft terms of reference covering the development of the business plan; and that I was confident that other aspects of the assignment would be negotiated successfully.

David Davies then read out selected passages of Pelham's note of the meeting, focusing on those issues where we had failed to reach agreement. He went on to read out some critical comments made by George Magan, from a letter he must have known I had not seen. He addressed the Trust, saying that I was holding everything up, and that the reason the Trust had not received adequate financial advice was because I had not co-operated.

I said that I had, that I was negotiating with Pelham Allen the terms of his involvement with the Royal Opera House, and that I was optimistic that we could resolve any outstanding issues.

David Davies turned his attention back to me. He said that I had been prevaricating. He said that until the Royal Opera House was able to provide assurance that it would meet the Floral Trust's conditions, the Royal Opera House Trust would not provide any further funds.

I said, choosing my words with great care, that the Royal Opera House Board was committed to meeting the conditions, and that I was committed to enabling the Board to meet the conditions. I chose my words so that I was not committing myself to stay with the Royal Opera House, only to ensuring that they would be able to meet the conditions even if that meant that I had to leave in order that they could do so.

Michael Pescod, another Trustee, tried to bring the temperature down by saying that all the Trust needed to know was whether or not there was a probability that the House will stay solvent. The distinction is between a *probability* it will go down, versus a *possibility* it will go down – if there is only a possibility then the Trust can give its funds.

David Davies insisted that I was impeding the agreement with the Floral Trust. I reminded the meeting that the Royal Opera House had only signed the agreement on 24 November; that since then a group of Board members and I had met twice in order to determine what we felt would be appropriate terms of reference; that it had then been agreed I should meet with Pelham Allen and that he and I should look at the practicalities of the assignment. It had been agreed that Pelham would contact me, which he had done the previous week. Since then he and I had met three times.

David Davies dismissed this and said that he was not interested in the sequence of events. It had been agreed at the last meeting of the Royal Opera House Trust that the Trust would use Coopers to obtain the necessary financial reassurances and I had prevented this from happening.

I repeated that Coopers had only contacted me the previous week.

Then Jim and Vivien joined in. Jim said, 'Mary don't you remember talking to Adrian Stanway?' I said of course I did, but that was long before the original agreement was even mooted.

Vivien asked about the appointment letter I had given to Coopers the previous evening, and what my authority had been to do this. I said that the appointment letter was that which I had tabled at the Board meeting two days earlier and, as she would recall, it had been agreed by the Board subject to one addition, which had been included precisely as the Board had specified.

I stuck to my ground and my guns. At that stage of the meeting I was angrier than I can ever remember being. I just clenched my fists under the table and chanted to myself, 'You will not do anything until after Christmas, you will not do anything until after Christmas, you will not do anything until after Christmas. You are not answerable to these people. You are answerable to the Board and only the Board can instruct you. Do and say nothing.' And I did and said nothing.

I was triumphant when I emerged from the end of the meeting, having gritted my teeth and listened to what they wanted to say. I picked up my stick and hobbled into my office, and sat in my chair trying to cool the beating of my heart. I felt surges of adrenaline rushing through my body.

Then Peter Davis came in and said that he, Jim Butler and Harvey Goldsmith had all been talking about their fear that I would leave. I said that if the Royal Opera House Trust really was going to insist to the Board that I had to agree final terms of reference by the Board meeting on 7 January I probably would have to leave. I said that Pelham and I had been progressing well in our negotiations and that I was confident we could sort it out by the middle of January but not by 7 January.

I travelled home feeling as though I was lit up from inside by rage. I don't know whether David Davies thought that by speaking to me in the way he did he would be able to make me do what he wanted, or whether this, to him, was merely an efficient way of doing business, but it had come across to me as the most extraordinary display of rudeness and aggression. There was no sense, during the meeting, of us all working together, only of difference and hostility.

My desire to leave is now stronger than ever. I must get through tomorrow. I have promised myself so firmly that I will do nothing until January. At least then there will be a gap between the Kaufman report and any decision that I might take about my future. Even if the Board comes down wholly on my side, and does not require a decision by me on 7 January, I do not know whether I can face working with these people during the next few years.

When I was talking to Peter Davis earlier this evening, I asked him whether or not Vivien wanted to get me out. He said that she did not, and that the two of them had discussed that issue earlier in the week. I did not ask him what had occasioned that discussion, but I noted it had taken place. I then asked whether or not Vivien realized that that was the direction in which she was pushing and he said that he thought she probably did. So I then asked why she wanted to achieve my departure and he said that he thought it was all part of a much larger and very dangerous game that she was playing with the Government.

I think he is right. Although I have not yet got the impression that

Vivien wants me to leave *per se*, I think it is possible she might want to remove anything that could create stability at the Royal Opera House, in order that she can demonstrate to the Government that they simply must give it more money.

I will do nothing. The time has long since passed when I could influence events.

Friday 19 December

Woke up feeling angry. Went into the office early and drafted a letter to Peter Davis, pointing out that it was the responsibility of the Royal Opera House Trust to obtain whatever advice it felt necessary in order to release the funds. The minutes of the Trust meeting on 1 December stated that if Cooper's were not able to provide that advice then the Trust would go elsewhere for it, and I wanted to register my concern that they appeared to have done nothing between 1 December and 19 December.

I wrote a short covering note addressed to Peter saying how very sorry I was that I was having to write to him in these terms, since he had been so kind, but I was sure he would understand the need.

Faxed the letter to Peter and the three other members of the Trust's *ad hoc* finance committee, including David Davies.

Anthony Everitt and Luke Rittner came in for our discussion about the Arts Council: where it had come from and where it was going to.[85] We had two hours of anecdotes, interrupting each other, and speculation. By the end of it I had almost forgotten I was running the Royal Opera House. My own position was that, following nearly thirty years of tension and argument between the Arts Council and the Regional Arts Associations/Boards, and discussions that

[85] Anthony Everitt and Luke Rittner had been my two most recent predecessors as Secretary-General of the Arts Council. Anthony had suggested to Luke and me that we write a joint article, for one of the broadsheets, about the Arts Council and possible ways forward for it, to coincide with the appointment of a new Chairman.

either one or the other tier of the funding apparatus should be abolished, the best thing to do would be to abolish the whole lot of them, and to replace them with a single national institution, which comprised a network of regionally-based groupings. Anthony and Luke were initially sceptical, but became quite interested as I described what I thought it should be and how it might work. Anthony is going to propose this as one of the ways forward in his article.

Midway through the morning, once Anthony and Luke had gone, I received a fax from James Spooner announcing his resignation as acting Chairman of the Board. I was sad. He has been a great supporter during the last few weeks, and chaired the last Board meeting with wisdom and authority.

Two down, seven to go.

I went to Judy's office and told her about my session with Luke and Anthony. She looked slightly steely and remarked that, since I need all the friends I can get, particularly at the Arts Council, this might not be the moment for me to start advocating their abolition in print. I know she is right, but I had enjoyed myself so much and feel so strongly that the problems of arts funding in this country ought to be addressed, that I am reluctant to go along with her. I know, however, that I will eventually do as she says. I told her that both she and Anthony will be at my party tomorrow night, and that we can all talk about it then.

After lunch I started going round the departments wishing people a happy Christmas. Sadly I missed Ron Freeman. I will write to him. A longer stop than planned in the development office where they had just returned from a long and boozy lunch and were opening further bottles of wine.

I returned briefly to my office to take a call from Pelham Allen, who asked me whether I had received any further instructions from my Board since the meeting last night. I said that I had not. I wondered whether James Spooner had been asked to order me to co-operate and had refused, knowing that I would resign as a result. I pointed out the difference between the work that he and I might do together and the work that he was doing for the Royal Opera House Trust, and said that I would fax through a copy of my letter to Peter Davis to his office. It was a tough conversation. I made it clear that he had *carte blanche* to start working for the Trust, but that our work, in whatever form it eventually finds itself, will not start until my return.

I went to the box office party, which was most jolly, and then off to the pub with John Seekings, John Harrison and Geoff Wheel. The technical department combines common sense, muscle and influence.

I eventually left and went on to our friends Angela and Bob's party, where I – insanely – danced. There was a very good piano and bass duo and at one point Waldemar Januszczak whisked me into his arms saying he had always wanted to dance with a woman on a crutch. Unfortunately the combination of Nurofen and alcohol meant that I could not feel any twinges in my knee at all and I danced energetically, first with Waldemar and then with Nigel, for some time. Rosie Millard was there and she said that when she had been doorstepping me outside the DCMS a couple of weeks ago she had been anxious that I would walk straight past her. I said that inside the building I had been equally anxious that I wouldn't be able to produce a single coherent sentence once I was standing in front of her.

I let on to several people that things were difficult, that I had been in the mood to go, but that I was determined to give it one last shot in January. At the end, just before I left, I was unwise enough to sing *Smoke gets in your eyes.* There are moments – thankfully only rare ones – when all good sense leaves me and my love of singing takes over. Nigel told me I didn't do it too badly, and I certainly had a very warm round of applause from the pianist – no doubt for bravery rather than any display of talent.

Partly, also, I think I was celebrating the fact that I had managed to get through to the end of the week without being forced either into an untenable position or into resigning. My strategy has worked – and I now have two weeks off.

Saturday 20 December

Woke up later than I had intended. Packed and drove to Suffolk, organized ourselves for our Christmas party. The party was great fun – about sixty people were there from various parts of Suffolk. Judy and her husband John were among the first to arrive, and Judy and I talked briefly about the Royal Opera House. I said that if all my attempts to deflect the adviser failed, we would need to have the strategy for how I left the Royal Opera House. She looked at me as if I was mentally deficient and said, 'You're not leaving the Royal Opera House.' She is implacable.

I also got her together with Anthony Everitt so they could sort out the business of his article. I had to confide in Anthony a little more than I would have liked, telling him that things were really extremely difficult at the Royal Opera House and there was even a possibility I might have to leave. Roddy, Anthony's partner, was most solicitous near the end of the party and he and I sat in the kitchen while he asked me if I was genuinely all right. I think he thought I probably shouldn't be after all that has happened. I am not quite sure myself whether or not I am. During the party I just felt extraordinarily light-hearted at not being in London and not being at the Royal Opera House.

Nearly everybody who came asked if I was all right and said in rather incredulous tones that I shouldn't be looking nearly as well and as happy as I appeared to be.

Christopher Howes (Second Commissioner and Chief Executive of the Crown Estates) in particular, was comforting and I said that I would like to ask his advice at some point over the Christmas holidays. I would be interested to hear his views on how far I have been damaged by the Kaufman report and how I might tackle the question of my departure if it gets as bad as that. I also had a long conversation with Clare Spottiswode, Director General of Ofgas about the difficulty of being a woman in the public eye. She pointed out that if I did go in January it would inevitably be seen as a belated response to Kaufman.

Sunday 21 December

Nigel and I collapsed in front of the fire for the day.

Monday 22 December

Christmas shopping. Tescos resembled Valhalla. Excellent lunch in the Spice Bar in Woodbridge. Home and back to the fire.

Tuesday 23 December

Woke at 3.00 with all of my worries operating at full stretch. I woke Nigel and we talked for three hours about the fall-out from the Select Committee, how matters might progress once I returned to the Royal Opera House, how my resignation might be handled and perceived, and how I felt I was going to be trampled by the Establishment again. Nigel was wise enough and courageous enough not to try and reassure me. He just said that I probably would be and there was little I could do about it.

At 6.00 I drifted back to sleep and immediately started dreaming about the Royal Opera House. I was on the stage, but at the back of the stage, helping people get on and off rather than performing myself. Suddenly I could see the auditorium: all of the plush and gold leaf had been removed and it was just wood and stone work and looked rather good. I then found myself on stage, and moving across the stage and through into the auditorium. I felt reluctant to participate in this way, although in my dream I had performed – sang in fact – on the Covent Garden stage several times before.

I then moved back from the auditorium and on to the stage with two other women and we were doing a dance routine. There was the voice of a director saying that we had to involve and draw in everybody else on stage, but also to make sure that there were two distinct and separate groups. We began dancing and drawing everybody in, and the first person who came over to me was Grey Gowrie. He took my hand and suddenly we were doing a line dance out in the country. Someone else was leading – I don't know who – Grey was second and I followed on. We kept on trying to get across and through broken fences, which made it rather unenjoyable.

Suddenly I was in the anteroom to the Select Committee, which had been reconvened. I moved close to the entrance, but where I could not be seen, and overheard Kaufman questioning Nicholas Snowman about the propriety or otherwise of my appointment. Nicholas said that he thought it had been wrongly handled. I was standing next to a very tall man holding a glass of whisky and I asked him what the penalty was for heckling a Select Committee. He did not reply. I moved into the entrance and stood with my hands on my hips right in front of Kaufman looking as obvious as I could. The proceedings paused and he then said, 'The next witness is Mary Allen.'

I turned on my heel and stalked back to where I had been waiting, trying to find my papers. I couldn't find them and couldn't find anything to write on; someone loaned me something and then began to explain how things had to be written down in categories and I said, 'For heaven's sake, all I want to do is make a few notes while I am being questioned.'

I walked into the Select Committee room and found that the Committee was on a high dais, rather like a stage. The little table at which I was to sit in front of them had been pushed off to one side and I pushed it back to the centre, with all its chairs, very easily. A sheet had been drawn down between me and the audience, so they could hear but not see. I turned towards Kaufman, took a breath and immediately began shouting at him, saying that it had been a vindictive, vilifying report, that the evidence had not been properly investigated and went on knowing that I must not draw breath or pause otherwise he would interrupt me, and that if I wanted to have my say I had to do so immediately and as loudly as possible. I was remarkably coherent for a dream.

Eventually my microphone broke away from its setting – it was something I wore round my neck and I moved my head back too suddenly. Kaufman asked me a couple of questions (I can't remember what they were or what I said). I was sitting down by this stage and kept on dropping a large key-ring full of keys noisily on the table. He produced his own key-ring which had a bag-like thing attached to it as well as keys. He walked around, jangling his keys, and looking much more benign – remarkably like Norman St John Stevas. He closed the hearing and I said I would like to ask him one question, viz. if, as he said in his report, I am tackling some of the management problems why did he also recommend that I should resign? At that point I woke up. My heart was thumping, and I felt pure rage. I immediately embarked upon a fantasy about what I would say if I was recalled to give further evidence and then stopped myself after ten minutes – it was a complete waste of time.

Got up. Left for London at around midday. Arrived at the house and opened some post and then went down to have my hair done. John, my hairdresser, asked me how I had been for the last couple of weeks but was rather muted. I don't know whether it's my imagination, but I get the sense that people feel awkward when they meet me now. I am not sure whether this is because they don't know how to tackle the ghastliness of all of that terrible press coverage, or whether they believe that I have done something wrong.

We went to our friends Richard and Jenny's for dinner; I did not know many of the people there. David Spanier, the gambling correspondent for the *Independent*, sat next to me during the meal. He, like everybody else, complimented me on toughing out the Kaufman report, and said that it was essential I now went on and made a success of it. How I so wish that might be possible. I told him that there were other circumstances which might mean I had to resign. He said that that would be a disaster and I should not even contemplate doing so. I said that if I had to it might become clearer what those circumstances were, but that I couldn't say anything at the moment.

Once we went home I fell asleep immediately I sat in the car. I was exceedingly difficult to get out of it at the other end, and kept telling Nigel to go into the house and I would stay there. I discovered later that he had in fact driven half-way round London on the way home and at one point had found himself going west along the Fulham Road – an unusual route to go from Kensington to Highbury.

Wednesday 24 December

Woke up at 9.30 – nearly nine hours' sleep, easily my personal best for about seven or eight months. This must mean that I am beginning to feel more relaxed and happy. Drove back to Suffolk and did some cooking, including making the gravy for tomorrow. Read in front of the fire in the evening.

Thursday 25 December

Woke up at 7.00: seven hours' sleep this time – what a relief. Opened our presents, most of which we knew about already because we had accompanied each other when we had been buying them. And then went to church. Felt unaccountably sad during the service, and prayed in a way that I haven't for years. At the beginning of *Away in a Manger* I felt tears at the back of my eyelids and had to concentrate very hard to control myself. I also took communion – again the first time I have done so for many years.

We returned home and made lunch together. The goose did not yield nearly as much fat as I had expected, which was annoying since I had been expecting to use the goose fat for frying things in. We sat at either end of the dining room table with lots of candles between us both wearing silly hats, and were fine until about two-thirds of the way through dinner when I broke down. There is something about winter festivities that bring to the surface lost hopes and disappointments. All my hurt and humiliation at Kaufman's criticism rose to the surface and I wept for a long time. I managed to recover and then we played scrabble in front of the fire. At least the day had a nice ending.

Friday 26 December

Left at about 11.30 to go to Cambridge for lunch with our friends Andrew and Antoinette. At one point I was talking to two entertaining people – one a consultant at Addenbrooks and the other a Foreign Office civil servant – and was delighted that we had managed to talk for half an hour without referring to any of our jobs, in particular mine. Suddenly the civil servant turned to me and asked, 'Do you mind all of that terrible publicity.' I said that of course I did, and then we started talking about the Royal Opera House. I then went through to another room and had a long conversation with another senior civil servant, and the subject turned once again to the Royal Opera House.

We drifted into the kitchen where I said to Antoinette that I didn't think I could bear it for very much longer. She said that my life was more important than the job, and that if it was too grim I should leave it.

Saturday 27 December

I woke up early and spent several hours sitting on the sofa thinking about what had happened and where it had all gone wrong.

I heard the telephone ring at about 9.00 and put my hand out to pick it up thinking that no one, surely, would be ringing me on Saturday morning, the day after Boxing Day, but caution made me let the answerphone take it. I heard a man's voice talking on the answerphone in the study. About half an hour later I went through and listened to the message and it was Jim, saying that he had some urgent documents to fax me and please could I phone him immediately. I did so.

The main document was a letter to Jim from Adrian Stanway at Coopers and Lybrand, written in his capacity as adviser to the Royal Opera House Trust, saying that if I was not prepared to agree the terms of reference for the professional support adviser immediately the Board should instruct him themselves, and that the adviser had to begin work on 29 December. I spoke to Jim again and he told me that the Board wanted me to go in to the office on Monday and begin working with Pelham Allen.

Nigel and I walked in the garden for a while, as I tried to think what I should do, and then we packed up and went back to London. I felt deeply despondent. I have worked so hard to try and make the relationship with the adviser one within which I could continue to operate fully as Chief Executive, or even one that didn't have to take place at all, because a new Chairman could instill sufficient confidence in the Trust. And I have now failed.

When we reached London I wrote a letter to Jim and faxed it to him, asking for written instructions from the Board, as I felt it important that I knew exactly what they wished me to do. And also that they took some responsibility for making events happen, rather than just allowing that responsibility to drift over to the Royal Opera House Trust and the Floral Trust.

I feel more miserable than I can describe.

Sunday 28 December

Spoke to Judy Grahame and Michael Berkeley in the morning, and waited for Jim's fax, which arrived just before midday. It does indeed instruct me to go into the office and work with the Floral Trust adviser tomorrow. I phoned Jim and said that of course I would do so.

I can barely think with anxiety and not knowing what to do. I was awake most of the night and Nigel, darling Nigel, was awake with me. He just lay there holding my hand, looking at me, talking to me if I wanted to be talked to. I could not manage any of this without him.

Monday 29 December

I phoned Michael Knight at 7.30 and asked if he would come to the first part of the meeting with Pelham Allen. He agreed that he would. I phoned Judy and told her how I was feeling and she sounded quiet. I also phoned Michael Berkeley and said that things were exceptionally difficult. He sounded worried. He, Colin Nears (a Board member) and Carolyn Newbigging are all rooting for me very strongly. Bob is too. Rudi is away. Jim sits uneasily between me and Vivien, and I don't know what Vivien wants at all. Michael told me that he was persuading Vivien that I had to stay. Obviously she has been through a period of thinking the reverse. That would account for why I feel so hedged around and persecuted. In some senses it would be easier if she could just come out into the open and say that she wanted me to go and make sure I did. At least I would get out, and possibly even with some semblance of honour. This ring-holding of other people between us is the most tiring, since she has far more influence through her money than I will ever have through any other attributes.

I went into the office and met Michael at 8.45 and we spoke briefly about how to handle the meeting and then Pelham turned up at 9.00.

He walked towards me smiling with his hand outstretched and I couldn't smile at him or take his hand. I have never done that before, but there was something physical inside me stopping me. We sat around the table and analysed the brief. Michael was helpful, pointing out where the organization could be confused and even compromised if there were two of us, me and Pelham, putting different recommendations to the Board. Pelham was thoughtful and careful in his replies.

Michael left after about an hour and a half and Pelham and I went into the small office that had been Peter's. I said that I wanted to talk to him on a personal basis, so that he could understand a little more about how I felt about the whole thing. We spoke for a couple of hours and he was exceptionally helpful: clear, firm, always making it clear that he was following the instructions of his paymaster – the Floral Trust – but that he wanted to make it work if he possibly could.

During the afternoon I spoke longer with Pelham about the generality of the assignment, and then we began to talk specifically. The moment we did so it became painful. He is a man of immense energy and he has not been through what I have during the last few months. I am sure that he will be able to point to things that I haven't done, or could have done differently or better. I felt threatened, but we managed to conclude the meeting in a business-like and amiable fashion.

Tuesday 30 December

Met Pelham at 7.00 so that he could get on with some work and I could get away by midday. We spent the first part of the morning talking tactics: I think Pelham is now beginning to appreciate the difficulties of a strong Royal Opera House Trust moving in on territory that should be properly occupied by the Royal Opera House Board. As I remarked, if the Trust wished me to take a particular approach to the closure period, that is a suggestion they should make to the Board rather than instruct me directly. Pelham agreed, and we talked about how we might manage the Trust meeting on 15 January.

Left at midday and took a taxi back to the house. We had some lunch and drove back to Suffolk. Changed, and went to Tizy and James's party. Met an interesting couple, Hugh and Mary Wooley. She is an art valuer and I envied her the possession of a technical skill which allowed her to do something the practice of which she enjoyed, without the stress of management. She, conversely, envied me the capacity to seek jobs with a higher and higher degree of responsibility. I remarked rather drily that there were some heights one would prefer not to scale.

Wednesday 31 December

We cooked some Toulouse sausages for lunch and then prepared for the New Year's Eve parties. That morning I had had to sort out which one we were going to, having accepted two invitations on the night of our own party ten days earlier. We eventually agreed that we would have a drink with Clare and Christopher Howes, and then go on to Piers and Caroline Feetham.

We arrived at Clare and Christopher's. I sat on the sofa and was soon joined by Jack Phipps, an old colleague from the Arts Council, who was now working on one of the larger lottery-funded building projects. He sat down next to me on the sofa and showed me pictures of his daughter Polly and her baby, who has been given a Tibetan name meaning peace and joy. When I heard him say these words I felt desolate. I explained that I was rather fragile at the moment because of the Royal Opera House. He was sympathetic and I told him everything. He was loving and wise – he said that he had been having to work with Coopers at Milton Keynes, and the best way was to work with them, and to use them to help you, not to fight them.

We left and went down to the Feethams, where we had a quick glass of wine while waiting for them to finish getting ready, and then went along to the Goods for the first course. It was an excellent party. John and Di Huntingford were there, Nick and Penny Heath were there, Piers and Caroline, and many others. Everyone was in a terrific mood, and no one wanted to talk about the Royal Opera House. My criterion for enjoying myself socially is rapidly becoming whether or not I can get away with talking to new people without the Royal Opera House being mentioned. We then went back to the Feethams for the main course, where I sat next to someone who, although he didn't talk about the Royal Opera House, talked at inordinate length about operas he had seen. John Huntingford was on my other side. We put our arms around each other and John told me how kind he thought Nigel was. Nigel was bravely doing his stuff down the kids' end of the table.

We then walked up to the Heaths' house, where we listened to the

New Year being chimed in and raised glasses of champagne and kissed each other. Jamie, Nigel and I raised a glass to Kate, who was not with us. Then there was a lot of 60s' music that Jamie and Ben – Piers and Caroline's son – put on for the sadistic pleasure of mocking us while we danced. God knows what they do nowadays – apparently it's cool not to move at all. Can't really see the point. Unwisely, having had a large amount of champagne to drink, I too started to dance, leaning on my crutch. At times I got carried away and will no doubt pay for it tomorrow morning.

Thursday 1 January

Lunch with our friends Jack and Joan. It was good to see them, particularly since they did not want to talk about the Royal Opera House. Both of them said I was looking well. I was feeling strained and was pleased it hadn't shown on my face.

I spent the evening lying with my head against the back of the chair, half asleep drifting in and out of waking and sleeping, listening to Kate, Nigel and Jamie play scrabble and watching the fire. The open fire is one of the best things about this house. I can listen to and watch the wood and just feel the time passing. I went to bed at about midnight.

Friday 2 January

I decided to spend the day in bed, partly to rest my leg and partly because I still feel exhausted. My sense of anxiety is heightening by the day. Nigel says that this is because everything is going on at the Royal Opera House out of my control, and it is the sense of being out of control that is making me feel so anxious. I'm sure he is right, but my rational mind cannot persuade myself that my anxiety is rooted in ludicrous fantasies.

I spent the day reading. I slept towards the end of the afternoon and then got up, and we went out to Wilf and Annie's party. Contrary to my expectations of earlier in the day I enjoyed myself greatly. I met an entertaining man called Thomas Hughes-Hallet, who was wearing a brown crushed velvet jacket and his wife's chiffon scarf. I sat next to Wilf at dinner and we talked, inevitably, about the Royal Opera House and the Kaufman report. He had no explanation as to why Kaufman would have wanted to single me out in the way that he did.

When we moved places I sat next to a man who owned an antiques shop in Yoxford, where we bought a cheap table and nearly bought a very expensive chest of drawers. His wife is about to do a course in garden design. I yearn for a life of that kind, rather than the terrors of insolvency.

Saturday 3 January

Slept nearly all morning. Got up briefly to have lunch and then returned to bed for another sleep. I suppose all this sleeping must be good for me.

Went out in the evening to see John and Miranda Margetson. They had a fire blazing away in their sitting-room, which was decorated in the same way as my parents' sitting-room: velvet curtains, old rugs, chairs and sofas upholstered in different fabrics and all blending together to create an effect of cosy informality rather than stark design. We ate in the kitchen and Miranda had prepared an excellent Thai chicken curry and some Tira Misu. Sadly, my stomach was so knotted I could hardly eat a thing. We only spoke briefly and occasionally about the Royal Opera House, otherwise the conversation was general, about their children and about our plans.

We returned home and I went to bed. I thought I did not sleep, but just swam along on a river of uncertainty, but when I looked at the clock it was 4.30. I then slept for two or three hours.

Sunday 4 January

Spent the morning either sleeping or reading a Ruth Rendell novel. I got up for a late lunch and then prepared to go home. I oscillate between feeling optimistic that I will be able to cope with everything and feeling anxious about how it will all be. During the last few days there has been a sense of being cradled in a womb, as I have lain in our bedroom buffeted on three sides by very high winds and rain spattering down on the roof. The marvellous thing about our bedroom is that if you sit up in bed you can look straight out of the floor-to-ceiling window opposite. As I watched the rain sheet down over the fields the Royal Opera House seemed artificial and far away. I wish it were.

Monday 5 January

Arrived at the office fairly early and read through the faxes that Pelham had sent through the previous afternoon. They were reasonable and I had comments on both, so I rang him and he came over by about 8.45.

I am not quite sure how it happened, but I explained to him that during the previous few days I had had long chances to think, and I had realized that the way in which events had developed during the previous four months had meant I had had virtually no chance to take the organization forward, and we had been circling around in our preoccupation with insolvency. I was worried that I was beginning to fail, and that without some help I would do so. He confirmed that that was indeed likely to be the case. We found ourselves agreeing entirely new terms of reference in which he will report to me, and do several important pieces of work with which I actually need help. It was an excellent meeting. I think I have managed to find a way through that will allow me to remain, work well with Pelham, and do my job properly. I am relieved beyond words.

He returned to Coopers. I saw some people, did some paperwork and then went out to lunch with Jim Butler. It was a good lunch and we were both relatively light-hearted. We ate tuna carpaccio and scallops, and drank a bottle of Chablis. Jim was affectionate, and keen to reassure me that all of the Board members very much want me to stay on. Vivien he was not so sure about. I got the impression that during the last couple of weeks there have been periods when she has not wished me to stay, and that she was still in the middle of one of those periods.

Tuesday 6 January

Arrived in the office at 6.45 and read through the first draft that Pelham had prepared of a report on the current status of the Royal Opera House. He came in at 8.00 and we spent an hour discussing it.

We talked again about the Royal Opera House Trust Trustees, and the possibility that they might challenge my decision to allow Richard Hall to go on holiday. I said to Pelham that Richard had already had to cancel two holidays because of the Royal Opera House, one at my request last autumn. Now that the organization was more stable, and he – Pelham – was available to oversee the finance department while Richard was away, we could cope with Richard's absence for three weeks. In any case I was sure that if I did cancel another of his holidays he would resign, and the likelihood of being able to find another Finance Director for the Royal Opera House at the moment was about zero. Pelham agreed.

A two hour programming meeting. There were about a dozen or so people around the table, Nicholas, Anthony, Anthony and I having been joined by the rest of the senior management in order to discuss the proposals for the first year's programme in the new House and determine how we were going to cost it and assess its income potential. It was an unsatisfactory meeting, in the Boardroom, with everybody lounging around the huge table, separate from each other and squabbling. Judy and Keith do not like the idea of starting with *The Fairy Queen*, which they regard as an obscure and specialist work. *Mathis der Maler* only did 50 per cent at the box office last time; and why the hell were we doing *Gawain.* I said that we were doing *Gawain* because I thought it was one of the best things the Royal Opera House had ever done, and pointed out that we were also doing *Nutcracker.*

When I asked the finance department how they were planning the costing exercise for the business plan they were reluctant to be specific, saying that it would be hard to arrive at any reliable figures until we had information about, for example, the number of staff it would take to operate the new House. I said that initially we were focusing on the production costs; that we would be doing some work on staffing but that for the time being we were just going to have to make a number of assumptions. So long as people set out what their assumptions were, at least we would know where we were.

Then I met with the Planning Group to talk about the business plan. It was frustrating in many respects, and I am recognizing now the degree to which my preoccupations with insolvency during the latter part of the autumn has set back the business planning process. There are too many instances in which the working groups[86] are not certain about what they are meant to be producing, because they have been left to get on with it in a vacuum. We finished by looking at a draft skeleton outline for the business plan produced by Richard Sadler. He was diffident about it but it was first class.

I then had half an hour in which to eat my lunch before Keith came in and we talked about the Select Committee. They have asked to see Chris Smith again on 21 January to ask him about his response to its report. I asked Keith what he thought they wanted, and he said he thought they might be after me. I said I had thought the same myself. I also said I can hardly even feel alarmed at the prospect. Keith said one of the reasons he thought that was because of the piece Rodney Milnes had written in *Opera* magazine. I had seen it the previous day: it was most unpleasant and headed something like 'One down and one to go'. Keith also said that he got the impression

[86] These were the staff groups that I had set up soon after I had arrived.

Vivien seemed to be against me.

He asked how Vivien and I were getting on and I said not well. He said that she had phoned him for a gossip and I asked what she had been saying. He prevaricated a little and said that she was in one of her moods in which she felt that all the staff ought to go. I said, 'Oh, you mean her, "Off with their heads!" mood.' He agreed. He also began to indicate that she had been asking him questions about me and whether or not he supported me. I said to him that I had already been thinking she might be trying to get me out of the job and therefore he shouldn't feel anxious about telling me things that would upset me – I knew them all already.

We also talked a little about Ian Albery. Keith had met him the day before, and he had expressed an adamant determination not to yield an inch in any direction to Harvey Goldsmith and me when we negotiate with him on Friday about changes to the Sadler's Wells contract.

Then went into a three-hour meeting of the senior management about the closure programme. It juddered and jerked and stopped and started as we moved from one difficult item to another, resolving whether or not to cancel things, or how we would market them. I am trying to cancel an orchestral tour to America, on the basis that it increases the *Dance Bites* costs. Nicholas asked whether we should be doing *Tosca* with Raymond Gubbay. Having indicated he was not that keen, he then fought bitterly when it was suggested we cancel it.

I then had a session with Mike Morris. He, too, has heard that Nicholas is on the short-list for the ENO job: apparently the interviews are tomorrow.

I went up to see Richard Hall and mentioned his holiday, and he launched off for about half an hour into an account of how anybody who worked at the Royal Opera House had their definitions of 'sanity', 'stress' and 'crisis' bent into entirely new concepts. I agreed with him, and said that of course I would not be asking him to cancel his holiday.

I went home, and told Nigel it was quite possible I would not last for long. I feel it will not be many weeks before I have to go, one way or another. Either Kaufman will call for my resignation again, in a way that makes it impossible for me to stay any longer. Or something else will happen. Or I will just feel too tired. But I won't give in until I am forced to. I am too curious. I want to know the end of the plot.

Wednesday 7 January

Arrived at 7.00 and read the Sadler's Well contract through, carefully, from one end to the other. Harvey came in at 8.00 and we went through it. Virtually every second line he was raising his hands in the air and saying, 'My God, this is the worst contract I have ever seen.' He said there was no point in arguing about the detail, but the fundamental principle underlying it was that we had been screwed to the wall by Sadler's Wells. He began saying that the only thing worth doing was to threaten to pull out of it. I said we needed to be careful because we wouldn't be able to carry through that threat, since if we pulled out of it we would not be able to perform for over a year.

Harvey asked what was wrong with that, and I said it would mean that the Arts Council grant would probably not be paid, which would mean that we would become insolvent immediately. He thought that that was probably the best thing and we ought to go into administration. I explained that everybody felt the same, but actually what would then happen was that the whole thing would come to a complete halt for years.

Unlike many of the other people who have been expressing a desire to go into administration, Harvey seemed to understand the sequence of events that would follow and why it was all so destructive. Like everyone else he hates to be trapped, but at least he recognizes that that's where we might have to stay: trapped.

Jim Butler came in at 11.00 to go through the agenda for the afternoon's Board meeting. Now that James Spooner has gone, a chairman for the meeting has to be agreed: it is virtually certain to be Jim, although Vivien still wants it to be Bob. Vivien and Bob were round at the DCMS hearing officially who the new Chairman is to be.[87] Unofficially nearly every Board member has told me that it will be Sir Colin Southgate. I have not met him and know virtually nothing about him. Jim and I agreed that Pelham would join the meeting after the terms of reference for the support adviser had been agreed, and would remain for the rest of it.

The meeting began at 2.30, with Vivien being chippy about the new Chairman. At one stage she referred to him as 'our little miracle-worker'. She and I crossed swords once, about the Edinburgh Festival, when I said that we would be going even without the sponsorship, because it was cheaper to go than not to go. She referred to a previous Board minute, when it had been agreed that without the sponsorship we would not go. I referred to the fact that a year ago the Board had authorized Nicholas to book up the season, and said that we now knew we would incur £150,000 of further losses if we cancelled at this stage.

Richard then took us through his six or seven linked papers on the development, its financing, and the sale of the retail properties. They were excellent papers, and enabled us to have a quick discussion, after which Richard, Pelham and I left so that the Board could discuss the new Chairman and the new Board.

Thursday 8 January

Arrived at the office at 9.30, wrapped my mother's birthday present, had a few words with Pelham, who was moving in to share the office

[87] Although the Royal Opera House Board has been criticized for being 'a self-appointed oligarchy', it is normal practice for the Trustees of a charity (and all subsidized arts organizations are charities) to appoint their fellow Trustees. It was not possible for Board members to be appointed by the Government, unless the Royal Opera House was also to be directly funded by the Government, which was not being proposed. In fact, in this instance, because of the criticism, most of the Board members were reluctant to be involved in the new appointment, and I believe Sir Colin Southgate's name was put forward by Chris Smith. Colin was formally appointed by the Board at a meeting during the following week.

opposite with Richard Sadler, spoke to Judy briefly and then had a pre-meeting with Sheila Forbes, Mike and Richard Sadler.

Sheila is quite clear that we cannot go through a consultative staffing exercise more than once. Until we know the outcome of the Eyre review, and whether or not we are going to split into two companies and a receiving house, we should not engage the staff on any bottom-up planning. However we agreed there was quite a lot of investigative work she could do before that, finding out how things operate at present and looking at the existing union agreements.

We then had a meeting with Sheila and the full senior management on the subject of staffing in the new House, during which a considerable amount of anxiety was expressed about re-negotiating the union agreements. Anthony Russell-Roberts said that he was beginning to talk to staff. I cut across him and asked whether he was involving Mike Morris, and he said that, well, it wasn't really that kind of talking. I said that I advised against *any* kind of talking so as not to raise expectations. Mike said afterwards that he was angry, and that Anthony had not mentioned anything at all to him. I went round to see Anthony later and said firmly that he must not talk to any of the dancers without involving Mike.

After lunch a meeting of the inner core of the Development Steering Group, comprising John Seekings, John Fairclough, Stuart Lipton and Kit McMahon. They were talking in a rather vague fashion about authority and it was only near the end of the meeting that I understood that what they actually wanted was for me to become more re-engaged with the development project now that the operating finances were secure. I said that I would certainly do that.

But until I know my position with the new Chairman I feel as though I am suspended in limbo. I'm sure that is partly why I feel so disengaged.

Friday 9 January

Richard Hall and I met Pelham: in addition to briefing him, prior to Richard's holiday, we discussed how we were going to manage the rapid transformation of the finance department with Richard away for three weeks. Pelham told me afterwards that Richard had been uncomfortable during a similar discussion the previous evening, but that he now seems to have accepted that there are some important issues about the leadership of the project with which he needs to be happy before he goes away.

Then, at 11.00, Harvey and Ian Albery turned up. It was nice to see Ian again. He folded me in a big hug, stepping on my foot as he did so, and then sat down. Harvey managed the meeting carefully, courteous most of the time, with an occasional foray into a raised voice and, 'How dare you even think of doing . . .' whatever it was. Ian surprised – even shocked – me and Harvey with his saga of how the contract had originally been negotiated, who had been involved and at what points. Apparently during the final stages of the negotiations there had been at times eight people from the Royal Opera House facing him around the table. He said that the only person with whom he had had discussions who had known anything about theatrical contracts was Jenny McIntosh, and no sooner had she made some progress than the Board had waded in and taken over.

We did not end up very far along the road. Harvey and I said that we would see if we could squeeze more performances out of the earlier weeks in each season, and in turn we would ask Ian to allow us to have access to a larger number of the tickets for those nights. After Ian had gone I reminded Harvey that I was proposing to chop off the final two months of the season, and replace a month of opera with ballet. I think Harvey had forgotten that. He said it would make it rather more difficult to negotiate with Ian. I said yes, but it would save us £150,000, considerably more than the amount of money we would gain through the kinds of marginal adjustments to the contract we had been discussing.

Lunch with Tom Sutcliffe, the Opera critic of the *Evening Standard*, who was far keener to tell me what he thought about the Royal Opera House than to ask me about my views, and then back to a meeting with Mike Morris. Mike always gives me a feeling of solid dependability. He is a tough person and I admire that.

Caught the train back to Suffolk and was in the house by 6.30. Then Judy rang me and said that one of the Sunday newspapers had contacted her about the Ombudsman's report on the dealings between the Arts Council and The Kosh.[88] Did I remember this? I said, yes, it had been about four years ago, and that most of the business had taken place some time before I took over as Secretary-General of the Arts Council. Judy said that, yes, the newspaper was aware of that but intended to play it as though it had all been my fault. They had some space to fill and wanted to create a story about me. I pointed out to Judy that I had nothing to do with these events and I could not be held responsible for them. She said that may be the case but, nonetheless, the paper wanted to get me. Apparently nobody else connected with the relationship between The Kosh and the Arts Council was of any public interest any longer, no one else was in the limelight, and I was the one who would make a good story.

I spoke to Graham Devlin later in the evening, who confirmed that the report's conclusions were mild, and although he had not read the main body of the report he therefore assumed that that would be too, and that there was only one mention of me, in relation to a letter that I had written to The Kosh, at the end of the whole affair, saying that enough was enough. I have promised Judy I will speak to the newspaper tomorrow.

[88] The Kosh was a dance company funded by the Arts Council. Several years earlier the Arts Council had reduced its grant, a controversial decision against which the company appealed. When the appeal failed the company had gone to the Ombudsman through their MP who – coincidentally – was Chris Smith.

Saturday 10 January

Decided I was going to spend the entire day doing absolutely nothing that required any effort whatsoever.

Spent the morning in bed and took a couple of calls from Judy. During the second one she told me the story had been spiked. God knows how she did it.

Got up at lunchtime and walked around the garden with Nigel. It was sunny and still. The grass is growing and the plants are too far advanced. No doubt in three or four weeks' time there will come a savage frost and all the delicate new growths will be burnt and killed. We watched a fox-hunt. We could see the fox quite clearly, running over the fields while the huntsmen faced the other way.

We spent the afternoon in front of the fire, listening to music and dozing, then a game of scrabble, which I refused to finish because my letters were so dismal. I was rather abashed when Nigel did finish, both hands, and I would have lost by only fifteen points. This confirms that Nigel is much better at scrabble than I am. More dozing in front of the fire and listening to music for the rest of the evening. To bed by midnight.

Sunday 11 January

A reprise of Saturday – in bed until midday, up for a brief lunch and then lying in front of the fire dozing and listening to music. During this weekend I have freed myself entirely from all pressure and just floated along. All I would like now is to be able to leave the job with honour, spend a month or so recovering, and then find a way of working with Nigel. It seems like so much more of a rewarding way in which to live. For lunch Nigel cooked a roast leg of lamb – very rare – and we had potatoes and vegetables. He also made some excellent gravy. Just the act of him cooking it and us eating it was so pleasurable.

Monday 12 January

Got up at 5.00 and we drove back to London, getting caught up in long delays. Finally reached the office at 8.45 and I opened my diary to see that I should have been having breakfast with Geoffrey Sterling at 8.00. This is a meeting that has already been cancelled three times. I phoned his office and explained that I had been caught up in an accident on the M11. We rearranged.

Nicholas gave me his resignation, saying that he had accepted the General Directorship of ENO. I said that I was very pleased indeed for him, but sad for the Royal Opera House. Although it will be a loss in some respects, I also think it will be an opportunity for us to think about the possibility of having a single artistic director. But of course it all depends on how we restructure.

Judy and I met at 4.30 and talked, among other things, about the possible announcement of Colin Southgate as the new Chairman. It is definite, as long as the Board agrees him tonight.

Tuesday 13 January

Arrived at the office at 8.00 and read Pelham's briefing document that he has been preparing for the Royal Opera House Trust. I then phoned Michael Berkeley, who told me that the Board meeting last night had been positive in that it had agreed Colin Southgate's appointment as Chairman, but otherwise confused and inconclusive in that the Board did not wish to have an active role in his appointment or the announcement of it. I said to Michael that we had to put some dynamite under this process and that we couldn't allow the Board to faff around now. Colin and I needed to meet, he should sort out anything he wanted to with the Secretary of State, and we should then go ahead with an immediate announcement about him.

Colin Southgate came in at 1.30 and the moment I set eyes on him I liked him enormously. He is a physically large man, with a loud deep voice that cuts right through to the heart of issues. We spent about an hour and a half together, and I tried to combine anecdote with briefing in order to provide him with a sense of what it would be like at the Royal Opera House.

I offered him my resignation, on the basis that a public report had recommended it. He rejected it, saying that if I was going to go it would be because it was what he wanted, not because of 'some idiot like Kaufman'. He said he was going to ask Chris Smith to set aside £10 million as a contingency for the Royal Opera House. I stared at him and could not stop myself from bursting into laughter. He also wanted to do an insolvency check before deciding whether or not to accept the job. I impressed upon him the urgency of his decision, because – apart from Chris Smith's desire to have a full Board in place before he goes in front of Kaufman next week – the organization was in danger of disintegrating. He accepted that, but nonetheless said he wanted to put all his own checks in place first. He also wants an indemnity from the Government if he is to take over the chairmanship of an organization that could be – or could become – bankrupt. I'll be surprised if they agree that.

Later in the day I spoke to Colin again and heard that he had not had much satisfaction from Chris Smith on the question of the £10 million contingency. He now seems to be keen to announce sooner rather than later, pending discussions with Vivien, John Eatwell (an economist and President of Queen's College, Cambridge, and who had been closely involved with several dance organizations) – one of Chris's favourite candidates for the Board – and, at my suggestion, Michael Berkeley. I would like to announce soon.

It is an odd feeling at the moment. We might be about to enter a period in which we will have much firmer governance and leadership and I will get the support I have been needing. It could be exciting. However the figures are still so dreadful that it is going to need a great deal of both effort and will, in terms of fund-raising and cost-control, to make it through to the end of the closure period.

I am still feeling passive, although not so tired. At the moment I just want someone to come in and give me proper support.

Maybe it will work. Hard to tell at the moment. I have the glimmerings of some optimism. At least now I have the sense of a strong and powerful presence beside me, who could help me make the organization function properly.

Wednesday 14 January

Arrived at the office at 7.00 in order to go through Pelham's briefing paper. There have been one or two changes made by Bob and Jim, notably a reference to making radical revisions to the closure programme. I told Pelham that the Board has already rejected that option and it will be up to Colin whether he wishes to revisit it.

We met Jim at 8.00. He was anxious about the Royal Opera House Trust meeting tomorrow and gave me the impression that discussions have been going on of which I am unaware. We adjusted the drafting so as to remove the implication of radical change, but kept in the material about making savings where possible.

What I find so frustrating is that neither the Board nor the Trust appear to believe that Richard Hall and I have already made all savings possible.

At 10.00 we went through the paper with Bob, who picked up on the references to external advisers. I am increasingly coming to realize that the Board did not take in any of the substantive recommendations that I presented to them in my paper at the end of October. They appear to have no recollection of what they authorized me to do. I reminded him about the restructuring exercise, and the fact that I had said I would be employing external advisers to help me with it.

Went to *Cinderella* in the evening. The show looked good on the Festival Hall stage, although when I went on stage afterwards it seemed a very small space for so many people dancing. Met Andrea Quinn, the new Music Director for the Royal Ballet, and had a drink with Anthony Russell-Roberts in the interval. Also bumped into Anthony Dowell, who continues to tell me to get something done about my knee. It has not got any better, and I will have to recognize that it will not improve of its own accord.

Thursday 15 January

Got up in a leisurely fashion. Judy rang me saying that she had read a draft of Anthony Everitt's article, and on no account must I let my name be associated with it.

At 2.30 Melanie Leech and Nigel Copeland came to my office, and they made it quite clear there was no question of an indemnity for Colin. I rang him, pulling him out of a meeting, and told him. We had a vigorous conversation for about ten minutes, during which he expressed himself forcefully on the subject of the Government, the Arts Council, and the public sector in general. I said, 'That might be how you feel, but you're still not going to get an indemnity.' He said he would not do the job.

Melanie spoke to Hayden. I spoke to Hayden. Melanie spoke to Hayden again. Hayden spoke to Colin. Possibly Cólin spoke to Chris. Anyway, Colin rang me later in the afternoon to say that he obtained a letter of comfort and was happy to go ahead. I asked Judy to confirm the arrangements for Colin to meet the press later in the day.

Colin had also said he was very unhappy about a piece in the press that had suggested there might be a conflict of interest between his EMI work and that with the Royal Opera House. I thought, but did not say, 'If you think that's bad you have a shock in store.' I hope he is not going to be too thin-skinned about the press – and indeed about difficulties in general.

We had the Royal Opera House Trust meeting at 5.00. Peter Davis came up to me at the beginning and said that David Davies had wished to amend the minutes, but that he – Peter – did not wish to discuss it at the meeting. I said I was happy to let it go. We presented the report, which went down well, and then Adrian Stanway gave his view as adviser to the Royal Opera House Trust. He said that the

Trust ought to take out security if it was to give any further funds to the Royal Opera House development. Several Trustees pointed out that the Trust was merely a conduit for funds, and that it was the Trustees' duty to give the money to the development since it had been given to the Trust specifically – and solely – for that purpose. Then another Trustee commented that the Trust had a moral duty to the donors not to give money to something that might be going bust. Someone else remarked that there was a moral duty to the contractors – not to mention the donors – not to take action which would ensure that the thing did go bust. Stanway continued to comment lugubriously about security. I couldn't wait to leave for the press conference.

First there were photographs, in the shabbiest part of our offices, with both Colin and I leaning against a pile of crates, and then we went in to meet the arts correspondents. He was good: charming, although relatively inarticulate. In particular he made a funny but unfortunate remark about not wanting to sit next to someone in a singlet, shorts and a pair of smelly trainers. Judy and I looked at each other. That will be the headline in tomorrow's papers. Michael Berkeley was there as well and Colin made it clear that he very much wanted Michael to stay on, which will have pleased Michael.

Then Colin went out to be filmed, and I took over the hot seat and provided much more detail about how we had nearly gone bust in the autumn and how we had dug ourselves out of the difficulties. The journalists went, I had a drink with Dalya Alberge from *The Times*, then I went home.

Nigel and I went out to dinner at Galiano's and I had their delicious scampi. They are cooked well, in a very light cream sauce, with thin slivers of mushroom.

Friday 16 January

Met Pelham at 8.00 and he told me that the amendment to the Trust minutes was critical of my conduct at the previous meeting. I made a note to ring Peter Davis later in the day.

Pelham and I met with Liam and Chris Sammes, who had been brought in by Richard Hall to help improve our financial procedures, and we went through Chris's proposals to change the way in which we monitor costs. They are good. I know that Richard has been bogged down in insolvency considerations for most of the last few months, but I wish he could have made a little more progress on some of these issues to do with financial controls. It has taken Chris Sammes only two weeks to come up with his ideas. When Chris and Liam had left, Pelham made a similar comment to me.

I then went down to the ballet company for physiotherapy. Lucy rubbed my knee, flexed it, made me stand, made me bend it and told me it probably wasn't cartilage but an inflamed tendon – apparently there is one that runs in front of the kneecap. She gave me the name of a doctor, told me to put ice on my knee for fifteen minutes each day, and to take a course of Nurofen. She also gave me ultrasound.

Back to the office. Sandwiches and then Bernard came in. He was gloomy about Nicholas's departure, and wanted to know more about the new chairman. I reassured him that we could survive if Nicholas went, and there were not going to be any cancellations of his major pieces during the autumn. He was surprised at that.

During the afternoon I phoned Peter Davis, who confirmed that the amendment was indeed critical and he would send it to me on Monday. I said that criticism was fine as long as it was accurate, and Peter implied that it wasn't. Peter also said that we had to stop having these nonsensical meetings, of which there is going to be another in February.

Colin came in to see me, after spending an hour and a half with Nicholas trying to persuade him to stay. I was slightly taken aback by that as I hadn't realized, when he had said he was going to speak to Nicholas, that it would be in person, for so long, and with that end in mind. I thought I had made it clear to Colin that although Nicholas's departure would be a loss in some respects, it was also an opportunity and we could achieve a great deal in terms of the development of the artistic philosophy and direction of the Royal Opera

House. Colin said he thought it wouldn't look good if Nicholas went at the same time as he arrived. I thought to myself that it might not, but that was in the short term whereas surely we had to be looking at what would be good for the Royal Opera House in the long term.

He then began talking about prospective Board members, and mentioned a number of people, all of whom were men. I said that in my experience, groups of this kind functioned better when there are roughly equal numbers of men and women.

'It's almost impossible to find women for non-executive positions: they're not tough enough,' he replied.

I told him that I knew a number of very tough women and, if he would find it helpful, I could give him a list of names.

'No, women can't be tough without being emotional.'

I roared with laughter. 'That's rich, coming from a man. Most of the emotion I have encountered at meetings comes from men and not from women.'

'Ah, yes, but that's because we have bigger hearts.'

Well, he can't have it both ways.

He grew tetchy after that exchange and talked about the development being late. I said that it was on time and on budget and he said 'Well, building projects are always late aren't they.' I said that Glyndebourne hadn't been and he said that yes but that was being built in the middle of the countryside. I said he should stop listening to outsiders and start talking to those who were actually managing the work, so he could form his own view. The most destructive thing about the Royal Opera House were self-fulfilling prophecies that everything would go wrong, and that it was his job to try and build up confidence rather than side with the whingers. He said, 'Well, if that's what you want why are you suggesting it would be all right if Nicholas went?' Altogether not a very satisfactory meeting.

Colin left and then phoned me about half an hour later to say that his wife was being doorstepped by the *Mirror*, who wanted to know what she thought people should wear to the opera. He wanted me to stop it. Get rid of them. I said I would do my best. I spoke later to Judy, who said yes, she had had the same message, and he was saying that if it was going to be like this then he wouldn't do the job. I hope he won't be too over-anxious and too sensitive to press comment.

Caught the train to Ipswich and a taxi home and felt a sense of physical pleasure as I walked into the sitting-room. I lit a fire and sat on the sofa, staring at the fire and feeling the tension drain away. I put on the Eddie Cogdon CD and listened to the jazz and read my book. Heaven.

Saturday 17 January

Stayed in bed until midday. Walked around the garden. Had some lunch. Lit a fire and sat in front of it. Snoozed a bit. Woke up and watched the fire some more and read my book. Snoozed some more. Went to bed.

Sunday 18 January

Woke up feeling lethargic. At the moment I feel I don't really care what happens, either to me or to the Royal Opera House. I feel apathetic, listless, lacking in energy, and with no enthusiasm or excitement about anything. It is as though having fought for so long last year, I have just run out of steam.

Monday 19 January

Michael Knight and Philip Heatherington came to see me at 11.00, in order to take me through their various structural options. There are three: the integrated whole; fragmentation (the Royal Opera House becoming like the Royal Albert Hall and the two companies separating from it entirely); and partial separation, with the two companies becoming resident but independent.

Went to *Figaro*. What a good show. Went round backstage

afterwards and congratulated everybody and then went to the party. Sat next to Patrick Young, the director, and stayed until about two in the morning. I should have been feeling exhausted but instead felt exhilarated.

Tuesday 20 January

Got up early after about four hours' sleep and into the office by 6.45. Stumped around Covent Garden trying to find a coffee shop open. Eventually persuaded the Seattle Coffee House to sell me a quadruple espresso, even though it wasn't yet open. Delicious . . . and after about thirty minutes began to feel an enormous caffeine high coming on.

Had planning meetings all day, and managed to conduct myself relatively calmly, even though the caffeine was making me feel as though I wanted to dance on the table.

During the afternoon, Nicholas wanted various decisions about *Tosca*, but without being able to give me sufficient information about the costs. I emphasized that I was not prepared to take decisions without having all of the details about the costs, speaking with a slight edge – if he is thinking about staying he needs to know what he will be staying with.

Someone remarked today that Pelham looks exactly like Tintin. He does.

Wednesday 21 January

Went to see Mr Strachan, a knee and joint specialist, at 8.30 – a brief meeting during which he confirmed he thought it was cartilage. He is going to book me in for a scan.

Back to the office. Various meetings until I went to see Angela Bernstein, a Royal Ballet School Governor. I thanked her for all her continuing good wishes and support. She told me what had been going on at the Royal Ballet School, and then about Gerry Robinson and what he might wish to do at the Arts Council. I told her my one or two more radical ideas for the Arts Council.

Then back to a variety of meetings, following which I went to Deborah Bull's book launch party. Deborah, a principal with the Royal Ballet, had written a fitness and diet book. It looked excellent, she exquisite and I enjoyed myself talking to a number of Royal Opera House staff.

Thursday 22 January

A meeting with Colin at 8.00 which left me feeling more positive than I have at any time since joining the Royal Opera House, and virtually for a year. Left the meeting feeling as though I was walking on air. I was impressed by his sense of clarity, his apparent ability to get things done, and his desire to get the right people in the right place.

Met John Sainsbury mid-morning, in order to hear his views on the opening programme – he does not like the idea of the Royal Ballet's first performance being *Nutcracker* and wants a more adventurous triple bill.

Went to the South Bank Show awards; met Tina Brown (then editor of the *The New Yorker*) on the way in and had a long talk with her and then talked to Peter Mandelson. Sat next to Anthony Whitworth-Jones at lunch. I asked Anthony what he wanted to do next year once he had left Glyndebourne, and he gave me a long list of things such as travelling round Europe and learning various sports and skills. Obviously not very persuadable to take over from Nicholas. We won the opera award with *The Turn of the Screw.*

Friday 23 January

Spent the morning with Colin and Pelham at EMI. It was a difficult meeting in some respects, inasmuch as Pelham and I were both trying to take the lead. He mentioned it afterwards, and we agreed that we were managing a difficult relationship remarkably well.

Went to the *Stage*'s new year party, where I saw Graham Devlin. He is looking like a live human being for the first time in months.

Colin came to see me after speaking again to Nicholas and said that he was moderately hopeful but no more of keeping him. Got the train back to Suffolk. The usual thing: fire, music, Nigel, relaxation.

Saturday 24 January

Got up late and went to Woodbridge, looked around various antique shops, did some shopping and then had lunch in the Spice Bar.

Sunday 25 January

Got up relatively early and looked around the garden. Cooked a lamb casserole for lunch, with flageolet beans and skinned cherry tomatoes and little green beans in with the lamb. Delicious. Particularly with Nigel's mashed potatoes.

Monday 26 January

Spent the morning thinking about the closure plans. Colin has indicated that he will be asking for a major review of them and, if possible, will try to get out of the Sadler's Wells contract. If he really is prepared to do that, I felt we should think again about the possibility of going to the Lyceum. Although the figures would be tight, given that we would be paying for two theatres during the period from October this year to the summer of next,[89] it might just work if we

[89] If the Royal Opera House had not gone to Sadler's Wells it was intended that the contract should nonetheless be paid in full, unless Sadler's Wells were able to mitigate the loss.

were able to negotiate a reasonably cheap rent for the Lyceum, given that the seating capacity was so much greater. I discussed the possibility with Pelham and we decided it was definitely worth putting together some prototype budgets. Rang Bob Scott and discovered that the Lyceum was still available. I will get people working on new plans quickly over the next few days so we can see if it is a runner. Agreed to see Bob Scott tomorrow.

Went down to the House of Lords at 6.00 in order to meet John Eatwell and had an amiable hour and a half in the House of Lords' bar. John and I talked about a number of issues relating to the Ballet Board, the kind of people we wanted on it and what we wanted it to do. We also talked about the two Anthonys, and how we might toughen them up; and some visits we would like to make to Paris and Frankfurt. John also wants to go to San Francisco.

When I got home I read the transcript of Chris Smith's evidence to the Select Committee. Kaufman's remarks about me have become even more outrageous, saying that I 'got the job' and 'hid it from Lord Gowrie'. Considered the transcript for some time before going to bed.

Tuesday 27 January

Woke up and found that Nigel had begun drafting an excellent letter to Kaufman. Spent an hour in bed reading papers. Up at 6.00, into the office by 7.00.

Programming Meeting at 9.00 once again attended by all the senior management group. We looked at the 00/01 schedule for the new House main stage, which is a better balance of rep than that for 99/00. We also had a presentation from Keith on pricing and marketing. It worried me, partly because there was nothing about marketing, and partly because of the notion that, instead of a subscription scheme, we should have a season ticket scheme, for which people booking tickets pay a premium. I cannot believe that our audiences will want to do this.

Bob Scott came to see me at 2.00, with David Rogers, to talk about a possible rent for the Lyceum. They tried to draw me into a negotiation but I refused and said that I would come back with an offer.

Then went into the senior management meeting. Most of the senior management group are interested – some of them bordering on the excited – at the possibility of going to the Lyceum. Colin joined us near the end of the afternoon and he had an hour with the senior management.

Returned home. Nigel and I went out to supper at Galiano's. When we returned I fiddled around with the letter to Kaufman. I am fed up with being the scapegoat. I am feeling tired and cross.

Wednesday 28 January

Spent the morning in a meeting with Vivien, Jackie, Keith and Jane Kaufmann. We talked about the notion of a 'ladder of giving' and the desirability of having a single set of coherent schemes ranging from Friends' membership to being a Premium Member of the Trust, with each category of member receiving benefits that are commensurate with the level of their payment.

At lunchtime went to see the Lyceum. *Jesus Christ Superstar* was rehearsing, so we couldn't go on stage, but Bob Scott showed me over the auditorium, the various hospitality rooms, and the dressing rooms.

Thursday 29 January

Went for my scan at 8.00. I was laid out on a platform, with my knee held immobile, and then the platform was electrically slid into a tube. Apparently the tube comprises a large magnet. I had earphones and was being played Vivaldi very loudly through them, but the moment the noise started I couldn't hear the music at all. The noise, apparently, is what makes the hydrogen atoms in my body go into different patterns, which then enables the technicians to take pictures of my knee across various planes. It was phenomenally loud. I felt as though I was lying in the middle of a battlefield. The whole process lasted about forty minutes. Later in the day I spoke to someone in the office who said that he had had a brain scan, which means that your head is in the middle of the tube and you cannot even wear the earphones.

I came back from the scan, and sent my letter to Kaufman, together with a number of documents, including the Arts Council's initial press release about my appointment; a copy of Lord Gowrie's letter to the *Times*; a copy of Lord Gowrie's statement to the Arts Council; and a copy of the relevant section of the Edward Walker-Arnott report. These make it plain that his – Kaufman's – comments about me were inaccurate. I have asked him to print my letter in the report which includes Chris Smith's evidence, in order to set the record straight. I also sent copies to the Arts Council and the DCMS, as well as to all the other members of the Select Committee.

Continued working on my notes for the Board discussion about the closure plans, and whether or not we go to the Lyceum.

Colin came at 1.30 and we talked through the Board papers and his impression of the Royal Opera House to date. He said that the general buzz on the street was that I was damaged goods, partly because of the Kaufman report and partly because I had come to the Royal Opera House from the Arts Council. When he had finished talking I said to him that every Chairman had the right to choose their own Chief Executive, that he – Colin – had not chosen me and that if he wished to have someone else I would step aside. He replied rather vaguely that he hadn't yet decided what kind of Chief Executive he wanted.

The Board meeting went on for hours. The discussion about closure was good, and the Board members gave strong support to my Lyceum idea.

Went off to *Figaro*, and arrived just after the show had gone up. Found Nigel and we had a drink in the bar, waiting for the interval. Saw the second half and it was just as good as I had remembered. Went round afterwards with Colin on to the stage for the party.

Friday 30 January

A long meeting with the senior management group about the Lyceum, during which I made it clear to Keith that I wanted marketing plans as well as pricing schedules and ticket income forecasts.

The results of the scan have come through: it is cartilage, and I will need to have an operation. It has been planned for Tuesday.

I'm in a better mood at the moment. I feel that I am in a win/win situation – either I leave the Royal Opera House with honour and dignity (and I believe that Colin would allow me that honour and dignity) or I stay at the Royal Opera House and we really have a good go at it. I would far rather the latter. I cannot say how much I would enjoy working at the Royal Opera House with the authority of the Board and Colin behind me, and *really* starting to make things happen.

Saturday 31 January

Nigel drove me down to Marble Arch, where I bought some clothes at Marks and Spencer. My bad knee means that I am getting even less exercise than usual and I have begun putting on weight. I need to start wearing clothes of the proper size, rather than trying to squeeze myself into my normal clothes. I am eleven stone, and a size 16.

Sunday 1 February

Stayed in bed until 10.00 and then cleared out the study, cleared out my filing, cleared out my clothes, and cleared my files from the old computer. Then I cooked a pheasant casserole with several vegetables. I was feeling energetic, positive and optimistic.

Monday 2 February

Spent the morning reading the marketing papers that have been produced by Keith's working groups.[90] The main thrust of the work has focused on existing audiences: members, Friends, and loyalty schemes. Interestingly, the best thinking about new audiences, and the activities of selling and marketing, came from Sofie Mason's group – Sofie is not in the marketing department but sells advertising space for the programmes.

The operation has been put back until Tuesday week.

To *The Enchantress* in the evening. Scintillating performances from orchestra, chorus and soloists. There was a Drogheda dinner afterwards. I managed to get away before the pudding and the speeches, as I had taken the precaution of booking a taxi for midnight. I exaggerated my limp as I made for the door.

Tuesday 3 February

Arrived as early as I could bear so that I could finally sort out all of my 'hot' files – those about immediate matters that I kept in my desk drawer. I spread everything out on the table and into about thirty or forty piles.

The Programming Meeting – still involving the full senior management – intervened, and we had a flaccid discussion about the studio theatre. Into the Planning Group, where we continued discussing the studio theatre and looked at some prototype budgets, prepared from information provided by Anthony and Nicholas. I

[90] Keith had been in charge of all the groups working on ticket pricing and new audiences.

was astonished when I saw that some of the production budgets had been put in at £60,000. These are far too large. I remarked that I had run something very similar in size to the Studio Theatre, and to have a cost base of £2.5 million, excluding all of the basics such as heating and lighting, was absurd. The discussion led us on to the artistic priorities for the studio theatre, which have in the past been described as the same as those for the main House but in miniature. I said that we needed to be tackling the whole question of programming the Studio Theatre in quite a different way, and that I would discuss it with John Eatwell and Michael Berkeley, as well as the Arts Council.

Then cleared up the remainder of my piles of paper. Everything is now impeccably in order, and I feel fully in control. I am starting to enjoy myself.

Wednesday 4 February

Spent several hours thinking about the marketing department in the morning. The whole thing needs to be restructured – and urgently. Unless we can start selling more tickets soon we shall be facing yet another financial crisis. We also need to introduce some radical new thinking into sales and marketing for the new theatre. We *must* attract new audiences. I would expect that the novelty value of the new theatre would mean that attendances will be very high for the first year or two, which means that we will be able to bring down ticket prices and still bump up earned income. But it is essential we get the marketing right.

A Friends meeting at lunchtime, to which Colin and I both contributed, with many interesting comments from the Friends about the relationship between the Friends, the Trust and the House's own marketing efforts and the need to brainstorm about linking it all together. It is always a pleasure when different parts of an organization start to have the same idea simultaneously – I have another ladder of giving meeting, with Jane, Jackie, Keith, Phyllida et al. next week, where we can sort all of this out.

Then Colin and I went to my office. He sat down.

'I have shown the Sadler's Wells contract to my solicitor who says I have only two options: I can either sue the Arts Council or sue the old Board. Well, I'm hardly going to sue the old Board, so I'll sue the Arts Council,' he began.

I wasn't entirely sure whether he was serious. 'I wouldn't advise suing the Arts Council: they're very careful about the way in which they conduct their relationships with clients. In any case, the Arts Council wasn't responsible for the fact that the Royal Opera House signed that contract, the Board was.'

Colin became irritated with me.

'The Arts Council's a *useless* organization – of course it was their responsibility.'

'Colin, it is entirely up to you whom you sue and how you go about it, I am just trying to offer you some advice,' I said.

'Well I don't want your advice,' he replied.

'But Colin, I have been working for five years on the relationship between the Arts Council and the Royal Opera House, and I know where the pressure points are and how you might be able to take effective action – are you sure you don't want me to advise you?'

'No, I don't want any advice at all,' he said, with some emphasis.

Mike Morris had come in to my office during this exchange and was looking horrified.

Michael Knight and Philip Heatherington then came into my office. They said afterwards the atmosphere had been electric. I sat us all down, went through a short introduction and then handed over to Michael. I watched Colin's body language and saw him unwind, as Michael's soft, careful presentation began to soothe him. We went through everything Michael had covered with me the previous week, talking about the different ways in which the organization could be structured – integrated, separated, or fragmented – and Colin made it clear from the beginning that he was only interested in one option: the integrated option. Michael made numerous references about how good it was that both he – Colin – and I had the same view, and how well it would enable us to work together. I wondered whether Colin would feel as positive about that as Michael appeared to think.

When the meeting was finished I caught a taxi to Paddington station and went to see my parents. It was a lovely evening – all of us feeling friendly, my mother's cooking at its best, some excellent wine, and terrific conversation. On occasions like that I feel I have the best family in the world.

Thursday 5 February

Got up reasonably early and caught the train back to London. Pulled together some papers for Colin to see, and went over to EMI at midday. We had a conversation about a number of issues and touched on the subject of my own future.

Colin said he found my presentational style rather confrontational: it was like being on the receiving end of a Tornado fighter with all guns going at the same time. He also said that he felt my time at the Arts Council had perhaps made me this way, with people asking me for money, me having to say no, and them being unpleasant as a result: it must have had an effect.

He then asked me about the autumn and what had happened, and why the Board and I had become estranged from one another. I said that it was not the Board and I who had become estranged from each other but Vivien and I, because I had stopped her putting the organization into liquidation. The other Board members, quite to the contrary, had been doing their best to keep me in place. I explained about the Floral Trust adviser, and said that because Pelham and I both wanted the relationship to work he and I had eventually managed to rewrite the terms of reference in a way that enabled us to co-operate successfully. I remarked that what with one thing and another the last few months had left me feeling rather embattled.

The discussion then turned to a letter Colin had received from the Arts Council saying, among other things, that they were looking for a gender balance on the Board. He made a number of trenchant comments about Kathryn McDowell, who had signed the letter, saying that surely no one thought like that any longer. He said, quite adamantly, that he didn't know any women who he thought were good enough to serve on the Board. He then said he didn't know of any senior women at all. I mentioned Carol Galley, whom he waved away as being in finance and not in business. He then mentioned Marjorie Scardino as a possible future Board member.

We then talked about future structures and he said he still hadn't decided what he wanted to do. I said, 'Do you mean whether you have me as a Chief Executive or bring in a big name intendant?' and he said yes, that was exactly what he meant. So I said that I was naturally worried about what my future was going to be, and he looked astonished and said, 'Why? Why on earth are you worried?'

This led me in turn to be astonished – I was flabbergasted he could ask the question. I said, 'Because I would like to continue working at the Royal Opera House. I think it could be very exciting, if you and I can develop a good working relationship, to take the companies through the next two years and into the new House. Besides, I might not find it very easy to find another job.'

He said, 'Oh, you'll have no trouble, don't worry.'

'As you have said to me yourself, I'm damaged goods in the public sector, and a report such as the one Kaufman wrote does not exactly make one attractive to potential employers,' I pointed out somewhat tartly.

He did not appear to hear that remark.

I left shortly afterwards, and returned to the office. I had not realized that the issue regarding my position was quite as clear cut as that in Colin's mind. Adding up Colin's various comments over the past two weeks I would give myself a 75 per cent chance of going. I told Judy later in the afternoon and she agreed with me. She said her gut instinct was that my prospects were not good.

Met John Eatwell[91] at the House of Lords at 7.00. John and I had dinner; we talked about the Studio Theatre, and the first three

[91] Colin had reinstated the Opera and Ballet Boards, chaired by Michael Berkeley and John Eatwell respectively.

months of the main stage rep in the new House. He too wants to do *Rite of Spring* and I told him about all the arguments that the two Anthonys kept advancing against it. An ally – we might finally get it into the rep this time. Huge victory if we can actually get it to be the first piece, too. We finished dinner by about 8.30. He went back to Cambridge and I went home. Brief discussion with Nigel about my conversation with Colin earlier in the day and then Nigel went to Suffolk.

Friday 6 February

Arrived at my office at 8.30 just in time for my meeting with Paul Daniel. At 8.45 we both rang each other – he, too, had been sitting in his office wondering where I was. His good manners and my bad leg meant that he came over to see me, and we spent until 10.00 together, talking about Richard Eyre, our respective companies and our difficulties.

I then wrote a letter to Colin in which I said that he seemed to have formed the impression I wished to leave the Royal Opera House; that although the period before Christmas had been difficult I now thought there was real potential to make the organization a success. I also set out how I would like to restructure the senior management, with an Artistic Director, who would manage both the opera and the ballet companies; a Marketing Director taking on the education, marketing, press and community relations departments, as well as the Friends and the Trust; a Director of Theatre Operations, who would be responsible for everything that happened both back and front of house; a Finance Director; and – while there were such important union negotiations outstanding – a Personnel Director. If he will allow me to begin restructuring along these lines, then I can start to make the integrated option work.

Lunch with Graham Devlin. We talked briefly about Peter Hewitt who had just been appointed Secretary-General of the Arts

Council.[92] I told Graham of my conversation with Colin the day before. Most of the time we talked generally. I suggested that if I left the Royal Opera House and he left the Arts Council we could start a consultancy together but he did not seem too excited by that idea – I think he regards me as rather dangerous to know, professionally speaking.

Saturday 7 February

Did nothing. Colin's comments have returned me to the state of apathy I was in a couple of weeks ago. We had a nice lunch at the Spice Bar. I read a cookery book during the afternoon and dozed in the evening.

Sunday 8 February

Much of the same today.

Monday 9 February

My train was late, and I joined the Lyceum meeting half-way through. It was going unsatisfactorily. No one seemed to want to take any decisions at all and everybody was dithering around and being rude to one another. Peter Katona, who was there in place of Nicholas, has a very different style. While Nicholas says, 'Oh well, I'll see what we can do,' Peter Katona just says, 'No it's not possible.' Others criticize this as being over-Teutonic – I find it refreshingly direct. We sorted out which parts of the programme still need to be confirmed, agreed who would do what during the next twenty-four

[92] Peter Hewitt had been Chief Executive of Northern Arts, and had been one of the more challenging – and effective – of the regional arts board directors.

hours, and I drew the meeting to a close. I went back to my office to sort out some papers.

Two people from the Charities Commission came in at 2.30 and I had the familiar experience of telling people the Royal Opera House story and watching them move from sympathy to fascinated horror.

John Seekings and I walked around the 45 Floral Street offices to see how much spare office space we could find – quite a lot, in fact, even though everyone had told me the place was crammed to the gunwales. So I can remove the European Opera Centre from that little office close to mine and put Pelham in.

Then I got on with writing various papers for Colin and my second letter to Kaufman. On Friday I had received a letter from the Select Committee saying roundly that it had no intention of publishing my letter to them as it does not add anything to its report. I was astonished. Kaufman makes remarks about me that are inaccurate, I send him information that demonstrates this, and he refuses to publish it. How ironic that his criticisms of me should be about process.

Home. Telly. Book. Bed.

Worrying now about the operation tomorrow. I do not like having a general anesthetic: I am afraid of not waking up again. I suppose it might be rather high profile if I died: 'Beleaguered opera chief dies under anesthetic.' Not good for business. I shall comfort myself with that thought tonight.

Tuesday 10 February

Senior management meeting at 9.00. We spent the first hour discussing the progress we had made, since the previous day, towards confirming the Lyceum programme. We then talked about the business plan for the new House. Still no information from either the finance department or the opera company. Pelham and Richard Sadler will chase respectively. I updated them on the Eyre review, talked about my ladder of giving meeting, and about the need completely to rethink the Studio Theatre.

Nigel collected me at about 12.45. We went to the hospital, which was more like a luxurious private hotel, and I was taken to my room where I undressed and put on some extraordinary paper knickers and a white gown that did up at the back. We watched television for a while. Various people came in and asked me questions. I became increasingly nervous. The anesthetist came in and I asked for a pre-med and – as I had expected – he said no, they didn't like giving them because it made people drowsier afterwards. He said he generally only gave them if people were on the point of running out of the hospital, and told me that there had been a patient who had quite literally done so. The anesthetist asked me what I was frightened of and I said that I was frightened of dying and that I wouldn't wake up. He said, 'Oh, most people are frightened that they will wake up in the middle.' This had not occurred to me before . . .

Eventually the trolley came to collect me. I lay down on it and at that point I wished that I, too, had tried to run out of the hospital. There is something terrifying about giving up control to that extent. We trundled along the corridors and went into the lift and then into the anesthetic room. All the nurses were very nice to me, and Mr Strachan and the anesthetist – whom I had previously seen in suits and who were now dressed in green with blue caps on their heads – were being very friendly. Then they stuck a needle in my inner elbow and started talking to me, and reassuring me, and saying everything is going to be fine, and that the anesthetic was now going in, and all I remember was saying, 'Oh, my head feels all prickly,' and then the next thing I remember I was lying on my side with my knee in agony. I opened my eyes and thought I saw Lucy from the Royal Ballet physiotherapy unit: I must have been hallucinating.

They gave me a morphine shot in my thigh, and then subsequently a suppository in order to kill the pain. After a while they took me back upstairs and I just slept. I spent the rest of the day sleeping – it was wonderful. Went home that night.

Wednesday 11 February

Slept. A glorious day.

Thursday 12 February

Went into the office, and had a meeting with Keith to talk about the marketing strategy that he had devised for the Lyceum. The concepts were fine but there was very little detail about what, in concrete terms, would be done to sell the tickets.

Then to the Development Steering Group. The most entertaining moment was when John Seekings was talking about catering. He had described the stainless steel goods, the white goods, the tables and other furniture, and was getting on to the cutlery and crockery, when Vivien threw up her hands and shouted, 'Don't you *dare* have anything to do with that – you have *absolutely no taste whatsoever*.' The whole meeting cracked up with laughter.

On to the Royal Opera House Trust. Quiet, uneventful, they are beginning to see sense – until I tried to leave the meeting at 5.45, in order to prepare for my Lyceum negotiation with David Rogers. Vivien said she wanted me to stay. I said firmly that I had to go into another meeting. Jeremy Soames opened the door for me, as I limped – using two crutches now – towards it, with a glower on his face. Some of these people give a very good impression of thoroughly disliking me.

Excellent meeting with David Rogers. We agreed a basic rent plus contra (what the theatre charges for various services). I also gave him enough information so that he could come back to me with an alternative based on a lower guarantee and a box office split.

Then off to *Barbiere* at 7.00. Nigel, Kate and Jamie came to my office first, and we walked up to the theatre together. Kate said afterwards she thought it was really cool – from a sixteen-year-old that is serious praise. We have been marketing it to the wrong audience.

Friday 13 February

Got to Lucy by 9.00. It *had* been her in the operating theatre – I had not been hallucinating. She had come to see my operation and that of one of the dancers. She said I was healing remarkably well and that I must be a very healthy eater. I said that was so if she counted Kit Kat and white wine as being healthy.

Back to office and saw Manon Williams at 11.00 and we talked about the possible reception being held for us at Sandringham. 17 March won't work because we are opening *Così* that night but 18 March might be possible. She said she would talk to Prince Charles. I will sort it out at my end.

Then at 12.00 Peter Katona, Richard Sadler and I met to talk about possibly doing another piece before *Tosca*, in order to put on performances in what would otherwise be a dark week and thus offset some of the costs of the Lyceum by bringing in more box office income. Having spent months trying to originate ideas with Nicholas, Peter and I were able to talk in under thirty minutes about whether it would be a new *Bohème*, the old 1950s *Butterfly*, or whether we would do a new, cheap *Rigoletto*. Peter gave me a costing; he's going away to see which he could cast most easily, and Richard Sadler will follow up. If only business could be like this all the time.

Then to lunch with Dennis Scard, the General Secretary of the Musicians Union. We talked about the way in which the Musicians Union wants to approach the negotiations, which I discussed with Mike afterwards and Mike said was useful. What Dennis does not want is for us to come along with a preconceived idea of how the working practices might develop. Rather he would like us to come along with a statement of what we aspire to for the new House, which he and the Union can then consider as to the impact on working practices. He is right – involve the workforce and one will get better ideas.

Saturday 14 February

Nigel gave me a Valentine with a long poem, written by him, inside. I gave him nothing. I comforted myself by reminding both him and me that last year it had been the other way round. Sat in bed reading until 11.00, and then went into the office. I completed some work on the Lyceum budgets, and then met Kate from Coopers and Lybrand and ran through some models for ticket-pricing schedules for the Lyceum programme.

I think we can make it – if we put the prices up even just a bit we can make another £1.6 million.

Sunday 15 February

Slouched.

Monday 16 February

Went to see Mr Strachan. He took my stitches out, told me I was healing well, and said that I would be running around in a couple of weeks. It does not feel like it.

Back in the office for half an hour before going off to the Laurence Olivier Awards, where I had long conversations with Dalya Alberge from *The Times*, Sally Greene and Stephen Daldry, the Director of the Royal Court. We won an award for *Paul Bunyan.*

Returned to the finance meeting, which lasted two and a half hours. I found Richard Hall's presentation about transforming the finance department disappointing. I made my frustration clear, and tried to suggest some more radical approaches. He has put together a complex series of change projects: each individually tackles an aspect of the problem but I couldn't see how they hung together.

After the meeting we had another session on the Lyceum. Then a quick word with Pelham. He said that Colin had rung while I was at the Olivier Awards and made a great song and dance about me swanning off to awards ceremonies when, 'She ought to know there is a business to run.' He is obviously not aware that I will be at the office until late tonight, will be at the office at 6.00 tomorrow morning and was at the office for most of the day on Saturday.

Worked throughout the evening on the Royal Opera House's submission to Richard Eyre.

Tuesday 17 February

Arrived at 6.00 and continued with my Eyre response, together with a letter to Colin setting out key issues we need to address.

The Planning Group looked at the budgets for the new House, the first version of which has now been completed. The budgets show a deficit of £18 million a year. I said which of the income and expenditure lines I wanted to be analysed further in the short term with a view to starting to bring them into balance: much resistance when I said that I would not look at the artistic numbers yet. That, to my mind, is a different order of decision. We have to see what other savings we can make first, before we start taking the really painful decisions about the amount of art and its quality.

We then looked at whether or not we could put a substantial shop in the Floral Hall. John Seekings pointed out that the Floral Hall is on the critical path of the overall building project and therefore any shop there could disrupt the timetable. I said that nonetheless we would have to present it as an option to the Board, so that they could take their own decision about our assessment of the benefits and the risks.

Richard Hall, Pelham and I then went off to see Colin. He said that he wanted to have a quick word with me privately at the end, but we found ourselves at 3.00 with him having to leave and no word having been said. Richard's presentation about the finance department was improved in certain aspects from the previous afternoon, but to my mind there was still not enough of an overall picture showing how the changes would work. Colin was very laid back during the entire meeting, although he had been threatening thunder and confrontation in a brief phone call with Pelham beforehand.

When we returned from the meeting Richard said he wanted five minutes with me. As we went into my office I kicked off by saying that I was worried about the presentation he had made, the complexity of the task as he had presented it, and the fact that it was not clear how the individual change projects hung together. We talked about the timetable for a few minutes, and then Richard said how very regrettable he had found the meeting the previous evening. He felt that the tone of many of my remarks had been inappropriate, and that some of my suggestions had bordered on the irrational. I apologized for the tone, and said that it reflected my deep sense of frustration and disappointment at how little progress we appeared to be making. I asked him for an example of an irrational suggestion and he said closing down the finance department. I said well that was a matter of view: it might not seem to be an irrational option to everybody. Particularly since I know that the last time Pelham encountered a finance department as dysfunctional as ours that is precisely what he did, outsourcing key functions while he reconstructed it.

I spoke with Pelham afterwards. I have been coming to the conclusion for some time that Richard is not the man to take forward the changes to the finance department. He is committed, loyal, well skilled, and very sound on processes, but he does not appear to have the speed and flexibility that is so urgently needed at the moment. The finance department continues to be in a shambles, and there is intense pressure being brought to bear on us by the bank, the Arts Council and both Trusts to sort things out very rapidly indeed. Richard sets himself very high standards: that's fine but at the moment we need a solution that is cruder, and more rough and ready than Richard seems temperamentally able to deliver. Pelham and I agreed that I would suggest to Colin that Richard left and that Pelham would take over as interim Finance Director, creating a task force, including Liam, Chris Sammes and Peter Morris to help him transform the department as quickly as possible.

A Lyceum meeting at 4.00 to begin reaching a view as to whether we should go there. We first discussed marketing, and spent some time talking about a complex variety of ticket pricing schemes. I wish Keith would stop talking about ticket prices and start talking about selling. We still do not have a clear marketing strategy, dealing specifically with how we are going to sell the tickets.

We then went on to review the budgets overall. We could be as much as £1.2 million better off than if we go to Sadler's Wells, but only if we achieved all our box office targets. These targets are ambitious and thus far during the closure programme we have underachieved our income targets to the tune of nearly £2 million. Also, the programme – most of which is confirmed – has been put together bearing in mind the audiences we are likely to attract to a 1,400-seat theatre in Islington, rather than to a 2,000-seat theatre in the West End. Even if we do add some more popular pieces such as *Tosca*, and *Butterfly* or *Rigoletto*, operas like *Masnadieri* are unlikely to achieve the 75 per cent or 80 per cent occupancy we would need to make the Lyceum financially viable.

At the end of the day the fact remains that Colin and I have been dumped with Sadler's Wells, and if it doesn't work we can say, 'Not our fault, guv.' If we decide to make a switch to the Lyceum and *that* doesn't work, then we are responsible. It will depend in part on how much Colin is prepared to take a risk. From what I've seen of him so far his attitude towards risk seems to vary between wanting to run blindly over the edge of a cliff to being exceedingly cautious. It will be interesting to see which end of that spectrum he is prepared to occupy in relation to the Lyceum.

Wednesday 18 February

Arrived at the office at 6.30. Sorted out a report for the Board on the Lyceum, evaluating risks and weighing them against the potential benefits; drew up a Board agenda; reviewed my Eyre paper, setting out a vision for the future and generally got myself in good shape.

I spent an hour or so talking to Pelham and then to Colin on the telephone. Colin is now feeling pretty risk averse as far as the closure plans are concerned, and we have very reluctantly agreed to recommend to the Board that we do not go to the Lyceum. Although I agree with the decision – and indeed recommended it – I am very disappointed. It would have been morale-boosting for the companies to have been resident at a theatre so close to our own, able to watch the development progress, and work towards reoccupying the House.

I think Pelham is becoming quite excited by the possibility of being interim Finance Director. He said he would want to move into the office opposite mine, and have it to himself, with Richard Sadler moving into the office about to be vacated by the European Opera Centre.

Thursday 19 February

Worked on Board papers for an hour or so until met with Pelham at 7.30. We talked for a long time about the whole organization, and what was needed now in order to enable it to begin functioning better, including the leadership. We talked about the marketing department and what I describe as the outward-facing parts of the organization: education, community relations, Friends – the whole lot. After a very long discussion about new audiences, our poor record at the box office, and the urgency of improving sales so that we don't incur even greater deficits, we agreed that Keith should be asked to leave and Judy asked to undertake a review of all the outward facing departments, with a view to restructuring the relationship between them and bringing them together under a single manager. Keith has been with the Royal Opera House for six years. His thinking is excellent, but he does not seem any longer to be able to turn it into practice. It is as though the organization has in some way emptied him out.

Later, after I had finished my session with Pelham, I thought that if we were going to make changes to the finance and marketing departments, now was the time to tackle the question of the technical department, making the position of Technical Director redundant, with the three technical and making heads – David, Lorraine and Geoff – reporting to John Seekings. I spoke to John Seekings, and started by saying that I was going to ask him a question that he would find very difficult to answer. He asked me whether he would have to answer it and I said yes, I was afraid he would. I asked him whether he had the capacity to take on those three additional reports. Although he looked very taken aback he said he had. He is upset at the prospect of John Harrison going because they are close personal friends. But he has known that this was likely, ever since he and I first discussed the role of Director of Theatre Operations last autumn.

Having left many messages with Colin's office he eventually phoned me in the middle of the morning sounding grumpy. I said to him that I was happy to send out the Board agenda and papers without having consulted him but that I would prefer him at least to know what I was proposing the Board should discuss. I took him through the agenda and he gradually unbent.

Lunch with Anthony Whitworth-Jones. I discovered that even if he was not about to go off on a year's sabbatical, he would not want to become Opera Director. I said surely it would be a much more fun job than that of Chief Executive, who just has to deal with all the shitty bits and Anthony said that yes, but when you have been a chief executive you are used to dealing with the shitty bits.

He can have no concept of just how many shitty bits there are at the Royal Opera House.

However this confirms Colin's fear that it will be difficult to recruit an Opera Director, unless they have a higher degree of autonomy than they have at present, or unless we go down the route of recruiting an Artistic Director. The problem with the latter course of action would be that there are not many people who have an equivalent level of knowledge and expertise in both opera and ballet.

Friday 20 February

Saw Lucy at 9.00 who was not pleased with me. She asked if I had been doing my ice. I said that when Mr Strachan had asked me the same question and I had said no, he had said that I was probably the only one of his patients who was being honest.

She snorted and said that he was a great big softy and that if I wanted my knee to get better and the pain to go I had to build up the muscles; and that I couldn't build up the muscles until the swelling went down; and the only way in which the swelling would go down would be for me to put on my ice four times a day. She's very good – she subtly withdrew affection from me throughout the session so that by the end I was frantic to do anything that would please her.

I went back to my office and said to Sue Murray, my PA, that we must unfreeze the little freezer compartment in my fridge so that I could put the ice pack in there.

Turned up at EMI at 3.00 and had a good meeting with Colin. As far as my own position was concerned he said, 'Look, it's going to take me months to decide what I want to do, so the best thing you can do, if you want to continue being Chief Executive, is just to get on with it and do the job.'

I said that in the interest of getting on with it and doing the job I had a proposal to put to him. I repeated my thoughts on Richard and the finance department, Keith and the marketing department, and John Harrison and the technical department. Colin said he completely agreed with Richard, reluctantly agreed with Keith, who he says is a nice man and has been damaged by the organization – I echoed both of those sentiments – and suggested that, rather than remove the post of Technical Director now, let John Harrison complete the closure period, make it clear that his job will no longer be there in the new House, and ensure that John Seekings is involved in all the new House planning exercises. When I reported this on my return, to Mike, John Seekings and Pelham, they all said they thought John Harrison might resign if that was the case.

I invited Sue and Ellie, her assistant, and later Richard Sadler and Kate (from Coopers) into my office for a drink. Kate is good – she helped us on the Lyceum work and gets on well with Richard. The thought of there being Kate and Richard working on the business plan, Pelham and I working on restructuring the organization, and a 'battle-team' of me, Pelham, John Seekings, Mike, and Judy managing the Royal Opera House is tremendously exciting.

I have decided that the time is right to change the format of the management meetings again. We have now completed the programme for the first two years of the new House, so I am intending to form a new senior management group comprising the 'battle team' plus Richard Sadler. It will be responsible for drawing up the business plan, developing policy in relation to access and resource management, and preparing Board agendas and papers. It is incomplete because there is no one from the opera and ballet companies, but that will need to wait for a further restructuring. In the meantime I will continue with the larger meetings on Tuesday afternoons, overseeing the closure operation, as long as they have any value.

Saturday 21 February

Went into Woodbridge in the morning, shopped, had lunch at the Spice Bar. Tried a new recipe for supper: thinly sliced salmon sautéed with thinly sliced cucumber, with yogurt and chives added – the whole thing takes about five minutes. Tasted delicious.

Sunday 22 February

Did nothing in the morning apart from wander around the garden, thinking about future gardening plans. Tried out two more new dishes: first pork and cabbage stir-fry, which was not very successful, and then for supper thinly-sliced seared beef fillet in horseradish and tomato sauce – that was good, particularly with mashed potato, and spinach sautéed in a little bit of oil with some pine nuts.

Monday 23 February

Ladder of giving meeting in the afternoon, which was about as frustrating as the finance meeting had been the week before. I was given lots of diagrams and told how services could be centralized. I said that these ideas were interesting, but that we also needed to be talking about money and how we were going to sell tickets. Keith is so good on structures and concepts, but he won't get down to the concrete reality of saying, 'Look, here is something really good, come and buy a ticket for it.'

Tuesday 24 February

Another long discussion about whether to put a shop in the Floral Hall. John Seekings feels strongly it would be wrong, both aesthetically and in terms of the timing of the construction programme. I agree with him but we must make some money somehow. I asked Peter Morris to write a paper pulling together all the potentially income-generating activities, such as tours of the building, for presentation to the Board. A long discussion about staffing. Everyone wanted to start immediately on clean-sheet planning. I said there was no point in tackling that until we knew what the Eyre review would be recommending, for example whether we would be sharing certain facilities with ENO, or whether we would be adopting a certain type of organizational structure. We must not push the staff through two successive organizational reviews – I remember the Arts Council in 1993, when we had to do three restructurings in quick succession, and how demoralized the staff became.

In the afternoon had the senior management workshop with Michael Knight and Philip Heatherington on organizational structures. Lots of pluses and minuses for each option, with the opera and ballet companies advocating total separation and the rest of us wanting to integrate.

Then John Eatwell, Nicholas, Anthony and I waited for Michael Berkeley. When he hadn't turned up by 5.15 we started examining the first three months of the main stage programme for the new House. We agreed that there would be a ballet triple – John and I eyeballed Anthony Dowell and said it *would* include the *The Rite of Spring*; he compressed his lips but didn't comment – and we agreed that we would try and open the whole new season with it. We also acknowledged that there would have to be some tinkering around with the numbers of *Nutcracker* performances. Nicholas chipped in but we weren't really able to hit the *Mathis der Maler* versus *Le Grande Macabre* question.[93]

I talked to Michael afterwards on the telephone. I can't remember what had happened – either he had been held up or there had been a mistake in his diary – anyway he agreed with me it should definitely be *Le Grande Macabre.*

Wednesday 25 February

Arrived early to plan for both the Arts Council liaison group meeting this morning and the Board meeting in the afternoon.

The Arts Council meeting was grim. I must say, now that I am on the other side, my erstwhile colleagues do seem on occasion slightly irksome. I can understand why they feel frustrated, but they don't seem to be able to regard our problems in a pragmatic light. We all know that what we are risking is the Royal Opera House going bust, and that in order to stop it going bust we have to be pretty fleet of

[83] It was planned to include a revival of the Royal Opera's *Mathis der Maler* near the beginning of the opening season of the new House. This was not a piece I liked and it had done badly at the box office the first time round. I thought it would be more exciting artistically – and potentially better business – to programme Ligeti's

foot with the cash. Equally, I know that the Accounting Officer has to ensure that the financial rules are followed.

But there must be a better way of doing it than lining up five Council members and six officers. The only decent exchange was between Nicole Penn-Symons,[94] who said that our development was *not* on time and on budget, and John Seekings who explained how and why it was. They were both straightforward, explained their positions clearly, listened to what each other said, and were mutually satisfied at the end of it.

Most frustrating for me were all the complaints about the marketing, and the quality of the financial information, when I knew all that we had tried to achieve during the last six months, what the difficulties had been, and that I was about to ask both the Marketing Director and the Finance Director to leave. Prue tackled me about it afterwards and asked me why wasn't I doing more. I said that it was particularly embarrassing to discuss it right now. She still didn't understand and I said I would phone her on Friday to explain why I was so confident – as I was being at the meeting – that all of this would shortly be under control.

Colin conducted himself considerably more calmly than the nature and tone of his comments about the Arts Council prior to the meeting would have suggested, apart from at the end, when the Arts Council members were trying to make suggestions about new Board members. All were brusquely dismissed by Colin.

All this took forever and we barely got back in time for the Board meeting. Another marathon. Colin's style of chairing strikes me as being rather meandering, becoming combative as soon as anyone challenges him. He went through a long series of items that interested him and then, when we reached my item on planning for the new House got up and started offering everybody coffee and tea. I stopped talking at one point and he said, 'Oh, go on, unlike most women I can concentrate on more than one thing at a time.' Carolyn

[90] Arts Council Project Director, in charge of monitoring all building projects in receipt of a lottery award.

Newbigging rose to the bait. I eventually obtained the decisions I wanted.

Usual dithering around when we got to the subject of the Eyre review, with Board members saying that there must be a paper saying what they want. So I said briskly that I had provided them with a paper, dressing up wanting the structural status quo into a semblance of a vision, with a number of aspirations for artistic development, increased accessibility and improved resource management. What *was* it they wanted? No one knew. So I said that I couldn't write a paper, or indeed anything else, until I knew what it was they wanted to say. Colin suggested I do bullet points and circulate them to the Board to see if they respond.

There was a vehement discussion about the opening night of the new House, with Vivien saying that her donors would not want to come and see a ballet triple.

Richard Hall presented his paper on improving financial controls, and John Eatwell said that he found it difficult to absorb something that did not specify either the problem or a solution, but just talked about a number of tactical actions. I felt sorry for Richard. It was only John's second Board meeting and any Board member with longer experience would have known that the problem was imminent bankruptcy and virtually non-existent financial processes.

At the end of the meeting the other staff in attendance left, and I went through my proposals for Richard, Keith and John. I explained the timetable; both the proposals and the timetable for implementing them were agreed.

After the Board meeting Colin came into my office and we went through the press release about Richard and Keith. Mike, Judy and Pelham were in my office and once Colin had gone we all started planning for the next few weeks. It was the first time at the Royal Opera House I felt the sense of there being a proper team that could really achieve something.

Thursday 26 February

Arrived at the office at 6.00 and spent two hours writing out all of the things I was going to say to the people I was about to ask to leave, and to the groups of their staff I would be meeting in the afternoon.

Mike joined me at 9.00 and we went through the legalities of it all. He showed me the various letters the lawyer had advised we give the three of them and then we just chatted. The horror of doing this kind of thing is such that I find I can only bear it if I have someone with me, even if we are just talking inconsequentially.

Both Pelham and Judy came in to check that we were ready to go. We confirmed the press release with Judy, Pelham was on standby to take up all the financial aspects, and Mike and I sat and waited, with me shivering. At 9.25 I could feel myself starting to sweat. It was the sheer treachery of asking someone to go who had given me so much support through a difficult time, as Richard had done all the way through the autumn. He came in at 9.30 and I sat down, and he sat down, and I took a breath and looked straight at him and said, 'This is going to be a very difficult meeting because the Board and I have decided that we do not wish you to stay at the Royal Opera House any longer, and that we would like you to leave immediately.' I outlined why. We started to talk about it but he then decided he didn't wish to continue the discussion. He took the letter and left.

Then we waited for John Harrison and at 9.55 I realized that all I had asked Sue to do was to make sure he was available, not to arrange a meeting, so I asked Sue to ask him to come round. John came in, I greeted him robustly, he sat down and I told him that his job would not exist after August 1999 and I felt it was right to tell him now that his job would not continue beyond that date. He went white and suddenly his skin looked as though it was stretched over his skull much more tightly than it had been before. He picked up his letter and said, 'Well, that's it then, isn't it,' and walked out.

Mike and I relaxed and waited, and waited some more, and then at 10.30 Keith came in and I said the same thing to Keith as I had said to Richard and I started explaining how I was going to manage the transition, and he said, 'I don't want to know – I wanted to do this work. Don't you think I could manage a new approach?' And I said, 'No, I don't, Keith, I think it has to be somebody else,' and he could barely speak and took the letter and left the room. Mike said, 'He was very, very angry.'

I had lunch with Nicholas Snowman at the South Bank Centre, and on the way back tried to get hold of Bernard on the telephone. By the time I arrived at Floral Street he had already gone into his rehearsal, which was just about to begin. I walked into the rehearsal and said, 'Bernard, can I have a quick word,' and he said, 'No, no, no I am about to rehearse,' so I said, 'Look, Keith Cooper's going and Richard Hall is going – don't forget you heard it first from me and not from the press.' I learnt afterwards he rather enjoyed that, though he had no idea who Richard Hall was.

Friday 27 February

Got up early and read the press – far better than I would have thought, with the general view being 'Southgate gets a grip'. Only one mention of my position. Excellent.

Judy and I had a very long meeting with Colin about public relations, market research, and visits to the site. Judy acquitted herself excellently. She was calm, matter of fact, took everything in her stride, and treated all of Colin's requests as being easy to fulfil.

One benefit of the meeting with Colin going on so long was that I did not have to sit through a meeting about several aspects of the commercial properties. I returned to Pelham and he said, 'Well, I was there, John Seekings was there, you sacked everyone else who was meant to be there, so we took the decision ourselves.'

Then I had a couple of hours with Sheila Forbes about staffing, which was – as usual with Sheila – full of cool common sense. We went through all of the departments and the approach being taken to, for example, the orchestra, the dancers and the technical teams. She has shown me that even before exploring new ways of working three must be an overestimation of at least 100 members of staff in the present plans for the new House. She also highlighted a fundamental issue about the way in which we are programming the Royal Opera House. Even though the technical facilities have been designed to allow us to work the stage harder, the very fact of working it harder costs an enormous amount of money. I asked her to go over to talk to Judy about the review that Judy is doing of the outward-facing departments.

Richard Hall came in to say goodbye near the end of the day. He was friendly and said he thought it would be good for him to leave, but that he thought it was a mistake for the Royal Opera House. I said I was very sorry things had turned out this way, after all the support he had given me in the autumn. We parted on as good terms as I could have hoped.

Saturday 28 February

Made up a new recipe for chicken curry, which worked well. I fried the chicken thighs hard, and got them good and burnt on the outside, and put in a lot of spices and juices.

Sunday 1 March

Made another casserole, this time from lamb, which I had been marinading from the day before with onion, celery and big pieces of orange. I browned the lamb, browned the vegetables, browned lots of mushrooms and then deglazed the pan with the marinade and poured it all in – it was fabulous.

Monday 2 March

This is the first day of my diet. I stood on the scales and was mortified to find that I weigh eleven stone nine. All I can think of is the torture of the next two or three or even four months as I try to get the whole lot off again. Back to bed where I lay feeling gloomy until the last possible moment and then got up and went to the office. Saw Peter Katona, and we talked about the possibility of replacing *Mathis der Maler* with *Le Grande Macabre.* He was rather pessimistic, and said that it depended on whether Peter Sellars would agree to direct the other show, and the only singer who could transfer across was Willard White. Frankly, *Mathis der Maler* is such a dire piece – apart from Peter Sellars' direction, which is in my view the only redeeming feature of an otherwise dull and undistinguished opera – that I would put up with a great deal to get it out of the rep, particularly at the beginning of the first season in the new House.

Then we talked about the conference in Leipzig, which we were both planning to attend in a few weeks' time and he assured me that he would do all the translation. It's funny, a year ago I would have been filled with horror – no, less, six months ago – at the idea of going to a conference with all these opera directors, imagining them sneering at me and saying that I don't know what I am doing. Now I don't give a fig. When you have nothing to lose – in my case no reputation to lose – all you have is something to gain. I am rather looking forward to it.

Then Matthew Evans, Chairman of Faber & Faber and a member of the Eyre review group, came in to talk about structure and management for the Eyre review. It was an odd meeting in some respects, because he did not ask me anything about the overall scene in London, with Sadler's Wells and ENO, but just about how I saw the future for the Royal Opera House. I told him how I thought things ought to be run – definitely emphasizing there should be a Chief Executive who was empathetic to, and knowledgeable about, the arts but not an arts producer him or herself. I might as well make my views known while I can.

But it made me realize that once the review team has made its recommendations it could mean substantial changes for the Royal Opera House. And indeed it could mean the end of my job. It also made me realize that, once the review team has produced its recommendations, if there is anything in the report about me or my job there will be howlings in the press.

I had a sushi for lunch, and was eating bananas all day to keep my blood sugar level up. Franchesa Franchi came in and we had the meeting that had been deferred since mid-November, to talk about her budgets. Then Ron Freeman and I went to tea. Ron is a darling, and we gossiped and talked and agreed we would do the same thing at Baden Baden – we both felt it would be rather smart to have tea at Baden Baden.

Tuesday 3 March

Having decided that yesterday's eleven stone nine was an aberration, due no doubt to the fact that I had drunk a great deal of water just before weighing myself, I weighed myself again this morning and found I was eleven stone ten. I looked at myself in the mirror and I could now see that I am eleven stone ten. I must have been deluding myself for the last few weeks. My appearance is very chunky indeed.

Got into work at 6.30, feeling immensely energetic. Wrote a new outline for the business plan, and determined the work we need to do in order to complete it. Sue came in for an hour of dictation at 8.00. Had a meeting with Jones Lang Wootten and our other property advisers at 9.00 and learnt that we were likely to make between £6 and £10 million more on the sale of the commercial property than we had anticipated – this is tremendous news, and will greatly reduce the development risks. Started the new style management meeting at 10.00 and had swept through a substantial agenda by 11.30. I gave out my business plan outline, and talked about the prose that I wanted everybody to write – in other words the philosophy, the policy and the strategy. The budgets still require further work from the finance department before we can begin to tackle them properly.

Then into a closure meeting when we tried, once more, to nail the closure programme. Anthony said that he might want to adjust the final month of the Sadler's Wells ballet season in the light of new thinking. I commented that surely the only new thinking that might be emerging would be some of the new pieces that have been choreographed for *Dance Bites* – otherwise the rep hasn't changed since they did their old thinking.

Nicholas and I had a chin to chin on the subject of *Duenna* and *Barbiere*. He insisted that there had been no discussions at all about changing *Duenna* before the possibility of going to the Lyceum had come up; I insisted that there had been.

I commented that Michael Berkeley shared my scepticism about *Duenna*, and whether audiences would want to come and see it. Nicholas said, 'Well, if that's how you want to run the opera company, with meddling amateurs.'

I pointed out that Michael was not a meddling amateur: he was an opera composer, he ran the Cheltenham Music Festival and he was chairman of the Opera Board.

Nicholas said, 'Well, I suppose you can have what you want.'

I said, 'I want *Barbiere*,' very slowly, very carefully, and looking directly into his eyes. Then I said, 'That will be minuted please.'

Finished drafting a letter from Colin to Ian Hay Davison, the Chairman of Sadler's Wells. I hope I have struck the desired note of bellicose aggression. Ian Albery keeps writing letters to me, and soon I will have to write back saying that the reason I have not been replying is because our chairmen are in correspondence. Nothing will happen, of course, but I suppose the male ego has to strut its stuff.

A quick look in at Judith Pleasance's leaving party and then off to *Der Freischutz*. Sat near the front, listening to the waves of music. The soloists were superb, Bernard was on top form, and the chorus were roaringly good – all seventy of them. Met James Spooner in the interval and told him that, at the last Board meeting, I had confessed that I found my ex-colleagues at the Arts Council somewhat irksome, and that the Board had fallen around laughing, with Vivien roaring at the top of her voice, 'That's *exactly* what James used to say about you.'

Wednesday 4 March

Arrived early, and managed to tidy up some stuff before Hilary Carty, the Arts Council Dance Director, arrived. Among other things I told her that we might be doing *Cinderella* next Christmas, although not exactly at the same time as the English National Ballet, certainly over the same season. She looked severe and said that the National Dance Co-ordinating Committee might have something to say about that. I said that indeed they might but, since ENB were not £10 million in the red and that we were, my duty was to do whatever was right for my company in order to get the best financial results.

During the morning I asked John Harrison about *Coq d'Or*, currently being planned for inclusion in the Sadler's Wells season. It was originally conceived as a co-production with Rome, but apparently no one in Rome can find the costumes and the set is far too large. During the course of the conversation he also mentioned that we had co-produced *Fidelio* with the same company. It had begun rehearsing in Rome but on the second day of rehearsal the Romans had decided that they didn't want to do the production after all. We built the set, which we never took out there, but they have the costumes – more to go and find. I wonder how many other productions have been mislaid, accidentally burnt, or are hidden under the snows of St Petersburg – as is, I gather, the case with *Fiery Angel.* I am going to ask Pelham to do a register of assets in terms of the productions we have, when they were 'killed', and for what reason.

I had a conversation with Michael Berkeley about possible replacements for Nicholas Payne. I said I was becoming increasingly worried at Nicholas's air of distraction and I was not convinced we should be making him serve his full notice period. I said that I would give some thought to interim arrangements and discuss the matter with Colin.

I spoke to John Eatwell and we discussed the early part of the 99/00 season – the ballet company is now proposing to open the new House with a Jerome Robbins/Chopin piece paired with the *The Rite of Spring.*

I asked Peter Katona how he was getting on with *Le Grande Macabre.* He started talking about it being necessary to decide where authority lay: with the opera company, with me or with the Main Board. I said that it was the job of the Board, advised by the artistic staff and the Opera and Ballet Boards to agree overall artistic policy, and mine to ensure it was being implemented by the two companies. I also said I felt it was right that the Main Board should have sight of the seasons' programmes.

Peter mentioned the *Duenna* discussion and I made it clear that Nicholas had first proposed pulling *Duenna* himself back on 20 January – I had checked it in the minutes.

An hour and a half with Colin Tweedy, Director General of the Association for Business Sponsorship of the Arts (ABSA). He repeated some excerpts of a speech that John Drummond had made to the Royal Philharmonic Society at the Royal Society of Arts. John disapproves of me vehemently, has done all along, believing that I have none of the necessary qualifications to do my job. Apparently he will be recommending to Richard Eyre that I am removed from my job. Colin Tweedy is having dinner tonight with the Chairman of ABSA, Cameron Mackintosh and Dennis Stevenson among others, together with Chris Smith and Melanie Leech in order to discuss the Eyre review.

Thursday 5 March

Arrived at the office, and drafted terms of reference for the Main Board, the Opera Board, the Ballet Board, and the Audit Committee.

Learnt from John Harrison that the *Coq d'Or* costumes in Rome still have not been found, and that the other production of *Coq d'Or* that he was following up – one from Copenhagen – was scrapped six months ago. Heaven knows what we are going to do and stay within budget. He suggested asking Peter Katona what we could do with the singers we have contracted, and then seeing if we can find a production of whatever Peter suggests to hire. I gave Pelham the *Coq d'Or* and *Fidelio* contracts and asked him to tell me who owed what to whom.

Went to a meeting of the Design Sub-Group. I made a speech about public art, and the importance of distinguishing between that which was recording the progress of the development – the photographs – and that which would add genuine aesthetic value to the development. We got so hung up on the first of those we never got round to discussing the second, but I shall ask Stuart Lipton to help me at the next meeting.

Back to the office for a meeting with Judy and Jane Kaufmann, about how we would tackle the review of the outward-facing departments. I said to Judy that if she wanted to make some immediate changes to the marketing department then that would be it. She couldn't make further changes as part of the wider review. If she needed more time, then she should take it. Both Judy and Jane had been rather taken aback by my statements to the staff that the exercise would be consultative, and told me that it would take far longer than if they just made up their minds. I said that it was better to take time over the consultation and engage everybody in the solution, otherwise there would be resistance to what they wanted to do. I pointed out that they could have lunchtime consultative sessions, with voluntary attendance, or that they could get people together in groups.

Friday 6 March

Started to look at the various objectives and tasks that we should be setting ourselves for the next two months, the next six months and the next year. Made quite good progress, but I need the input of the others. I have already been through with Pelham what he wants to achieve over the next few months, and I have asked the others to let me have their targets within the next day or so. I then need to talk to Nicholas, Anthony and Malcolm Warne Holland, the Orchestra Director on Monday.

It is odd: although I am consciously excluding the artistic heads from the main management process there seems to be a willing collusion on their part. They do not seem to wish to be involved in the management of the organization as a whole, as well as the operation of their own separate groups. I am having individual sessions with them as and when I need to, but it is not a satisfactory position.

Waited for a phone call from Colin. I had faxed him that morning requesting permission to go ahead and recruit a Commercial Director and a Studio Theatre Director. Although the Board had discussed my papers about planning for the new House, and broadly endorsed what I had recommended, nothing had been explicitly agreed about recruiting for these posts. I had also sent him the redrafted Eyre bullet points, for his comments before I sent them out to the Board, and the various terms of reference I had drafted the previous day.

Caught a train to Northampton and read outstanding paperwork on the journey. Then just stared out of the window. I love being on trains with nothing to do. It is like being suspended in time. The motion of the countryside moving past the windows is hypnotic and it is the best way to see changes as the seasons rotate. The trees are just tipped with green, a couple of weeks earlier than usual.

I went to physio with Lucy, who was pleased with me – I told her I had been doing my ice – and as a reward she gave me a neck massage while I was having the electric shock treatment. I then had to wait for two hours before the show went up, and I went in to the theatre to watch the dancers do class – they really are extraordinary in their discipline and their physical ability.

Dance Bites was variable: the first piece – *Las Hermanas* by MacMillan – was based on Lorca's *House of Bernada Alba* and the choreography was highly expressive. I found the design of the set old-fashioned and cramped – there was a kind of pot plant thing, half-way up the set on the audience's right hand side, that could be removed. The second piece was by William Tuckett. It was too short to develop its idea properly, but I found it satisfying. Then there was a rather unsatisfying piece by Christopher Wheelan based on

Beethoven's 'God Save the Queen'. The final piece, by Ashley Page, I thought was stunning: dark and aggressive.

I travelled back in the train with Jan Parry who completely disagreed with me about the Ashley Page. She found the *pas de deux* repetitive and the whole thing unpleasant. We talked about a whole range of work, and she told me about the biography she is writing of MacMillan. It was a disgusting train; the man in the seat behind us threw up all over the floor and there were men slumped and snoring in other seats.

Saturday 7 March

Nigel took me to Marble Arch, where I returned some of the clothes I had bought from M&S a few weeks earlier and instead bought a blue trouser suit. I am still immensely fat and have only lost three pounds since the beginning of the week.

Sunday 8 March

Spent an excruciating hour exercising. Not only am I much more bulky at the moment, but the three months of being unable to walk properly has left my legs with very little strength in them. I am trying to follow the fitness plan in Deborah Bull's book, so I warmed up gently on the bike for five minutes, then did the stretches, then did thirty minutes on the bike, which left me barely able to stand up even though I had been deliberately going as slowly as possible so as not to exhaust myself. There is no question of doing the strength exercises after that, so I have decided that I will do the warm-up and the stretches every morning, and then alternate between the aerobics and the strength exercises. It is going to take a very long time indeed to improve.

Lunch with Janie and Douglas. I spent a long time talking to Bruce Higham about theatre and opera production and also to Douglas about his food-combining diet, and about various mathematical theories. He was in excellent form.

Went home and tried to watch *Tess of the D'Urbervilles.* It was an unsatisfying production: too slow, with the actors too self-consciously Hardy-esque, and very little spontaneity or naturalism. We turned it off half-way through.

Monday 9 March

My exercises were much easier, since I did not do the aerobic section. The stretches are quite easy, even though I now feel very stiff, and the strength exercises are easy if one does them lightly and for a short time. I know that the long-term intention is that one does them intensely and for a long time. But at least you can moderate yourself, unlike aerobic exercise where you just have to keep going.

Into work by 9.00. My 10.30 meeting with Melanie was cancelled. Pulled together targets for the organization as a whole.

Colin rang from Antigua. He said that the wind was too strong to sit on the beach and it was like being sandblasted. I commented it might be good for his skin. Surprisingly he laughed. He said that he wanted the response to the Eyre review to be done differently and started reciting, in some respects almost to the word, what I had presented to the Board. I pointed out that I had already tried it that way and he harumphed for a bit and I just remembered to say yes, yes and nothing but yes. I'll try and combine the two approaches. He then said he wanted to wait until he returned to England in order to discuss the terms of reference. I said that was fine, that was what I had intended, that they should only be a stimulus for further thought not a solution. He agreed I could go ahead with recruiting a Commercial Director and a Studio Theatre Director.

I then met with Mike and Judy to discuss the changes Judy was proposing to make to the marketing department. She explained her strategy: it will result in two people being asked to leave, three posts being made redundant, and four further jobs being combined into two.

Francesca Zambello came in for a drink at 6.00 and we had an excellent discussion. She would make a first class Opera Director. She has a clear artistic vision and a sense of how that vision links to the relationship between the Royal Opera House and its audience. She is also a superb manager, making everyone feel part of a team and excited about working together. We agreed to talk again, although I said that until my own position was clarified there was no point in taking the matter further.

Tuesday 10 March

Senior Management meeting at 9.00. We debated the closure budgets and decided to give Nicholas, Anthony and Malcolm Warne Holland star chamber treatment in order to ensure that there are no further costs that could be reduced over the next eighteen months. Then we looked at the business plan for the new House. The deficit is now sitting at about £16 million. We reckon we can knock out at least £2 million by keeping staff numbers down, although we can't do any specific work on these numbers until after the Eyre review has been completed. We can probably raise ticket income by £3 or £4 million since the initial attendance forecasts are excessively cautious given the novelty value of the new House; and we should be able to save substantial overtime if we played in stagione, or seasons, rather than rep. I also said we should begin looking at guest and production costs: at the moment they are aspirational in the extreme. I have asked Richard Sadler to investigate what exactly is already committed for the first season in the new House. He has already discovered that only Willard White has a contract for *Mathis der Maler*. This will no doubt continue to be a difficult negotiation, particularly in view of the row Nicholas and I had last week.

Sushi in the middle of the day – this is the best food experience I have on my diet– and I then rewrote the Eyre material to send back to Colin in Antigua.

At 2.30 had the closure programme meeting. These meetings have almost come to the end of their useful life and I think I will now delegate the responsibility for monitoring the closure programme to Richard Sadler. Once we have had our star chamber sessions, and the closure programme is nailed in blood to the wall, he can keep an eye on it.

Star chamber meeting with Anthony Russell-Roberts. This was frustrating, because what we were in fact doing was demonstrating to Pelham that we had taken every possible step to keep the costs down on the closure programme. Work we had done several months ago was having to be regurgitated.

Reached Michael Berkeley's house at 6.00 and had an excellent hour and a half with him. We both dismissed the idea of not having an orchestra, which some have been mooting. We also both agreed that it would be interesting to have a director, for example Francesca Zambello, as the new Opera Director. It will be important that the Opera Director should complement Peter Katona's skills, rather than overlap them. We talked about what we should be saying to Eyre, our artistic policy, ticket prices, broadcasting, and about whether or not Colin would go for an intendant. I said that if he did I would step out of the picture.

Wednesday 11 March

Went into work in the pouring rain. At 9.30 I realized that I was meant to be going over to the Arts Council, rather than Peter Hewitt coming to me, so I immediately dropped my plans for showing him round the development, grabbed a taxi and got over there. We met in Grey's office, rather than in what had been my old office, and I had the impression he felt a very slight awkwardness about the reversal in our positions. I talked enthusiastically, and I hoped persuasively, about the Royal Opera House, the difficulties we have been facing, and why I was now feeling more optimistic about the future. When I finished he said, 'Well, Mary, you have always been bullish and positive, and you still are. How much of it can I trust, since Graham and Kathryn are both very jittery and worried?' I said that I wouldn't blame either of them for being jittery and worried since they had spent the autumn watching us discover that the budgets were £10 million short. We agreed that I would come in with Pelham to present to the three of them our financial position.

I enjoyed seeing him. He said he thought he had the best job in England. I said that the Royal Opera House was one of the worst aspects of the Secretary-General's life, beaten only by the regional arts boards, and that I was looking forward to seeing how he dealt with them. I wonder whether he really will be able to create that bridge between the Arts Council and the regions. It would be marvellous if he did. I think perhaps that everyone is so exhausted with fighting they might just now be in the mood to co-operate. But no doubt that is my perpetually over-optimistic nature.

Lunch with Peter Allwood, from EMI, which I think went well and will be useful. We talked about Colin, my vision for the Royal Opera House, and why I think there ought not to be an intendant. He thinks we ought to look to Europe for the Opera Director, although he also thinks Sally from the Met would be a good idea. He asked at the end how he could help me, and I said by telling Colin what I had said about an intendant, and also by telling Colin that Judy was one of the best – if not the best – arts marketing people in the country. He said that he already had, but that Colin blames Judy for the criticisms arising from his first press conference. Apparently he felt he hadn't been properly briefed. I remarked that the only criticism had been about the 'smelly trainers' comment and that in any case Colin, thus far, has shown himself a man who was not much interested in being briefed, but preferred to shoot from the hip.

At the end of the lunch, Peter said he could see Colin and I working well together. I hope he tells Colin that. He also said he thought I would intimidate most Opera Directors since I was so formidable. I roared with laughter at that, since I was the one who was meant to be being so intimated by the world of opera.

Pelham came in just before I went off to see Dennis Stevenson, and said that the meeting with the two possible purchasers of the commercial properties had gone well, and that we have a definite offer from the highest bidder. This will change quite radically our cash flows for the development.

I then went to see Dennis, who spoke alarmingly about Eyre. He is persuaded that the Eyre solution will be to take all the houses under one management, and to have the companies run separately. He said that if I thought otherwise I had to be prepared to develop very clear arguments backed up by figures rather than emotion, and certainly not by market research, as Colin is presently intending. He also told me that Colin, whom he knows very well, tended to feel his way round an issue and then suddenly he would make a quick decision. He was quite clear that Colin had the right to choose his Chief Executive. I told him that I had already said as much to Colin, but I couldn't spend too long in limbo not knowing whether or not I was going to be the one chosen.

It was a useful occasion, if not reassuring but then, as I said to Dennis, I didn't want reassurance, I wanted reality. His comments about Eyre were particularly useful. He advised me not to get backed into either the integrated corner or the separated corner, but to be prepared to move pragmatically between them.

Thursday 12 March

Went over to Cameron Mackintosh's office at 11.00 and listened to him talk about what he thought ought to happen as far as the lyric theatres are concerned. His vision – and I gather that of many others too – is that the Royal Opera ought to be resident at the Royal Opera House, which would in addition become a sort of high class Royal Albert Hall, with a variety of orchestral, operatic and solo concerts; that the Coliseum should become a dance house, with the Royal Ballet resident there; and that the English National Opera should move to Sadler's Wells. The three theatres would be put together under a single Trust, with a single management and a single Board.

I said that there might be difficulties in implementing such a plan, not least the interests of those who owned the theatres, who were in effect the Boards of the companies, and also those of people such as John Sainsbury. Cameron said that Dennis Stevenson had said that he thought John Sainsbury would not be against it. I was surprised to hear that.

I asked Cameron whether or not, in his view, I had been personally damaged by the events of the last twelve months, and he used the analogy of the *Martin Guerre* reviews. You get bad reviews and then whatever you do subsequently to improve the show you are tarnished by the reviews. In other words, I am tarnished by all the controversy over my appointment. His advice was that I should not bleat – 'Oh, we can do it, we can do it, please let us alone' – and that I should be prepared to support change, whatever form the change might take.

We had our star chamber meeting with Malcolm Warne Holland at 2.30, to discuss the orchestra variable costs. Then a long conversation with Judy who was worried about the impact upon the press of the staff changes she had been implementing that day.

Near the end of the day a call came through from Hugh Canning, the *Sunday Times* opera critic, wanting to speak to me personally. It was a tirade, about Judy's changes to the press department. At one point I said to him, 'We have not met, or even spoken before. I am happy to engage in a conversation but I am not prepared to listen to a rant.' He then rang off. By that time in the evening I was tired and unable to concentrate.

I had been feeling downcast after my conversation with Cameron, as though everything I have been trying to achieve, and in my moments of self-delusion kid myself that I can achieve, were as of nothing. I recognize the value of Cameron's comment about not bleating, since I haven't earned the right to claim I can do what is necessary to change the organization. But even so, we are now so focused on change, and the building is coming on so well, that I believe that we could get there with an organization that can pay its way.

The sense of a *deus ex machina* coming in is dispiriting.

The conversation with Hugh Canning didn't discourage me in itself, but it brought to the surface all of the depression that had been gathering during the day. I had been going to a party in the Serpentine gallery but I missed it and went out to dinner with Nigel instead, completely blowing my diet.

Friday 13 March

Mainly paperwork. I suggested to Pelham that I did not go to the meeting with Nicholas to review the opera closure plans. I felt if Nicholas and I had to discuss them one more time across a table from each other, one or both of us would end up screaming.

I made this observation to Nicholas as I passed him in the corridor. From the look on his face I could see he agreed with me. Pelham later reported that the meeting had happened, but that nothing had emerged. We can now report to the Board that we have investigated all possible avenues for cost savings.

Saturday 14 March

Went over to Woodbridge, did some shopping and then lunch in the Spice Bar.

I did some gardening of the fiercest kind during the afternoon, wielding both the secateurs and my very large pruning instrument with great vigour over some of the mallows. I hope it is not too early and that they will not be too knocked back.

More dozing and drifting in front of the fire during the evening, after I had made a stir-fry of pork in creamy mushroom sauce.

Sunday 15 March

Spent half the morning in bed thinking about getting up and doing some gardening. In fact moved all of the stuff in the old study over to the new study, so that we were able to move two beds into the old study and start creating another bedroom. I stayed the night, and spent the evening listening to music.

Monday 16 March

Brainstormed all morning about the business plan for the new House. There are some key decisions that the Board needs to take before we can move forward, about the way we operate the new House and whether we programme in stagione; how we cut down the production costs; and how we structure the organization to enable outsourcing that will yield substantial savings. Although we can't make much progress until the Eyre review has been completed, we can start drawing up prototype alternative budgets, showing the financial effect of different types of operation. Had to leave the brainstorming midmorning to brief Stuart Lipton about being a Board member.

David Lees, another new Board member, came to see me at 5.00 and I gave him a full briefing. He spotted straight away that one of the effects of the Eyre review would be not only to destabilize but also to demotivate everybody, since we did not know towards what we were working. I left him with Pelham and went home.

Tuesday 17 March

Received a letter from Hugh Canning, covering a letter to Bernard Haitink, in which he repeated all his criticisms about the changes we have made to the press department. I had also received a letter from Andrew Clements, another opera critic, who was equally critical. I copied them both to Colin, saying I would give him a short briefing if he would like one.

Had a good senior management team meeting. It is now beginning to resemble a proper senior management team, with matters for report, two or three items for discussion and then a review of the Board agenda and Board papers. We discussed the business plan for the new House, but we are more or less coming to a halt now, until we can begin taking some of the more radical decisions that were starting to be flagged up yesterday.

At 1.00 Pelham and I went to the Arts Council to meet Peter Hewitt, Kathryn McDowell and Graham Devlin, in order to discuss the Royal Opera House's financial position and the question of the Arts Council grant. Graham's hair seems to be turning blacker, sleeker and glossier by the day and he is looking far, far healthier than he has done for the last year. He also has a mischievous glint in his eye. Kathryn was looking faintly harassed, and Peter was very earnest. He mentioned the words 'Accounting Officer' at least four times during the meeting and I smirked internally. He used to hate it when I did that during discussions with the regional arts boards. Now that he is faced with the Royal Opera House and the possible collapse of a very large building project he understands exactly what those words mean. Anyway, he was gruff, Pelham was brisk, I was emphatic, and we did not really get anywhere at all except to say that yes, we all knew the Arts Council grant would be paid, and the issue was whether or not they wrote us a letter saying so. I pointed out that there was the need for a paper trail, both for us to be able to give something to our bank and to give Peter the protection he required.

Colin came over late in the afternoon, after his meeting with the Education Department. He was in big, brusque, breezy form, looking quite tanned after his Caribbean holiday. I told him about everything that had been going on. We talked about targets: he said that he only wanted my short-term targets to go to the Board, and not those for 1998/99.

We talked about Eyre. He said he does not want to make any submission to Eyre until very near the point at which Richard reports, and even then probably nothing very specific. He also asked about John Harrison, who had written to him asserting that I did not understand his job. I said this was not the case: I knew all about John's job and had made arrangements for every aspect of his responsibilities to be looked after once it had ceased to exist.

Late in the afternoon I decided to ring Vivien to discuss the possible Eyre proposals. I set out for her a version of what had been told me by Cameron; she said she agreed that the companies and the House should be separated and would fight for it. I then tried her on bits of the rest of it and she said absolutely not.

We then launched into a conversation, which reached heights of rudeness I have never experienced before. It was a prolonged scream of rage – or perhaps pain.

'Why haven't you told *the Board* about the changes in the marketing department? It's only *good manners* to let the Board know about something that's going to be reported in the press.'

I apologized for the fact that she had not been told, although I subsequently found out that she had been.

'How *dare* you only give Keith Cooper five minutes to clear his desk,' was her next attack.

'That was entirely his own choice,' I said, 'I had given him until the end of the following day.'

'That's an *outrageous* way to behave,' she shouted.

'If you are asking someone to leave it is better for them and for the business if they leave quickly – the end of the day following the notification is reasonable,' I replied.

'What do you mean "the business" – this is an *arts organization*,' she countered.

'Yes, but it's also a £40 million business, and we have to run it in a business-like way.'

'What *on earth* do you know about running a business, or running anything for that matter – look what a *complete mess* you made of the Arts Council.'

'Vivien, you began this conversation with a reference to manners. I think good manners are something to which we should all aspire,'

I remarked.

'You're *all* absolutely hopeless, the Board has no confidence in *you*, the *senior management* doesn't know what it's doing – if the Trust had had any confidence in the management it wouldn't have been so difficult in the autumn.'

'I don't blame the Trust at all,' I said, 'I found out within days of joining the organization that it was bankrupt. No one else seemed to know – it was the Board's responsibility to make sure the March budgets added up, and according to the minutes they didn't even see them.'

'Ah, so you *do* think that Boards ought to know something do you?'

'Well certainly the Finance and Audit Committee should have known about the budgets and should have reported to the Board, but they didn't see them either.'

It was like a high-pitched and fast-paced fencing match. At one point we were talking about giving people forty-eight hours to leave and she said, 'Well, see how *you* like it when it happens to *you*.' Whether she is going to propose to Colin that he sacks me on the spot next week I am not sure.

Near the end of the conversation she began to slow down and said, 'Oh, Mary, we should be on the same side.'

'Of course we should – that's why I rang you in the first place,' I replied. I thought for a while after I had put the telephone down. When Vivien is really upset I never feel personally attacked by what she says, rather that she is using the conversation to express a general sense of anxiety and distress. Whatever she had said to anyone else about me, most of the clashes between us have been about what we feel would be best for the Royal Opera House and the different ways of achieving that. I am not entirely clear what is bothering her so much at the moment, but she gives the impression of being extremely agitated. And of course she is right: we should be on the same side.

Wednesday 18 March

Arrived at the office at 6.00, in order to complete the Board papers. Just managed to do so before Elijah Mojinsky came in at 10.15 to complain about the *Masnadieri* schedules for the Edinburgh Festival. I was brisk: I called in John Harrison, got Peter Katona on the telephone and we agreed that if Elijah was prepared to do his Sunday rehearsal with just a piano then we would not incur the costs of orchestra overtime and he could have the extra rehearsal he wanted.

Then Sofie Mason came in with Mike Morris, wanting to know when we were going to introduce a proper grading structure for the BECTU administration jobs. I agreed with her in principle that we should have a grading structure, but pointed out that there was no point in trying to grade anything while the organization is in such a state of flux, and that at present no one knew what jobs there would be, doing what work, or at what grades, in a year's time. I formed the impression that she was slightly taken aback at my bluntness, but Mike and I had agreed that was the best tactic. I said that we couldn't afford to run the new House at the moment, and we were going to have a look radically at how we organized ourselves. I also said that I had no idea what the results of the Eyre review would be, and that some of the rumours were pretty wild. We agreed we would keep in close contact during the summer, so that we could at least look at a timetable for the grading.

Off to speak at the Royal Fine Art Commission. I had done no preparation at all, except to take along a copy of the Eyre review paper that I would be presenting to the Board. Scribbled a few notes on a piece of paper just before I started, and was blessed with tongues. I spoke articulately, in long, perfectly-formed sentences, covering all the points I wanted, astonishing myself.

Back to the office to sign a few letters and then on to the bus with the opera company – mainly the chorus and orchestra – to go to Sandringham. Prince Charles, the Patron of the Royal Opera, had invited the company to join him for a drink at Sandringham and we'd chartered a coach for the occasion. The driver decided to go along the Limehouse Link – a disaster at that time of day. Then he lost his courage at the bottleneck at the top of the tunnel, and decided to go along the A13. More delays. It took us an hour and a half to get to the M11, whereas it would have taken forty minutes if he had gone the conventional route up Rosebery Avenue. We were then going along the M11 and he missed the turning. I was the only one who saw he had missed it and everyone else said to me, 'No, it's fine, just calm down,' so I thought, well, I don't want to play the little leaderette with the troops so I'll shut up. It was only when we arrived in Huntingdon that people realized that we had now gone about twenty or thirty miles out of our way. I was then deputed to sit in the front with a map, together with Nigel, the percussionist, to direct the driver.

The main reception room at Sandringham is extraordinary – I did not have a chance to look at it as much as I would have liked but there were some magnificent tapestries on the walls. We all drank as much as we could as fast as we could, given the stress of getting there, and stayed from 7.00 until 8.20.

At one point, I called Prince Charles 'Sir', my first conscious act of deference towards a member of the Royal Family. Progress indeed.

Thursday 19 March

I am feeling a little less bruised and anxious about the putative Eyre proposals as set out by Cameron, partly because I have had the time to absorb them, partly because I have managed to detach myself a little more, and partly because I have had time to forget them.

Had lunch with a group from Camelot, the lottery company. I was sitting next to Alfred Scardino, and there were a number of journalists and a couple of MPs around the table as well. We really were made to talk for our lunch, right from the word go – none of Grey Gowrie's two courses before 'going general'. It was quite good, but it could have been better still if we had had a chance to talk more to each other first.

I returned to the office, where I had a long chat with Pelham about the meeting he had had with David Lees, one of the new Board members. They had been together for a total of six hours: a couple of hours in the office, three hours over dinner and a further hour over a drink. Pelham reported that David Lees thought Colin and I were too similar to get along.

At 4.30 Melanie came over and I talked about my various anxieties: the Eyre report and what might happen; the fact that the Royal Opera House was not preparing a submission for Eyre; that Colin Southgate was being difficult and things were little better than they had been before. Melanie was her usual calming, wise self. And told me to stick in there if I could. She confirmed, in response to a question from me, that if there was a straight showdown between Colin and me she would have to back Colin.

Friday 20 March

The changes Judy has made to the marketing strategy for *Traviata*, including bringing in Saatchis, combined with some excellent reviews for *Cosi*, have kicked our ticket sales into the stratosphere. Thank God we are finally making some money.

Had a meeting with Sofie Mason and Alex Hull Lewis (from the production department) to talk about union matters at 10.00. I said that in my experience the management/union relationship could range from collaborative to confrontational, that I preferred to operate collaboratively myself, but that I was good at being confrontational if that was what was required. We talked for some time about the specific redundancies in the marketing department. Once Sofie and Alex had gone I phoned Judy and told her that I had suggested the union go back to her, and that my advice was to be as open with them as possible.

Richard Sadler and Sue Banner, the Company Manager for the opera company, came in at 11.00, to discuss the management of the opera company in the event Nicholas left early, and we agreed that the best arrangement would be for Sue Banner to be General Manager of the opera company, for Peter Katona to remain as Artistic Administrator, and for Cormac Simms to become Company Manager. I now have to sell to Colin the idea of an earlier departure date for Nicholas. Nicholas is so mentally absent, now, that if we do not put alternative arrangements in place soon, something will go seriously wrong. It's all very well for Colin to tell me to 'hold Nicholas's feet to the fire', but not surprisingly his mind appears increasingly to be engaged with ENO matters, and both companies would be better served if he went there sooner rather than waiting for his contract with us to expire in August.

Jane Kaufmann and Judy arrived at midday. We talked about Colin. Apparently he has spoken to Jane about the Royal Opera House and how much work there is to do. Jane suggested to him that he asked me, Pelham and Judy to help him but he just said, 'Oh, they're far too busy.'

Jane gave as two examples the response to the Eyre review, and terms of reference for the Opera and Ballet Boards. I asked Jane whether or not he had said that I had provided any of that material. She said he had told her that I had provided one response to Eyre, which he hadn't liked. I then told Jane that I had in fact provided three versions of the Eyre response, the third almost directly taken down from what he had said on the telephone – even though I did not agree with some of it – and that I had provided him with extensive work on terms of reference. Jane said he had not mentioned any of that.

She reported a meeting between Colin and Vivien during which they had had a bad row – far worse than the one I had had with her. Vivien is feeling excluded and upset. We agreed it would probably be a good idea if I started to indicate to her that she and I had interests in common. I dictated a fax to Vivien, suggesting that we meet regularly, and sent it off before I left.

Lunch at the Paul Hamlyn Foundation, with Camilla Whitworth-Jones and Paul Hamlyn. We talked about the Royal Opera House, we talked about the South Bank Centre, and we talked about the Arts Council. I loved it.

Saturday 21 March

Stayed in bed for quite a long time, then did some gardening. Went into Woodbridge. Had lunch at the Spice Bar. Returned and did some more gardening. Made a delicious kidney dish with a sauce comprising chevre, sherry and mustard. Listened to Bach.

Sunday 22 March

Gardened all day.

Monday 23 March

Got up at 9.00 and arrived at the office at 10.15. Spent the morning with Sue going through my in-tray. Received a very warm fax from Vivien.

Judy came to see me at 12.00. She said I would not like what she was going to say. She explained that Colin had come to see her last Tuesday – immediately before he had told me that he did not wish me to continue with the submission to Richard Eyre – and had asked her to write a paper for Richard Eyre. That paper was to include some comments about the leadership of the organization, saying that it should be led by an artist rather than by an administrator.

She had phoned him back on Thursday saying that yes, she would do it, but only on condition that he spoke to me first. He said that he would. It had become apparent to her when she and I and Jane Kaufmann had been talking on Friday that he hadn't. She had spent the weekend feeling troubled, and had phoned Pelham who agreed that she should tell me herself. Basically, she was saying to me that Colin was putting in a response to the Eyre review which would recommend I was no longer Chief Executive and that she had asked him to talk to me about it but that he hadn't done so.

I was shocked. Even if you're expecting something, it doesn't make it any easier when it actually happens. I was also extremely angry.

I went out to lunch with Sally Greene. I explained my slightly over-emphatic mode at the beginning by saying that there had been a newspaper article by one of the opera critics saying that I should go and although there had been other such pieces by opera critics that I had waved away into the bin, this one had particularly got to me. After a while I admitted that actually my chairman had indicated to one of my colleagues that he didn't want me to remain as Chief Executive and that was what was upsetting me.

When I returned to the office I rang Colin's secretary and said that I had just had a discussion with a senior colleague at the Royal Opera House that made it imperative that he and I meet as soon as possible, by tomorrow lunchtime at the latest. I did not care whether we had to meet at 7.00 in the morning, or whether he had to cancel something, but we had to have that meeting.

Tuesday 24 March

I got into the office early, and rang Judy at about 7.30. She was in her office and she came over and sat with me. She told me there is a feeling building against me among the journalists, that the Royal Opera House ought indeed to be run by an artist and not by an administrator. I found this helpful to know. When the rest of the team arrived at 9.00 I explained that I would be going over to see Colin and why. They were subdued but, as always, very supportive. I went through the agenda of the senior management meeting, explaining what I wanted to get out of each item, and then left at 9.30 to go over to see Colin.

I arrived at 9.50 and sat outside his office drinking mineral water, waiting. I went in at 10.00 and he explained that the person who had been in his office before me was his son. He talked for a while about the difficulties his son found in getting projects – he is an independent film producer – to overlap.

I then told Colin that I was extremely angry he had spoken to a member of staff about my position in the organization without discussing it with me first. He accepted that and apologized. I asked him what he wanted, and he told me that he wanted an artistic director. I then asked him what he thought would happen as far as I was concerned. He was vague. Gradually I realized he had anticipated a structure for the organization which had a General Manager as a number two, and he had thought that I might move across to that position. He said that no doubt I was insulted by that suggestion.

I said that I wasn't insulted by it but that it was a job that would require different strengths to those I possessed. What I was good at was the leadership of change.

Colin said that he would want to have a discussion with the Board sometime in April about the artistic leadership and then go to Eyre, but not publicize anything before Eyre. In any case, if Eyre recommended solutions with which he, Colin, disagreed – such as the separation of the companies from the theatre – he would resign, so I should wait and see whether I could survive him.

I said that left both me and the organization in an untenable position. There were things that needed to be done, and decisions that needed to be taken, none of which was happening at the moment because the situation was unresolved. The organization had reached a dangerous stalemate. This all needed to be sorted out as quickly as possible. I asked whether we could talk about it at the Board meeting the following day. He demurred and then said, 'OK, we'll talk about it at the end.' I said, 'No, you must talk about it at the beginning – I cannot sit through a Board meeting not knowing what my authority is.' It was a very, very difficult meeting.

I went back to my senior management team and told them what had happened. When I came into my office they were all ranged around the room, slouched on the sofas and easy chairs – God knows what they had been talking about. I hoped they had been discussing how they were going to manage the organization after I have left.

I went home, and saw Nigel, and we talked about the best way to handle things. We agreed that I will offer the Board a compromise whereby I stay for eighteen months after the opening of the new

House to work it in, and to give a new intendant the opportunity to work his or her way in. I don't know if it will work.

In the early evening we went to the BECTU rally about the Eyre review. Both companies had co-operated in organizing it, and I had helped to put them in touch with several possible speakers. I felt I had to show my face in support, although I explained that I would not be able to stay because – I said – I had a migraine.

When I saw the Royal Opera House banner over the stage, together with the ENO banner, it was the greatest act of self-control not to show any emotion. And there was Nicki, and everyone from press and community affairs, and everyone who was organizing it, and I so much wanted to be part of it. And there was a little band, playing some music from *Cosi* and that aria from *Gianni Schicchi* that moves me so much.

Just before the rally began I said to Nigel, 'I want to go now,' and the moment we got outside I wept. I wept all the way back in the car, and I wept for sometime after that. I feel very unhappy – what has always underlain my feelings about the Royal Opera House is a passionate desire to do the job, a sense of real joy that I could do that job, I could do it well, and make something grand and brave and new out of the Royal Opera House. The trouble is that so many people feel I shouldn't be doing the job, either because I haven't earned the chance to do it – I haven't done a proper apprenticeship – or because they believe I got it the wrong way, that I will not be allowed to do it. I realize that now, but it saddens me.

Wednesday 25 March

I woke up early and got into the office by about 7.00. I needed to prepare what I was going to say to the Board. I knew what was going to happen, and I knew I had to make it happen rather than let it be done to me.

I spent some of the time in the morning just being with people, those of whom I was fondest. I said goodbye to John Seekings. I talked to Judy about the press.

I briefed Pelham about the changes that I thought ought to be made, the people he should aim to keep, and those whom I thought should be allowed to leave.

Mike was kind and fair about negotiating a settlement.

Richard Sadler and Sue were both very loving.

I had prepared my presentation by the middle of the morning, and rehearsed it in front of various members of the senior management. Once I was happy with it I just sat with Richard.

It was as though I was having to psyche myself up to go through some rite of passage – something that I knew, once I had started it, would inevitably continue with waves of unpleasantness. Resigning when you know it's going to be on the front page of all the newspapers is a difficult thing to do. Richard bought a large bottle of excellent whisky. I refused to have any before the meeting – I wanted to be clear headed.

Colin arrived at the office an hour before the Board meeting was due to start and waited in the Boardroom. I went in to see him. I said, 'I think we both want the same thing, don't we?' and he said, 'Yes, we do.' I was matter-of-fact and so was he.

When the meeting began, I went into the Boardroom and asked them if they would like to talk among themselves first and then come and collect me, and they said they would, so I continued waiting in my office.

Then Pelham came in and said, 'You're on.'

I joined the Board meeting and sat down. Since I had more or less agreed the outcome with Colin beforehand I was not sure whether it was appropriate for me still to make a presentation. I asked whether the Board wished to hear what I had to say. Vivien said, speaking with great emphasis, that she thought it was essential that the Board heard what I had to say.

I stood up.

I began by saying that within the last few days my position within the organization had reached a crunch point.

When I arrived at the Royal Opera House there had been no

management structures, no management processes, misconceived closure programmes and no plans for the future of any kind. Within my first three months the organization had gone bankrupt, the chairman had resigned and the remainder of the Board had offered their resignations, and it had been a period of perpetual crisis management.

During the last two months I had been able to start putting improvements in place, but until Colin decided whether or not he wanted an administrator or an artist to lead the organization I would not be able to do my job properly. I told them what job I wanted to do: I wanted to construct an organization that could be well-managed. I wanted to strengthen the management of the opera and ballet companies. I wanted to clarify the artistic direction of the whole organization, and I wanted urgently to tackle the plans for the new House, which would require taking some very tough decisions.

In the longer term I still believed that the organization ought to be run by a Chief Executive so that opera and ballet were held properly in balance and that if they went down the intendant route there would invariably be an operatic bias at the top of the organization and that the ballet company would become once more the poor relation.

In any case the intendant model should only even be considered in the longer term, and that what was needed urgently now was strong administrative management – through the closure programme, into the new House, and through the first year or two of the new House.

I concluded by saying that I passionately wanted to do the job but I did not want to do it under the present circumstances, and that if they wanted me to stay I would ask for a firm commitment into the first year or two of new House and 100 per cent support before, during and after the Eyre review.

Michael Berkeley asked me if I would stay as general manager if an intendant was appointed and I said that no, I would wish to leave. And then I left the room.

Richard was already drinking the whisky and I started while we waited for them to come out and tell me what they decided. They were considering it for forty minutes before Colin came into my office. Richard left us. Colin shook my hand and said 'Well, that's that, then.'

I continued to drink with Richard – he and I had agreed a strategy whereby he would give me enough whisky so that I was feeling moderately euphoric, and then he and Sue would take me out of the building down the back stairs, so there was no risk of meeting anyone. We managed it – we booked a car and when it was there they took me out. I hugged them both and then got into the car.

And so I left.

INDEX